D1614431

C001478909

History of British Agriculture
1846—1914

HISTORY OF
British Agriculture
1846 – 1914

CHRISTABEL S. ORWIN

and

EDITH H. WHETHAM

DAVID & CHARLES : NEWTON ABBOT

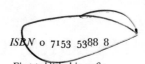

ISBN 0 7153 5388 8

First published in 1964
by Longmans, Green & Co Ltd
This edition published in 1971 by
David & Charles (Publishers) Limited
South Devon House Newton Abbot Devon

C001478909

50 11

Reproduced and Printed in Great Britain by
Redwood Press Limited Trowbridge & London

Contents

Preface

MESSRS Longmans originally commissioned Dr C. S. Orwin and Sir James Scott Watson to write a history of British agriculture covering the century from the Repeal of the Corn Laws to the end of the Second World War. Two volumes were planned, of which that by Dr Orwin was to deal with agricultural policy and social change, while Sir James Scott Watson undertook the volume describing the technical and scientific developments in farming. After the death of Dr Orwin in 1955 and the retirement of Sir James, the work was replanned. One volume dealing with all aspects of the period from 1846 to 1914 was undertaken by the present authors, who had the assistance of preliminary drafts of certain sections from the original writers. Nevertheless, the form in which this book now appears is our joint responsibility, since its plan and structure have evolved, as the work progressed, in ways which were not at first foreseen.

Lord Ernle's *English Farming Past and Present* is still the best comprehensive account of the development of agriculture in England over six centuries. But it does not cover Scotland or Wales; and those living in the second half of the twentieth century inevitably have a different attitude towards the events which Ernle lived through but could not see in historical perspective. Modern research has thrown further illumination on the great technical, economic and social changes which occurred both in agriculture and in the British nation between the Repeal of the Corn Laws and the outbreak of the First World War. It appeared that the time had come for a reappraisal of that part of the history of British agriculture which most nearly touches contemporary problems of farming practice and policy, and which is yet separated from us by the disappearance of the farm horse and the arrival of the tractor.

The radical changes in social and economic policy and in public opinion during this period affected not only the land of Great Britain, but also the status and mutual relations of the people who lived by it,

Preface

whether as owners, farmers or workers. In tracing these changes, we have tried to follow a chronological plan, with some inevitable overlap in subjects. Chapters 1, 2 and 3 deal respectively with the state of farming at the time of the Repeal of the Corn Laws, with the political and social status of the landed gentry, and with the condition of farm workers in the years following the passing of the new Poor Law. Chapters 4, 5, 9, 10 and 13 carry the story of changes in farming practice through the period of prosperity and the ensuing decades when international trade exercised an increasing influence upon the markets of British farmers, when scientific discovery and technological inventions gave farmers greater control over biological factors and when the State gradually assumed responsibility for agricultural education and research. Chapters 6 and 11 examine the relations of landlord and tenant, the legislation freeing farmers from landlord control and the gradual decline in the prestige of the landowning interest. Chapter 7 traces the administrative rôle of the State towards the land, culminating in the setting up of the Board of Agriculture. Chapters 8 and 12 describe conditions of labour on the land from 1850 onwards, State intervention to control the employment of women and children, the attempts of farm workers to organise themselves, the 'drift from the land' and its social and economic effects. We realise that it is not possible in a volume of this size to do justice to the incredible variety of farming practices and traditions, of social relations and living conditions, which were to be found in Great Britain during the period, but we have tried to hold a fair balance between the generalities of national policy and the local problems of a country which extends from Caithness to Cornwall, from Anglesey to Kent. We have not, however, attempted to deal with the history of forestry and we have but lightly touched on that of horticulture, two specialities beyond our competence.

The authors have incurred a large debt of gratitude to those many people who have helped them, by the provision of information, by the reading of certain sections, or in other ways. In Cambridge, Sir Frank Engledow, Emeritus Drapers' Professor of Agriculture, gave most generously of his time and knowledge by commenting on Chapters 1, 4, 5, 9, 10 and 13; parts of the same chapters were also read by Mr M. Barker, Mr F. Hanley, Dr A. Lazenby and Mr H. H. Nicholson, all now or formerly of the School of Agriculture. Professor Edgar Thomas, of Reading University, Dr Joseph Duncan, formerly Secretary of the

Preface

Scottish Farm Servants Union, Miss H. A. Beecham, of the University of Nottingham, and Mr George Houston, of Glasgow University, helped with sources and information; Mr J. J. MacGregor, of the Department of Forestry at Oxford, and Miss E. M. Tatham kindly read much of Chapters 2, 3, 6, 7, 8 and 11. We express our cordial thanks to Mr F. C. Hirst, Librarian at the Ministry of Agriculture, Fisheries and Food, to Miss E. Handlen, Librarian at St Andrews House, Edinburgh, to Mrs Fasnacht, Librarian at the Agricultural Economics Research Institute, Oxford and to Mr F. A. Buttress, Librarian at the Cambridge School of Agriculture, for their willing help throughout the long work of preparation; also to the Trustees of the Houblon-Norman Fund of the Bank of England for a grant in aid of research. We owe the charts to the kindness of Mrs Pahl, and the index and much help in proof reading and amendments in style to Mrs Anderson. The Department of Applied Economics, Cambridge, nobly undertook the typing of the final draft.

C.S.O

E.H.W

Preface to Second Edition

The authors are grateful to Messrs David & Charles Ltd for undertaking a reprint of this book, and to Messrs Longman, the original publishers, for facilitating the transfer of the copyright. For the second edition, alterations have been confined to a few corrections of words and figures.

Since the first publication of the book in 1964, the authors have noted, in addition to articles in the *Agricultural History Review* during the past six years, the following works dealing with the same period in the history of British agriculture:—

J. D. Chambers and G. E. Mingay, *The Agricultural Revolution, 1750–1880*. Batsford, 1966.

D. Spring, *The English Landed Estate in the Nineteenth Century: Its Administration*. Johns Hopkins Press and Oxford, 1964.

Ernle, Lord, *English Farming Past and Present*. 6th edn, edited with introduction and bibliography by G. E. Fussell and O. R. Mcgregor. Heinemann and Frank Cass, 1961.

E. H. Whetham, 'The London Milk Trade 1860–1900', *Econ Hist Review* vol xvii second ser, 1964.

E. J. T. Collins, 'Harvest Technology and Labour Supply in Britain, 1790–1870', *Econ Hist Review*, vol xxii second ser, 1969.

P. A. David, 'Labour Productivity in English Agriculture 1850–1914: Some Quantitative Evidence on Regional Differences', *Econ Hist Review*, vol xxiii second ser, 1970.

E. H. Hunt, 'Quantitative and Other Evidence on Labour Productivity in Agriculture 1850–1914', *Econ Hist Review* vol xxiii second ser, 1970.

C.S.O.

E.H.W.

January 1971.

Acknowledgements

We are grateful to the following for permission to include copyright material: the Editor of the *Farm Economist* for a table from an article by F. D. W. Taylor in the *Farm Economist*, Vol. VIII, No. 4, 1955; Her Majesty's Stationery Office for extracts from *Hansard*, and the Trustees of the Hardy Estate and Macmillan & Co. Ltd. for extracts from *The Dorsetshire Labourer* by Thomas Hardy.

Principal References

This is not a bibliography but a list of the full titles of those sources most frequently mentioned in the footnotes. The names of other authors quoted appear in the Index.

ROYAL COMMISSIONS

R.C. Children's Employment, 1862 .. Children's Employment Commission 1862, Sixth Report on Organised Agricultural Gangs, 1867.

R.C. Hypothec, 1865 .. Landlords' Right of Hypothec regarding Agricultural Subjects, 1865

R.C. Employment, 1867 Employment of Children, Young Persons and Women in Agriculture, 1867 (1867–1870)

R.C. 1881 .. .. .. Depressed Condition of the Agricultural Interests, 1881

R.C. Crofters, 1884 .. Crofters and Cottars in the Highlands and Islands of Scotland, 1884

R.C. Depression, 1886 .. Depression in Trade and Industry, 1886

R.C. 1894 .. .. .. Agriculture, 1894 (1894–97)

R.C. Wales, 1894 .. Land in Wales and Monmouth, 1894 (1894–96)

R.C. Food, 1905 .. .. Supply of Food and Raw Material in Time of War, 1905 (Cd. 264-5)

STATE PAPERS

Poor Law Commissioners Report on the Employment of Women and Children in Agriculture, 1843 (510)

S.C. 1848 (Customs) .. Select Committee on Agricultural Customs 1847–8 (461) (reprinted in 1866)

S.C. 1868–9 (H.L.) (Hypothec) .. Select Committee, House of Lords, on the Law of Hypothec, 1868–9

Principal References

S.C. 1873 (H.L.) (Lands) Select Committee, House of Lords, on the Improvement of Lands, 1873 (81)

J. M'Neill, 1851 .. .. Report to the Scottish Board of Supervision of the Poor Law on the Western Highlands and Islands, 1851

BOOKS

A.B.H,S. .. .. B. R. Mitchell and P. M. Deane, *Abstract of British Historical Statistics*. C.U.P., 1962

J. Caird (1) .. .. .. *English Agriculture in 1850–51*. London, 1852

(2) .. .. .. *The Landed Interest and the Supply of Food*. London, 1878

R. Haggard .. .. .. *Rural England*. 2 vols. London, 1906

A. D. Hall .. .. .. *A Pilgrimage of British Farming*. London, 1913

C. W. Johnson .. .. *British Husbandry*. 2 vols. London, 1847

J. C. Morton .. .. .. *Cyclopaedia of Agriculture*. 2 vols. London, 1855

E. M. Ojala .. .. .. *Agriculture and Economic Progress*. Oxford, 1952

V.C.H. .. .. *Victoria County History*

D. Williams .. .. .. *The Rebecca Riots*. Cardiff, 1955

PERIODICALS

Agric. Hist. Rev. .. .. *Agricultural History Review*

Econ. Hist. Rev. .. .. *Economic History Review*

J.R.A.S.E. .. .. .. *Journal of the Royal Agricultural Society of England*. Of the two numbers (e.g. 8.ii) the first refers to the volume and the second to the series.

J.R.S.S. .. .. *Journal of the Royal Statistical Society*

Tr. H.A.S. .. .. .. *Transactions of the Highland and Agricultural Society*. Of the two numbers (e.g. 8.ii) the first refers to the volume and the second to the series.

Charts

The charts provide a summary, for quick reference, of the main trends in British agriculture from 1846 to 1914, so far as these can be measured quantitatively. It must be realised that the data on wages, rents and prices, on which the charts are based, are themselves abbreviated summaries of complex and often conflicting evidence, and may conceal wide divergences between markets, regions and qualities.

Title	*Source*
I Area under Corn, Tillage, Temporary and Permanent Grass in Great Britain, 1870–1914 (Million Acres)	Abstract of British Historical Statistics p. 78–79.
II Numbers of Cows and Heifers, Total Cattle and Sheep in Great Britain, 1870–1914 (Million Head)	Abstract of British Historical Statistics p. 82–83.
III (a) Index of Average Earnings in Agriculture in a Normal Week (1891 = 100), England and Wales, Scotland 1846–79; Great Britain 1880–1914	Abstract of British Historical Statistics p. 349–350.
(b) Index of Rent per Acre in England and Wales, 1870–1914 (27s per acre = 100)	D.K.Britton, The Rent of Agricultural Land in England and Wales, 1870–1914. Central Landowners' Association. London, 1949.
IV Wholesale Prices of Food, 1846–1914 (a) Vegetable (b) Animal (1867–77 = 100)	Abstract of British Historical Statistics p. 474–475.

Charts

Introduction

The fifth census of Britain taken in 1851 revealed a total population of 20·9 million persons, where 10¾ million had been counted in 1801; in the intervening years, the population had almost doubled and the country had become the largest manufacturer of industrial products in western Europe. Of this population, some 1¾ million were engaged in the cultivation of the soil, the rearing of animals and the care of woods. Those employed on the land were, in fact, already a minority of the British people, representing only about one-fifth of the total occupied persons, or one-quarter of the males over twenty years of age. Thus for every adult man engaged in agriculture or forestry, there were three others working in industry, in trade, in domestic service or in the professions.

But the economic and political importance of agriculture far exceeded the confines of its employment. With the exception of tropical products such as sugar and tea, it provided most of the food consumed by the British people, and the state of the harvest still exerted a strong influence over commercial life. Low yields of grain and potatoes forced up the prices of the basic foods and reduced the volume of purchases of other commodities, especially textiles; compensating imports might strain the balance of payments and add to the dearness of credit; dear credit, lack of employment and dear food stimulated many forms of social unrest. High crop yields and low food prices encouraged extra employment both for the casual workers who helped with the harvest, and for the workers who supplied other domestic needs, on which the urban population spent the money they could spare from food.[1]

In addition to food, the land supplied important materials for industrial use – wool, flax, leather and tallow, timber and fire-

[1] W. W. Rostow, *British Economy in the Nineteenth Century*, Oxford, 1948, p. 109.

wood, charcoal and tanning bark, osiers for baskets, as well as horses for all transport. The prosperity of British agriculture also supported the fortunes of innumerable trades and crafts – those concerned with the marketing of farm products such as the cattle drovers and dealers, or with the processing and distribution of foodstuffs, the implement makers and blacksmiths, the wheel-wrights, saddle and harness makers, the carpenters, masons, saw-yers and tilers who repaired the farmsteads or built them new, the land agents and surveyors, as well as those who owned the land. In the census of 1851, 19,989 men and 14,638 women classified themselves as landowners; these 34,600 persons owned the greater part of the 29,213,312 acres 'under culture' in Great Britain, though many small parcels were owned by their occupiers, or by others who did not enter themselves in this category. It was these 34,600 almost professional landowners and their families who wielded the political power emanating from British agriculture in 1851. The rents received from agricultural land supported not only the great estates and the great mansions, the intricate family settlements and the marriage portions of the peerage and the gentry, but also the expense of duties in both Houses of Parliament.

The political power of the landed interest and the concern of the nation over its food supply had been brought into conflict over the Corn Laws, that dominating topic of the previous generation. The Restoration Parliament of 1660 had imposed duties on grain imports, and later offered bounties on grain exports so as to encourage a level of production which would supply the nation's requirements, even in years of bad yields, and at prices which fluctuated less than they otherwise might have done. Frequent amendments of detail in the regulations roughly maintained this position until the outbreak of war with France in 1793. Twenty years of war and price inflation, of rising population and expand-ing acreage, culminated in the bad harvest of 1812, when supplies of cereals were short, imports unobtainable, prices soared and the poor starved unless their earnings were supplemented by subsi-dised bread and doles in money from the poor rates. The men who sat in Parliament after Waterloo had therefore vivid experience of the effects of a scarcity of bread grain; it is not surprising that they attempted to guard against a repetition by protecting the growers of wheat in the post-war world through a revised system of import duties on all forms of grain.

The argument behind the Corn Laws was twofold – that ample supplies of the basic food for the rapidly growing population could only be secured from British agriculture, since supplies of foreign grain could not be relied upon for any regularity; and that the profits of British farmers must therefore be safeguarded against competition from such foreign grain as might be available in years of plenty in northern Europe. The attack launched in the 1830s by the Anti-Corn-Law League in part recognised the widening area from which supplies of grain could be drawn, as steam power increased the speed and size of ships and reduced the cost of transport. But the protagonists of free trade in grain were also carrying to its logical conclusion that general policy of removing barriers to exchange which had been adopted in the 1820s and which had been accompanied by such startling expansion in the volume both of foreign trade and of industrial production. And these general arguments were reinforced by the teaching of the Anti-Corn-Law League that protection to farming profits benefited not the farmers but mainly the receivers of rent, to whom was transferred, by competition among tenants, any excess of profits over a 'normal' level. Whether the Corn Laws kept up the price of bread in most years, and the level of rents in all years, as was claimed by the Anti-Corn-Law League; whether the Corn Laws kept down the price of bread in years of poor harvests by the maintenance of a higher average area, as was argued by the landed interest – these arguments over a particular case were swept aside when Sir Robert Peel was already converted to the general principle of tariff reform, and when that conversion was dramatically reinforced by the failure of the Irish potato crop in 1845 and 1846.[2]

[2] J. H. Clapham, *Economic History of Modern Britain*, Cambridge, 1926, vol. 1, pp. 495–506.

The repeal of the Corn Laws in June 1846 (to take final effect in 1849) destroyed the old Conservative party which had been pledged to their support, and threw into confusion the party alignments in many country neighbourhoods. 'In politics, Mr Thorne was an unflinching conservative. . . . When that terrible crisis of free trade had arrived, when the repeal of the corn laws was carried by those very men whom Mr Thorne had hitherto regarded as the only possible saviours of his country, he was for a time paralysed . . . to be so utterly thrown over and deceived by those he had so earnestly supported, so thoroughly trusted, was more than he could endure and live. He therefore ceased to live as a politician and refused to hold any converse with the world at large on the state of the country. Such were Mr Thorne's impressions for the first two or three years after Sir Robert Peel's apostasy; but by degrees his temper, as did that of others, cooled down. He began once more to move about, to frequent the bench and the market, and to be seen at dinners, shoulder to shoulder with some of those who had so cruelly betrayed him'.[3]

Sir Robert Peel was himself a landowner on a considerable scale in Staffordshire. He faced the results of his own policy by offering to his tenants in 1849 an investment equal to one-fifth of the current rent in such immediate improvements on each farm as might reduce costs or increase output, together with further investment in drainage on agreed terms. He suggested that the effect of free trade in lowering the price of wheat might well be offset by the reduction in internal transport costs brought about by the new railways, and by the increase in agricultural output which would result from drier fields.[4]

[3] A. Trollope, *Barchester Towers*, 1857.
[4] J. Caird (1), *English Agriculture*, p. 245. See also p. 40 below.

1

British Agriculture
1846-1851

*The Farms – Crop Rotations – Implements and Machinery – Crops and Livestock –
A Farm in the Lothians – Grass and Livestock – Markets – Agricultural Science – The
Profits of Farming – Progress and Prices*

THE FARMS

THE population census of 1851 included an investigation into the
number of agricultural holdings; it recorded a total of rather more
than 285,900 separate units in Great Britain and the adjacent
islands (Table 1). A comparison of these returns with those taken
in 1885 indicates that the recorders in 1851 must have overlooked
considerable numbers of the smallest holdings, those under five

Table 1. *Number of Agricultural Holdings in Great Britain*

Thousands		1851	1885
1–5 acres*		19·0	135·7
5–50 acres*		118·3	233·0
50–100 acres		53·3	64·7
100–300 acres		73·5	79·6
300 acres and over		19·3	19·4
Not stated		2·6	—
	Total over 5 acres	267·0	396·7
TOTAL		285·9	532·4

*It is probable that many holdings of these size groups
were omitted from the 1851 census. Table XXXIII, *Census of
Population*, 1851; *Agricultural Statistics*, 1886.

acres and probably also many of those between five and fifty acres in size. But the returns of 1851, as printed, showed that there were no less than 190,000 holdings under a hundred acres in size, just under 70 per cent of the recorded total; there were nearly 140,000 recorded of fifty acres or less, and there were 128,000 which employed no hired man or made no return under this heading. The family farms were therefore numerous, and probably more numerous than the census stated, yet they did not impress the public mind. Not many agricultural tourists explored the areas dominated by these farms of less than 100 acres, which comprised 87 per cent of the total in the north-western counties where the 'statesmen' of Westmorland and Cumberland pushed up the average; 79 per cent in Scotland, again especially in the north and west; and 72 per cent in Wales. Farms under 100 acres comprised less than half the recorded total only in the south-east and southern Midlands of England, and just over half in the eastern counties; yet the total area of these farms represented a much smaller proportion of the land under cultivation. In England and Wales 'there are nearly as many acres (2,152,000) in the hands of 2,038 farmers holding 700 acres or more as there are acres (2,142,000) in the occupation of 97,800 small farms (under fifty acres)'. It was the broad acres aggregated in large units and farmed by men of capital that upheld the reputation of British agriculture for advanced technology and large-scale business. But the ranks of farmers included also the thrifty cowman just starting an enterprise on ten or fifteen acres; the village tradesman who cultivated a couple of fields and kept a house-cow and horse; the upland farms with twenty or thirty acres in meadow and turnips and rights of grazing the hill in common with their neighbours; as well as the wealthy Lothian farmer with his 500 acres under grain and roots and ryegrass, his herd of Shorthorns, his flock of Cheviots and a dozen cottages for his men.

Most of these recorded holdings were well established units. Over the English Midlands, and thence south and east, the boundaries and buildings of many farms derived from an Enclosure Act dated somewhere in the sixty years before 1820; but Cambridgeshire, a backward county, was still completing its enclosures in the parishes of Newton (1854), Wilburton (1855), Bartlow (1863), Eltisley (1868), Willingham (1873) and Hildersham (1889).[1] On the Lincolnshire and Yorkshire wolds, and all up the eastern lowlands of Scotland, the land recently brought into arable cultivation in the previous century was distinguished by the large size of the farms, the methodical layout of their buildings and fields, their isolation from the older villages. In the East Anglian fens, additional land was being brought into cultivation as the new steam pumps drained the last of the meres, and new farms were going up along the droves which stretched from the villages on their clay islands to the new intakes. Reclamation of heath and moor was continuing on Exmoor under the Knight family; in Wychwood, near Oxford, disafforested by the Crown in 1853[2]; and in Aberdeenshire it continued until the end of the nineteenth century, but added to the size of farms rather than to their number. Those who wanted new farms, farms to own rather than to rent, went overseas.

CROP ROTATIONS

Over most of the light lands, the basic pattern was a variant of the Norfolk four-course rotation, the alternation of grain crops with fodder crops. A spring corn undersown with clover or rye-grass which was cut for hay or seed, and then grazed; wheat (if the land permitted), followed by turnips heavily dunged, thoroughly hoed and fed off by sheep, or carted for the bullocks: some variant of this rotation could be found from Kent to Moray-shire, from Norfolk to Lancashire. But turnips and clover when repeated were apt to fail, through unknown causes; especially on acid soils, turnips were stunted by finger-and-toe disease, and clover faded away before it was established. The contemporary remedy lay in the introduction of other crops – potatoes, beans and peas, rye, tares or kale, or in keeping ryegrass in pasture for

[1] The dates are those of the Enclosure Awards.
[2] C. S. Orwin, *The Reclamation of Exmoor Forest*, Oxford, 1929; C. Belcher, 'Reclaiming of Waste Lands', *J.R.A.S.E.*, vol. 24.i, 1863, pp. 271–85.

a longer period at one spell. Johnson gives for a light land farm an eight-course rotation of turnips, barley, seeds for three years, oats, pulse and wheat. A southern light land farm under superlative management gave fifteen crops on a twelve-year rotation based on grain for sale and crops for folded sheep: 'the practice of double cropping light lands is indeed pretty generally carried on in some of our southern counties.'[3] Aberdeenshire farmers had generally extended the four-course rotation to five, six or seven, because of finger-and-toe disease in turnips; but their ryegrass pastures quickly dried out in summer in the absence of clover and left them short of grazing at an awkward time. Caird noted that a second-year ley was often badly infected with twitch and was therefore avoided in parts of Durham by a six-course rotation which included one year in grass, peas and a bare fallow. Two straw crops or two cash crops in succession were regarded as bad farming for the lighter soils, and many landowners forbade such practices; but the better land, with more loam to it, might stand such a sequence occasionally which helped to pay for the higher costs of cultivation. Round Seaham in Durham, Caird observed a rotation of clover, potatoes, wheat, turnips, potatoes, wheat, allowing four cash crops in six years. Near Thorney on the fen soils, he found a seven-course cropping, three of wheat and one of oats, interspersed with roots, clovers and beans[4]; while Jonas recorded, on the best fens, successive crops of wheat and oats, with only an occasional fallow or year in clover to keep down the weeds.[5]

The heavy clays of the English Midlands had seen little change in their cropping during the half-century that had revolutionised the light lands.

Upon all wet thin cold clay soils, the wisdom of antiquity has long established that you are only to plough three or four inches deep; that you are to ridge up your lands into a certain round-backed shape which the rain may run off, as it would from an umbrella or the roof of a house; that you are never to

[3] C. W. Johnson, *British Husbandry*, London, 1847, vol. 2, p. 100.
[4] J. Caird (1), pp. 332, 336, 181.
[5] S. Jonas, 'Farming of Cambridgeshire', *J.R.A.S.E.*, vol. 7.i, 1846-7, p. 70.

cross plough or otherwise disturb this consecrated form . . . but to keep scratching it, up and down, shallow enough to ensure a seed time by having a dry surface two inches deep, leaving the furrow and about a yard on each side of it, as the perpetual channel or bed for water or ice in the winter, and baked sterility in the summer.[6]

Wheat, beans and fallow was the main rotation, with minor variants, for the regular summer fallow gave the only opportunity to kill the weeds by desiccation and cultivation. Wheat, the one cash crop, had to pay for three years' cultivations of land that was costly to work. 'I cannot fancy a more unhappy person than a small farmer on a cold clay soil with half capital', remarked a witness to a Select Committee in 1848.[7] But the previous decade had seen the development of one new technique – tile drains – which would do for the clays what the turnip had done for the light land; three pipe-making machines had been tested at Shrewsbury in 1845 by officials of the Royal Agricultural Society.

Judging by the lists of seed merchants in 1850, there were many varieties of each of the principal farm crops, but Morton observed that many of them were merely old-established favourites grown for a few years in different environments.[8] It was difficult to secure clean unmixed samples and therefore farmers inevitably sowed a mixture of varieties, often of their own growing. The favoured white wheats, grown extensively in Scotland and on the poorer soils in England, were mostly derived from the Lothians; Fenton, Hopetoun and Hunter were all varieties recently developed there and it was still the best source of seed. On the richer and moister soils in England, red wheats were more favoured, especially Lammas for the south, and Spalding, a stiff-strawed variety, less likely to lodge than Lammas but not much liked by millers as it gave a weaker flour. Three quarters (24–26 bushels) were regarded as fair yields on average land but the best wheat land well managed might exceed a ton an acre.

The common English barley sown on the lighter soils was probably not of any specific variety, but on the heavier soils

[6] C. Wren Hoskyns, *Talpa, or the Chronicles of a Clay Farm*, London, 1854, p. 29.
[7] *Select Committee on Agricultural Customs*, 1848, p. 66.
[8] J. C. Morton, *Cyclopaedia of Agriculture*, London, 1855, vol. 2, p. 483.

Chevallier was widely grown, as having both a stiff straw and good malting quality; six-rowed barley or bere was commonly used in the Scottish Highlands and in Ireland. Morton noted more than forty named varieties of oats, but only half a dozen were widely used.[9] Of these, the white Potato oat was the most popular in Scotland; it was often sown in a mixture with the Sandy or Angus oats, both of which had stiffer straw and therefore helped to support the Potato oat. On peaty soils, the black Tartarian oat stood best and was generally judged best as a fodder oat, but its colour made it unpopular with the millers. Lodging was a perennial problem as soil fertility was slowly built up with clovers, turnips, heavier stocking and the new fertilisers; both the Potato and the Hopetoun oats were especially liable to lodge on good soils and the former also shed its grain too easily at harvesting. But length and quality of straw were almost as much regarded as the grain, since oat straw was one of the principal sources of winter fodder.

More than 150 so-called varieties of potato were recorded in Lawson's Agriculturalist's Manual, of which a second edition was published in 1842. Many of these were undoubtedly synonyms, different names for the same product, and the majority were swept out of existence by the potato blight; a scant half-dozen survived as field crops. A small white round potato known as Regents was grown for an early crop in Yorkshire, Lincolnshire and Scotland; for the main crop, those most commonly grown were Hens' Nest, a prolific white potato susceptible to blight; and the red-skinned Orkney, almost the only survivor of the coloured varieties previously favoured. On heavy land, the sets were dropped by women or boys into raised drills in which manure was deposited under or over them; but ploughing the sets into furrows was more common on light soils subject to drought. Five tons to the acre was regarded as a fair average crop; but yields had been nearly double that level before the blight. Production was limited by the high costs of transport; Johnson remarked that 'the demand is such as always to leave a fair profit to the grower in the vicinity

[9] J. C. Morton, *op. cit.*, vol. 2, p. 483.

of large towns; but the cost of the manure and the expenses of culture are so high that unless in such situations or in those that possess advantage of water carriage to a market, it can seldom repay its cultivation on a large scale'.[10] The coming of the railways was to alter the location of this crop as of others.

IMPLEMENTS AND MACHINERY

Mr Ransome, of the famous firm of Suffolk implement makers, could proudly write in 1843 of the variety of implements available to farmers and of their gradual progress towards the current state of perfection.[11] His firm employed nearly a thousand craftsmen on the manufacture of ploughs, subsoil ploughs, scarifiers, harrows, drills, rakes, rollers, mole ploughs, threshers, winnowers, seed dressers, feed mills, chaff and turnip cutters. He, his father and grandfather had each in their generation experimented, adapted, invented and improved the basic tools, so that ploughs, for instance, were available in more than 300 varieties, tailored to suit the variety of soils, crops and local preferences. Ransomes had recently introduced the chilled iron share, with a harder working surface kept sharp by the more rapid wear on the softer inner edge; and also a plough frame to which the working parts could be bolted and thus easily renewed when worn. A dynamometer had been devised to measure the comparative draught of different ploughs in varying conditions, though its performance was acknowledged to be as yet imperfect. Ransomes also offered a self-clearing horse rake, whose prongs could be cleared by raising them through a row of bars; haytedders, 'one of the best instruments ever invented'[12]; and combined seed and fertiliser drills which placed the fertiliser 'two or three inches deeper in the ground than the seed but from ten to twelve inches in advance of it, so as to give the soil time to cover the manure before the next coulters deposit the seed'.[13]

[10] C. W. Johnson, *op. cit.*, vol. 2, p. 282.
[11] J. Allen Ransome, *The Implements of Agriculture*, London, 1843, p. 1.
[12] C. Wren Hoskyns, *op. cit.*, p. 187.
[13] J. Allen Ransome, *op. cit.*, p. 108.

As well as the great firm of Ransome, the intensive farming of East Anglia nurtured the slightly smaller firm of Garretts at Leiston, whose horse hoes and drills were to be found all over the country; recently, the firm had added steam engines and threshers to their lists. The steam engines provided on some large farms stationary power to operate a variety of barn machinery – pumps, hammer mills, bone crushers, chaff and turnip cutters, as well as steam for cooking potatoes and other fodder; they also provided mobile power for threshers. The large farms of the north of England and the Lothians often threshed by steam or by water power, but the threshers in general use in the eastern counties of England were usually mobile. 'They are frequently the property of individuals who itinerating from farm to farm thresh at a certain price per quarter, the farmer finding horses, and . . . the necessary complement of men.'[14] The recent invention of the shaking mechanism produced a more thorough separation of the grain from the straw than had been possible with the old beating mechanism; the operation of a rough riddling for the separation of broken ears and of a rough winnowing for the separation of the bulk of the chaff were performed by most threshing machines.

Although the flail was still in use on many farms, the threshing of grain was sufficiently well mechanised by 1850; minor improvements continued to be made in the process but the basic principles had been soundly established. The mechanisation of the harvesting was a more complex affair, for a thresher was stationary while it worked, while a reaper was required to operate on a variety of crops while moving over fields that were often rough or hilly, and might be soft or stony. The moving parts could only be powered from the main axle, but the gearing added to the draught; the standing corn prevented the horses from exercising a straight pull, so that they had either to push from behind or to operate on one side. The reaper invented in 1820 by Mr Bell of Carmylie adopted the first principle; oscillating shears were pushed from behind into the standing corn which was bent towards them by a revolving reel; the cut stalks were thrown on to

[14] J. Allen Ransome, *op. cit.*, p. 151.

8

an endless band of canvas which deposited them on the land side of the machine. In favourable conditions, this reaper cut and laid the swathe more evenly than the average gang of scythesmen; but it was awkward to turn and heavy on the draught, and few machines were built in the twenty years during which the original was working on Mr Bell's farm.

McCormick's American reaper, shown to the British public at the Great Exhibition of 1851, had its cutting mechanism placed to the side of the shaft, giving a much more compact machine; otherwise it followed closely two points of the earlier model – the revolving reel which brought the corn against an oscillating saw edge. But the cut stalks had then to be raked off the platform by hand, bound and thrown clear before the reaper came round the field to cut the next swathe, or the horses would have walked on them. Consequently its speed was limited to that of the dozen or fourteen people still required to gather, tie and stook, while Bell's reaper could operate independently of the speed of the hand work. Much inventive power was applied to the reaping machine, for it was urgently needed on the larger farms, whose high yielding crops required larger numbers of workers at harvest time than were easily obtainable. Drier fields and the new drills were intensifying this pressure on the harvest labour, for

the rapidity and accuracy with which the sowing of grain is now accomplished, frequently issues in the whole crops of a wide district being simultaneously ready for the sickle. The consequence is, that the supply of labourers proves insufficient – there is a scramble to get them – the rate of wages becomes exorbitant, employers are fain to submit to much sauciness and turbulence; and all the while the crops are suffering from over-ripening and are exposed to shaking winds. . . . The call for reaping machines is now, therefore, more urgent than ever.[15]

In spite of the variety of implements available and their progress towards perfection noted by Mr Ransome, there were in 1850 still large numbers of farmers who preferred the old-fashioned tools inherited from their fathers. The new implements cost good

[15] J. Wilson, *British Farming*, Edinburgh, 1862, p. 311. Plates of early reaping machines will be found in A. J. Spencer and J. B. Passmore, *Agricultural Implements and Machinery*, Science Museum, H.M.S.O., 1930.

money and their iron frames were brittle; their movable parts were quickly worn and the hand-forged replacement seldom fitted well. Broadcast sowing, hand weeding, the sickle and the scythe were still generally used on many farms, especially where rough or stony soils shook to pieces the new-fangled inventions of the agricultural engineers, whose workshops were nevertheless springing up in every market town. To be effective and economic, the new implements required a new system of farming – large level fields with straight hedges and wide gateways, and with no boggy patches and land-fast stones. It is not surprising therefore that the new implements and the new type of farming were to be found mainly on the eastern side of the country, from Lincolnshire through Northumberland and the Lothians to Aberdeenshire, on the big fields newly created from marsh and stones, and farmed in large units.

CROPS AND LIVESTOCK

The feature of British farming which commanded the admiration of the informed stranger, such as Leonce de Lavergne,[16] was the intricate weaving of arable crops and livestock into a combined business whose individual parts supported each other. These arable farms with their rotations of grain, potatoes and fodder crops were also meat producers on an enormous scale. Their sheep and fattening cattle required a carefully planned succession of vetches, tares, grass, turnips, hay and straw, whose regular production and economic use required a nicety of judgment both of the condition of the crops and of the needs of the growing animals. It was the root crop that linked the two together, for the root crop was the winter food for the animals whose muck went back on to the land to swell the grain crops and increase the volume of the fodder crops. The root crop, whether rape, turnips, swedes or mangolds, required a fine tilth upon clean land and a heavy dressing of last year's well-rotted manure; fifteen or twenty loads each acre was not too much for the lighter soils. Harrows followed

[16] Leonce de Lavergne, *The Rural Economy of England, Scotland and Ireland*, Edinburgh, 1855.

the seed drills and then came the hoers, hand hoers to single along the lines and horse hoes to control the weeds between the rows. Finally the crop must be lifted and topped, and part, if not all, carted to the homestead for the winter feeding of the stalled or yarded cattle. The maintenance of this link year by year taxed the resources of men and horses, with the ploughings and cross-ploughings, the harrowings and hoeings, the cartage of the muck and the hauling of the roots. Yet a well done turnip crop was vital to the continued production on the improved scale for two reasons; the amount of muck made depended on the winter food available, and the cultivations and manure given to the root crop served the rotation as a whole. Many farmers added guano and phosphates in some form, either as crushed bones or as super-phosphate produced by treating bones or coprolites with sulphuric acid; but even these aids to higher output could not give their full effect unless the crops were well started on clean soil, a fine tilth and with plenty of manure at the bottom.

The great aim in the culture of the farm is the early preparation of the land intended for the turnip crop; to this all other work is postponed after the corn crops have been secured in autumn. The stubbles are then stirred in one direction by Biddle's 'scarifier', the sharp-pointed tines being used in this operation, and the ground torn up to a depth of five or six inches. After the field has been gone over once, the 'scarifier' is fitted with the broadshare tines, and made to cross the former stirring at right angles, thus tearing the ground to pieces, and disengaging the stubbles and roots of weeds and twitch, which are drawn together on the surface with the harrows, then gathered by the horse-rake and laid in a heap. . . . The land, now thoroughly pulverised, is ploughed with a clean deep furrow, and in that state is left exposed to the influence of the weather till spring, when it receives one furrow more, and is found in fine condition. . . . The swedes are sown on the ridge, twenty-eight to thirty inches apart, eight loads of well-rotted farmyard dung and $1\frac{1}{2}$ cwt of guano per acre being previously applied and covered in on the weakest land. . . . On the better land 14 tons of dung and $1\frac{1}{2}$ cwt of guano per acre are applied.[17]

The type of livestock used in this mixed farming varied greatly. The light land farmers in the south and east relied principally on folded sheep, for which purpose Southdowns were favoured in England and the Cheviot-Leicester cross in the Border country

[17] J. Caird (1), pp. 323, 324, referring to a farm in Yorkshire.

and across into Scotland. Southdowns were reckoned to 'stand the fold' better than any other breed and they were to be found on almost all the chalk land farms, from Dorset through the Chilterns and their home territory in Kent and Sussex to Cambridgeshire where Jonas Webb (d. 1864) maintained his famous flock at Babraham. Southdowns had eliminated the old Wiltshire breed from that county; on the death in 1858 of Stephen Mills, of Elston near Shrewton '4,180 prize Southdown breeding sheep were auctioned at one of the largest sheep auctions ever to have been held in the south of England'.[18] Such farmers kept full-aged flocks, breeding their own replacements, selling some surplus lambs fat in the autumn with the draft ewes, but folding most of them on turnips over the winter to sell as hoggets in their second spring.

From Leicester and Lincoln northwards, the influence of the 'improved Leicesters' was to be discerned on almost every lowland farm. The pure breed itself, as developed by Bakewell, was out of favour, for its fertility was low and its propensity to fatten too high. But most of the existing breeds of sheep had been judiciously improved by a dash of Leicester blood which gave them quicker maturity; and as a cross, the Leicester was supreme for the production of easily fattened crossbred lambs which might be ready for the butcher at twelve to fourteen months on turnips with a little supplement. Rams of the Dishley Leicesters were commonly used for this crossing throughout the Midlands and the southern light land farms, but on both sides of the Tweed, a separate strain had gradually evolved which was becoming known as the Border-Leicesters, taller, more fertile, with shorter, closer wool. The improved Cheviots, the sheep of the green hills from the Border country to Sutherland, were the foundation stock for much of the lowland fattening trade; the ewes drafted from the hills were crossed with Leicester or Border-Leicester rams to produce either wethers which, when fat, sold well in the industrial towns, or half-bred ewes for further crossing with a Leicester or Down ram. For genuine flavoursome mutton, the three- or four-

[18] R. Molland, *V.C.H.*, *Wiltshire*, vol. iv, p. 86.

year-old mountain wether was preferred, whether from the Welsh mountain breed, the Scottish blackface or the speckled-faced breeds of Derbyshire and the Lake District, but the arable farms found in the Cheviot-Leicester cross a docile, quickly maturing commodity with a ready sale. In Cumberland and the northern counties, the Blackface-Leicester wether or 'mule' was also finding favour for the same purpose.[19]

But not all land was dry enough to carry a flock of folded sheep throughout the winter; many farmers had to rely on cattle for their muck-making, and many combined both enterprises. Here again, the farms newly established in the last half-century often had the advantage of buildings especially designed for this purpose – yards, or covered courts, or stalls in which the animals spent the last few months of their lives tied by the neck to a well-filled manger. The big arable farms found it profitable to fatten more beasts than they reared, or often to fatten rather than to rear; and their demand was supplied at the great autumn fairs with three-, four- or five-year-old cattle from Wales or Scotland. Youatt found that the light land farms in Norfolk and Suffolk preferred the Kyloes and Galloways which fattened quickly after their long walk; the Midland farmers bought the Devons, the Welsh blacks or the Herefords; while the north of England and the Scottish arable farms favoured the Shorthorn, either pure or in one of its many crosses. The Longhorns were almost extinct, for they had acquired a delicacy of constitution inconsistent with common management and keep, and the improved Shorthorns 'presented equal aptitude to fatten and greater bulk and earlier maturity'.[20]

The Shorthorn was established as the dominant beef breed by 1850 because of the successful inbreeding by three generations of Booths at Killerby and Warlaby in Yorkshire, by Cruickshank at Sittyton in Aberdeenshire, and by Thomas Bates at Kirklevington in Northumberland; they all possessed stock largely derived from

[19] W. Dickinson, 'On The Farming of Cumberland', *J.R.A.S.E.*, vol. 13.i, 1852, p. 263.

[20] W. Youatt, *The Complete Grazier*, London, 8th edn., 1846, p. 23.

the famous herds of Charles and Robert Colling, near Darlington, which were dispersed in 1810 and 1818. The emphasis laid by the Colling brothers on easily acquired flesh had produced by the middle of the nineteenth century the fashionable model of a compact, square-framed animal capable of laying on both flesh and fat in response to good feeding. Ten years of successful shows by the Royal Agricultural Society of England and the twenty-eight shows of the Highland and Agricultural Society had increased the renown and stimulated the competition for the progeny of the few early established herds. The breeding of pure Shorthorns had already become a speciality of a comparatively few farmers and landowners who could pay the costs of frequent exhibition as well as the risks of a chancy market. Prints of the early shows reveal the gigantic size of some of the prize-winning beasts whose judges took no evidence on milk yields or fertility, or economy in food consumption. It is not surprising, therefore, that the Shorthorns were steadily losing their reputation as a dual-purpose breed; even Bates's strain of milking 'Duchesses' does not seem to have possessed a greater inheritance for milk than less highly bred cows of other breeds. The Shorthorn was still favoured by many urban dairies which bought large quantities of brewers' grains and cattle cake, and sold their animals fat to the butcher at the end of their lactation; but the ordinary commercial farmers were content with a Shorthorn cross for fattening or for the dairy. A Shorthorn bull on Highland cows, on Galloways, or on the Scottish black polls produced quickly fattening beasts valued on every arable farm and they were less expensive to buy than the purebred animals.

The other beef breeds were more localised than the widely favoured Shorthorn. The horned Highlanders and the polled Galloways were both primarily hill or mountain stock, whose hardiness made their crossbred progeny by a Shorthorn bull a rewarding beast for the fatteners; the Welsh black cattle supplied a similar function for many of the English midland farms. In east Scotland, a small number of farmers – led by Hugh Watson of Keillor and William M'Combie of Tillyfour – were selecting from local material a compact, quickly maturing strain of the black polls commonly known as the Angus. On the borders of Wales and England, the local strain of red-and-white shorthorn cattle had crystallised into the Hereford, renowned by the Midland graziers as beasts which fattened excellently at three or four years old on lowland grass alone. Another variety of the red-and-white cattle had been evolving in Devon under the tenant farmers there, notably John and James Quartley, at South Molland; the all-red Devons, like the all-red polls being developed in Lincolnshire and Norfolk, were still dual-purpose animals, useful both for the butcher and the dairy, but best known outside their county of origin as beef breeds. The shows held by the Royal Agricultural Society at Norwich in 1849 and at Windsor in 1851 had separate classes only for Shorthorns, Devons and Herefords; all other cattle were judged together, whether 'Norfolk' polls, Suffolk duns, Longhorns, Ayrshires, Channel Island breeds, the horned Sussex or the black polls exhibited at Windsor by M'Combie. The Highland and Agricultural Society distinguished Shorthorns (by far the most important of the classes), Ayrshires, West Highlanders, polled breeds, which in 1852 and 1854 included both Angus and Galloway, and the Fifeshire, a dual-purpose black breed with horns which ceased to be recognised as a separate entity before the end of the decade.[21]

A FARM IN THE LOTHIANS

It was the Lothians and the Border country that set at this period some of the best examples of modern mixed farming. George Hope, for example, was the third of his family to farm Fenton Barns, 653 acres near Dirleton in East Lothian, but the first to farm it profitably, thanks partly to his own ability, partly to thorough drainage and partly to the new 'portable manures'; his business was described by Charles Stevenson for the Royal Agricultural Society in 1853. Two-thirds of the land, resting on traprock, was kept in a five-course rotation of turnips, potatoes, wheat,

[21] A. Ramsay, *History of the Highland and Agricultural Society of Scotland*, Edinburgh, 1879, pp. 312–25.

grass seeds and oats; one-third, on boulder clay, was worked in a six-course of turnips, wheat or barley, grass seeds, oats, beans or potatoes, wheat; there were only three acres of permanent pasture. His average yield of turnips was reckoned at 23 tons per acre; of potatoes at 7 tons for Regents and 9 tons for Reds; of wheat (the variety Fenton) 40 bushels; of barley 52 bushels; of oats 66 bushels.

The wheat was sown in October or November and given in spring a top dressing of about 3 cwt of Peruvian guano per acre; at the same time a mixture of 9 lb of red clover, 6 lb of white clover, 1½ lb of yellow clover with 4 lb of ryegrass was harrowed in, or, when the wheat was drilled, the seeds were hoed in by either a horse or hand hoe. About one-third of the grass was cut for hay and for feeding green in summer, and about two-thirds were grazed; a small area was kept for two years for the ewe flock but otherwise all the grass was ploughed up after one year for oats, after it had received a top dressing of 84 lb of nitrate of soda and 170 lb of Peruvian guano per acre. The grassland was ploughed in December and January and the oats sown in February if possible. When wheat was sown after the turnips as a spring crop, the grass seeds were sown shortly after; the Fenton wheat was found to do quite well as a spring-sown crop. About £800 was spent annually on portable manures, chiefly guano, but this figure included an allowance of 30s for each ton of cake or corn purchased for the stock, on account of its manurial value. Twenty-two horses were kept, nine pairs for the ploughs, two horses for stock work and two for the farmer's own use, and there was a fixed steam engine with thresher at each of the two steadings. A Bell's reaper was employed for the first time in the summer of 1853.

All the turnips were consumed by stock on the farm, about one-half by cattle, the other half by folded sheep. The cattle, usually half-bred shorthorns, were started on turnips at the beginning of October, sometimes by the second week of September and continued for about five months; for the last two months or more, they also got about 5 lb of linseed cake per head per day, or rather more of oats and beans ground into meal if linseed cake was too dear. Over the winter of 1852–3, 74 cattle had been fattened on 25 tons of cake, 90 quarters of oats, 20 quarters of beans and about 30 tons of hay; in addition another 20 cattle were kept on half-turnip for fattening the next autumn. All the cattle were kept in open courts with comfortable shedding.

About 900 sheep were fattened, usually Cheviot and Blackfaced wethers or the half-breds between these and the Leicester; in addition, there was a breeding stock of about 500 ewes, partly pure Leicester, partly pure Southdown and partly the half-bred between Cheviot and Leicester. Some of the breeding stock was grazed during the summer on adjoining links and about fifty shearling Leicester rams were sold annually for breeding at about four guineas each. The sheep were folded in winter on the turnips, being moved twice or thrice a week but being allowed to run back upon the cleared ground. Cake or beans were allowed after the middle of December at the rate of 1 lb per head per day, with hay as required; in the previous season, the sheep had consumed 35 tons of cake and 20 quarters of beans. About 100 pigs were kept, to be sold partly fat and partly when weaned; they were fed on the refuse of potatoes, steamed with turnips and a little bean or barley meal, and allowed on grass and tares in the summer.

There were fourteen regular workers engaged by the year, paid £2 annually in cash and otherwise in oats, wheat and the keep of cows which were fed along with the four cows kept for the farm house. About £400 was spent annually on wages to the out-workers and casuals who performed the field work, and another £200 on harvest work; tradesmen's bills cost about £100 annually and local taxes another £40. The farm was held on a nineteen-year lease which had been renewed in 1852 at an increase of 15–20 per cent in rent; the previous rent had been the equivalent at the current market price of 450 quarters of wheat, about £900 at the price ruling in 1850. Within the currency of this last lease, the tenant family had spent some £2,500 on field drains, 18 inches apart and 30 inches in depth.

GRASS AND LIVE STOCK

But there were many farms in Britain whose main crop was still grass, perhaps supplemented only by a few acres of crops for winter fodder. Round London, much of Middlesex and the Thames marshes were under grass, supplying milk to the towns, hay to the urban horses and beef from autumn-fed cattle. Half Warwickshire and most of Derby was reckoned by Caird to be under grass, mainly for the production of meat from Shorthorn cattle sold fat at three years, or from cross-Leicester lambs marketed at twelve to fifteen months.[22] Dairying was common round Birmingham and round the Durham coalfield, where the pit ponies also required a large supply of hay and straw. Cheshire was almost entirely in grass, its dairy farms selling cheese, pigs and veal from their seasonal output. There were grassland cheese makers in the Lancashire Fylde but 'nearly the whole of the lands within a circle of four or five miles radius round the principal towns were in grass', to supply liquid milk. The price of milk varied from 8*d* to 10*d* a gallon, but in Liverpool it had been from 1*s* to 1*s* 4*d* a gallon, the producers either retailing it themselves or consigning it by railway to the wholesalers who had recently begun to operate in Liverpool, Manchester and Bolton; it was noted that 'the profits of the land, for a considerable number of miles round Liverpool, have been somewhat diminished since the opening of the railways in consequence of the abundant supply of milk obtained by that means of conveyance, which has tended to diminish the average price of that commodity and reduced very considerably the number of cows kept in the town for milking purposes.'[23]

Another type of milk production had developed on the small farms above the industrialised valleys in Yorkshire and Lancashire; the high prices obtained for retailed milk were here balanced by the high costs of buying grain and hay and linseed cake since this poor, thin soil could supply only spring grazing and an exercising yard. This type of dairying was carried to the ultimate

[22] J. Caird (1), pp. 227, 392.
[23] G. Beesley, *Agriculture in Lancashire*, Preston, 1849, pp. 6, 17.

divorce from the land in the urban dairies where newly calved cows succeeded each other in the stalls and were fed on brewers' grains and purchased feeds, while their milk was retailed fresh in the early mornings, and was not shaken into curd by the vibration of the railway wagons. All the large towns had such dairies, and many filled their stalls with cows from overseas, the western dairies from Ireland and London and the eastern towns from the Low Countries and the Baltic. There was dairying for the liquid milk trade round Glasgow and Edinburgh as well as in those towns; but the Ayrshire dairy farmers used their grassland for the manufacture of cheese and for a flourishing trade in ryegrass seed. Cheese- and butter-making, supplemented by pigs and veal, were indeed found on all the lands that were too wet or too heavy for the plough and too far from the towns to sell milk liquid – Carmarthenshire and Pembroke, the Gloucester vale, the valleys in Somerset and Dorset and Wiltshire, the clays of Oxfordshire and Buckingham. On such dairy farms, the skill and attention to cleanliness of the farmer's wife largely determined the profits of the enterprise. Cheese and butter-making were mysteries, unexplained by science, and the cheese ferment in particular was liable to peculiar changes. The two processes were sometimes combined: cheese was made from the skim milk left by the butter, as Blue Vinney was made on many Dorset farms which supplied the London wholesale market with regular consignments of fresh or salt butter; and butter for household use could occasionally be made from the cheese whey.

These types of grassland farming had changed little in their methods in the previous half-century. They still relied almost entirely on the seasonal growth of grass from which they produced a fluctuating output of milk, most of which was converted into butter or cheese on the farms. Few of the dairy farmers attempted to provide winter keep other than hay, and few attempted any form of grassland improvement. The cheese-making farmers of the Cheshire plain were indeed regular users of crushed bones which they had found to bring a marked increase of clover in their swards and therefore in stock capacity, but elsewhere dairy pastures were likely to receive only 'little heaps of dung, the exhausted relics of the hay from which the cows derive their only support in winter, [which] were being scattered thinly over the ground, to aid in the production of another crop of hay'.[24] Lack of drainage in these pastures, the shortage of winter fodder, inadequate buildings to house the dairy cows were the usual handicaps towards increased production.

Most upland stock farms must also have been farmed in 1850 as they were in 1800; a correspondent to the *Farmers' Magazine* in 1853 commented that 'a look into Smithfield Market shows the improved animals to form a small exception to the number of coarse, ill-shaped and half-fatted carcases that are weekly exhibited there'. Shortage of winter fodder has always been the limiting factor on the output of the upland and mountain farms, but contemporary observers noted how little was made of such possibilities as existed on many farms. Turnips were seldom seen in the valleys and lowland of Wales; Sewell Read commented that the Welsh cropping was mainly a succession of grain crops with peas, until the land was run out and left to seed itself with grass and weeds. Some farmers supplied winter sustenance by 'fogging' – laying up a field in summer to grow what it would for the following spring, a practice destructive of good grass.[25] On the western slopes of the mountains, Thomas Rowlandson found that black cattle were wintered in small groups in sheltered spots which supplied a little marsh hay, as no other fodder crop was grown or preserved.[26] The sheep were generally of the small mountain breed sold at four years old to the drovers. 'The first object ought to be to produce nutriment capable of sustaining superior breeds', but this could not be done without capital to invest in drains and the knowledge of improved rotations.

Scottish agriculture north and west of the Great Glen had undergone drastic changes by 1850, as the result of a complex of

[24] J. Caird (1), p. 43, referring to the Vale of Gloucester.

[25] C. Sewell Read, 'The Farming of South Wales', *J.R.A.S.E.*, vol. 10.i, 1849, p. 138.

[26] T. Rowlandson, 'Agriculture of North Wales', *J.R.A.S.E.*, vol. 7.i, 1846–7, p. 582.

economic, technical and demographic forces. The improved Cheviots had been taken north by Sir John Sinclair and other landowners at the end of the eighteenth century, and had showed themselves to be profitable stock for the moors, provided they had access in winter to the glens and were farmed in large units. Throughout Sutherland, Caithness and Inverness, the commercialised, capitalised sheep farms were a dominant feature of the economy; it was their output of wool, of draft ewes and of young stock that was sold annually at Georgemas Fair or at Inverness market; it was their profits and their rents which supported the ducal estates of Scotland. But the same part of Britain also exhibited a tragic case of a type of farming in process of deterioration rather than improvement – the Highlands and Islands along the west coast. The destruction of the potato had plunged into acute distress the precarious life of the crofting communities, in proportion to their dependence on this crop. Thus the impact of the potato blight was worst in west Inverness-shire and in the islands north of Mull; moderate in Argyll and the eastern Highlands, where commercialised farming had already largely transformed the crofting communities; sporadic in Caithness and Sutherland where the previous 'clearances' had turned some glens into large sheep farms leaving patches of acutely congested settlements. The potato blight eliminated the staple item of food which could be grown in bulk on the small patches of arable land; it eliminated also the principal green crop in the customary rotation. Sir John M'Neill, in his Report to the Scottish Board of Supervision of the Poor Law in 1851, noted that in Stornaway 'previous to the failure of the potato crop, it was the general practice . . . to cultivate their arable land on a three-shift rotation taking two white crops successively after potatoes, and applying more or less of manure to the land with each of the white crops. . . . Since the failure of the potatoes, they have diminished the extent under green crop and increased that under white crop. The consequence has been to exhaust the land; and from it not being cleaned under green crop, a large portion of the ground is occupied with weeds.' He calculated that the crofters sowed 'about six bushels per imperial acre, often not so much, and the average return is certainly below eighteen bushels per acre. After reserving seed, there will remain but ten or twelve bushels to send to the mill; the grain is, moreover, of inferior quality. . . . The produce might no doubt be increased by better farming; but if the crofter is to be absent for six months of every year, it is vain to expect that his crop can be well managed.' (p. xiv.) Since the ordinary produce of the vast majority of crofts could not keep an average family in food for six months while providing only an occasional yearling for sale, paid employment of some sort had become essential. 'From the Pentland Firth to the Tweed, from the Lewis to the Isle of Man, the Skye men sought the employment they could not find at home; and there are few families of cottars or of crofters at rents not exceeding £10 from which at least one individual did not set out, to earn by labour elsewhere the means of paying rent and buying meal for those who remained at home. Before 1846, only the younger members of the family left the district for that purpose – since that year, the crofter himself has often found it necessary to go.' (p. xii.)

Many left the crofting districts in these years to take up permanent residence in the fishing ports on the east coast, in the lowland towns or in the new lands across the Atlantic. But the tenacity of the crofters to their land and to their community brought many back from seasonal work to spend the winter months in their crofts, even though regular employment could be found on lowland farms. One Skye crofter is quoted as saying to Sir John M'Neill: 'If I was employed at wages all the year round, I should make more than I get from the croft and six months' wages, for the croft does not pay half the rent by stock and whatever articles I have to purchase with money must be paid from wages; but I would not be so comfortable as with the croft and six months' wages.' (p. 63.) This continued occupation of crofts whose rents and money expenses could only be paid out of wages automatically prevented others from acquiring the area of land that might give a family a reasonable subsistence from commercial farming. Sir John noted that 'the distribution of land into crofts each of which would be sufficient to give them food would therefore imply the removal of a large proportion of the present population . . . the inhabitants of the distressed districts have neither capital enough to cultivate the extent of land necessary to maintain them, if it could be provided, nor have they land enough were the capital supplied to them.' (p. xxxi.) In a society without security against sickness, unemployment or old age, the occupation of a patch of land provided for many the essential basis of an ordered life; but without potatoes, the smaller crofts did not even prevent starvation in those districts where population continued to increase and the area of cultivatable land remained stationary, those districts in which the landowners had tolerated or encouraged the crofting system. Lord John Russell, who had held Lewis since 1844, had spent £67,000 more than the revenue on wages for work on improvements and the reclaiming of 1,368 acres of waste land, yet the growing population was in acute distress since the potato blight had deprived them of their basic food; the landowners who had bribed their crofters to emigrate or had forcibly expelled them in earlier years were relieved of such calls on their income and their charity. Sir John M'Neill's Report is a vivid and tragic description of communities ground between rising population and falling food supplies which were isolated from the main stream of economic life by difficulties of transport and differences in language.[27]

MARKETS

The farms of Britain were linked to each other and to their customers by a network of markets, ranging from the ancient fairs to the new Corn Exchanges which were rising in many county towns in the 1850s. Trade was growing and it was also shifting its course, as railways increased the importance of some markets, bringing them more business at the expense of those still dependent on footpaths and droving roads.

Most towns and the larger villages had their weekly market, to which the farmers' wives and daughters brought their poultry and

[27] A comprehensive account of the crofting districts at this time is contained in Malcolm Gray, *The Highland Economy, 1750–1850*, Edinburgh, 1957.

eggs, their butter and cheese and honey for sale direct to the housewives. They travelled by gig or pony cart, by side-saddle on a quiet nag, or came by carriers' cart or on foot. And most towns had also a regular day for the cattle sales when the local butchers haggled over the pigs and sheep, the calves and cattle that had been driven in from local farms. The main street thus regularly became a pandemonium of bargaining men, bleating sheep, frightened bullocks and pathetically muzzled calves unable to suckle their unmilked dams. These markets supplied the local demand for provisions and meat as well as the local trade in milking stock, calves and fattening stock among the farmers themselves. They were supplemented by sales made on the farms to the agents of the wholesale dealers; the larger farmers were thus saved the trouble and expense of conveying their corn and cattle to market, at the risk perhaps of being less up-to-date than the traders in their knowledge of market trends. Butchers and corn merchants might maintain regular rounds among the large farms with regular quantities to sell.

In conjunction with these retail markets were the wholesale markets in corn and cattle, butter and cheese, seed and feeding stuffs and breeding stock, which supplied the growing urban areas with food and the farmers with their supplies. Ancient custom had established certain centres for the wholesale trade in which London was both an ultimate market for a great volume of produce and also a distributing centre through which supplies flowed for resale in other areas. Chippenham in Wiltshire sold large quantities of cheese made on the dairy farms in that and adjoining counties; Reading supplied a similar function for the pastures of the middle Thames valley and both towns supplied London, as did the dairy farms in Essex and Kent and Surrey. Gloucester gathered in cheese from the Severn and Teme valleys for resale at its monthly markets; Chester sold cheese to the industrial towns of the north-west; and cheese from the Ayrshire pastures was pitched both at Ayr and Glasgow. Fresh Dorset butter was regularly quoted on the London market, together with butter in casks or barrels from Ireland, France and Holland.

The London meat market extended its influence to the remotest parts of the British Isles, and across the North Sea as well. Calves reared in the Hebrides and Caithness, in the west of Ireland, or in South Wales, might finish their days in the shambles at Smithfield or Newgate, having passed through a chain of markets and of ownership. Of the wholesale cattle markets, perhaps the most famous of the northern ones in 1850 was Falkirk. The autumn sheep and wool tryst was held on the second Tuesdays of September and October; the cattle and horse tryst on the second Wednesdays of August, September and October. In 1849 it was reckoned that there were at least 80,000 sheep actually present on the tryst days and uncounted hundreds of black cattle of all ages and sizes.

The almost universal colour is black ... the smallest, called 6 quarters, will clean up rough pastures and eat a little straw in Clydesdale, Dumfries-shire, Cumberland and the neighbouring districts. The older of the small cattle will proceed to Brough Hill, a very favourable fair with dealers because it is said to be attended by more gentlemen's bailiffs than any other in the United Kingdom. The finest West Highland heifers are for Yorkshire and the bullocks for the counties of Leicester, Northampton and Buckingham. The heavy north-eastern bullocks will supply the Lothians with stall feeders and will go in large numbers for the same purpose to Northumberland, Lincolnshire, Norfolk and the south east counties of England. These are all Norfolks when they get to Smithfield market ... A novel feature ... is the marquee of the London and North-Western Railway Company in which orders are received for the transmission of stock to all parts of England.[28]

In the west, Abergavenny, Knighton, Hereford, Ludlow and Worcester all had their autumn markets for the Welsh black cattle or for the red cattle with white or mottled faces so greatly favoured by the Midland graziers. From these collecting centres, the cattle walked east across England in long droves to the other markets in which dealers were selling to farmers rather than buying from them – the midland markets at Aylesbury, Evesham, Banbury, Maldon with 1,500 beasts and 6,000 sheep on one day; and to the famous fairs at Norwich patronised by East Anglian farmers looking for bullocks for their fattening yards and sheep for their turnip fields. These eastern and southern districts had a

[28] *Farmers' Magazine*, xxxi, 1849, p. 543.

regional trade in sheep passing from the breeders who sold their surplus lambs to the farmers, who bought in accordance with their supply of keep and the area of barley land to be sheeped over the winter. Thirty thousand sheep were reckoned to be sold on the downs above Lewes on fair day; 40,000 on the first day of the Ipswich lamb fair; 60,000 at Andover.

Linking these markets to each other were the professional dealers – the drovers, salesmen and jobbers who kept the supply flowing along the old drove roads to whatever market promised the best price for each particular type and age.

> The farmer sells to the drover, the drover consigns to the cattle-salesman, the cattle-salesman sells to the jobber, the jobber consigns to the carcase-salesman, the carcase-salesman sells to the butcher and the butcher to the consumer. . . . Upwards of one-fourth of the oxen sold in Smithfield are bought in this manner by jobbers . . . in the provinces, he is not unfrequently a drover and butcher besides a jobber . . . consigning part of his purchases to the salesmen of the metropolis in a live state – slaughtering the remainder, sending the hind quarters to Newgate, and cutting up the forequarters among his own provincial customers.[29]

The successful among these professional dealers in livestock were men of experience, integrity and capital, who would take the annual output of a rearing farm for sale in distant markets, or buy four or five hundred crossbred sheep for fattening on an order by a lowland farmer. They might sell, at Inverness in August to a Northumberland grazier, sheep that were still on the hills, and gather them later in the year from the breeding farms whose stock they knew as well as the owners. But another side of the droving trade was described by Thomas Rowlandson in his account of agriculture in North Wales in 1846: 'The drovers are generally men of the immediate neighbourhood who mostly buy partly on credit, paying at the time of delivery about one-fourth or half the amount of sale, by which custom the farmers are often great losers . . . [the drovers] often decamp with the produce of the sale or become bankrupts.'[30]

[29] 'Progress in the commerce of butcher meat', *Farmers' Magazine*, vol. xxxix, 1854, p. 50.

[30] T. Rowlandson, *op. cit.*, p. 569.

But everywhere the livestock trade was running into difficulties over the shortage of pasture along the established routes and the high cost of the frequent turnpike tolls and charges for lairage. The previous half-century of enclosure and consolidation had in many areas eliminated the open commons and grassy droves, and forced the animals into fenced roads where neither grass nor water was easily available; as a result, the drovers met with increasing hostility from the farmers and landowners whose crops suffered from the constant passage of animals to the main markets. In the decade before 1850, some of the Scottish cattle were brought south from Aberdeen or Kirkcudbright by steamship to Newcastle, London or Liverpool at far less expense though at some risk in winter.[31]

The railways were the logical answer to the problems of moving large numbers of animals long distances, and as railways spread in the 1850s and 1860s so the long-distance droving trade declined and with it, the importance of the intermediate markets such as Falkirk. The markets which gained in importance were those at railway heads near to the rearing districts, such as Lairg and Muir of Ord for sheep from the north Scottish farms, Lockerbie and Lanark for the Borders, Craven Arms and Ludlow for the livestock from north and mid-Wales, Crewe and Banbury for the imported Irish cattle.

As the importance of the drovers declined, the importance of the auctioneers increased, a shift in emphasis within the same profession from sale by individual bargaining to sale by public auction. The livestock salesmen could spend less time on travel but more time in their chosen markets. Perhaps the most highly specialised of the salesmen were those who conducted auctions for the famous breeders of pedigree sheep and cattle, such as the Mr Stafford who wielded the hammer in 1853 at the dispersal sale of Lord Ducie's shorthorns and of the Grant Duff herd at Eden in Aberdeenshire – a man of 'most intimate knowledge and judgment of short horn stock.'[32] A few breeders held annual

---

[31] A. R. B. Haldane, *The Drove Roads of Scotland*, London, 1952.
[32] *Farmers' Magazine*, vol. xxxix, 1853, pp. 296, 563.

auction sales on their farms for their surplus stock, with luncheon for the buyers and toasts of the Queen, the Agricultural Interest, the auctioneer and the breeder. Such was the 'annual sale of stock and ram hiring' which had been held by Jonas Webb of Babraham near Cambridge for his Southdown sheep for some twenty-five years before 1850, continuing a tradition laid down by Bakewell in the previous century and Lord Leicester at Holkham during the Napoleonic Wars. Since 1803, Sir Tatton Sykes had held at Sledmere in Yorkshire an annual sale of his Leicester sheep; his fifty-eighth and last sale took place in 1861, eighteen months before his death at the age of 91.

AGRICULTURAL SCIENCE

The modern farming of 1850 owed little to the work of agricultural scientists but a great deal to the farmers and landowners who experimented, adapted and published the results of applying new ideas in their business. The improvement of livestock, for instance, was still being carried on by men who had no knowledge of genetics but who had a practised eye for stock and a belief that like produced like, in spite of some startling exceptions to this general rule. Henry Stephens in his popular *Book of the Farm* lent his support to the theory current at this time that 'in regard to the breeding of domestic animals, the thinking organs are, in equal and distinct portions, derived from both parents; while the dam gives the whole of the nutritive and the sire the whole of the locomotive organs'.[33] Whether they believed this theory or not, the livestock breeders selected animals which possessed the qualities they sought – early maturity, flesh in the right places – fed them well to attain maximum growth, and bred from them. The practice of inbreeding produced a few potent strains which subsequently dominated the livestock industry as well as a number of failures, such as the Longhorns with which Bakewell did his early work. The pattern established by the leading herds was popularised by the shows of the two national agricultural societies,

[33] H. Stephens, *Book of the Farm*, 3rd edn., Edinburgh, 1871, p. 581.

the Highland and Agricultural Society of Scotland (founded in 1784–5) and the Royal Agricultural Society of England (founded in 1839), and by the shows of the many local agricultural societies. Indeed these exhibitions had already established some 'show-yard fashions' in shape and colour and size which had little connection with other qualities required by practical farmers, such as sound constitutions, high fertility and economic food conversion. Such fashions induced a pressure of demand for the breeding stock of the favoured herds which tended to create and perpetuate a high level of prices for the progeny of certain pedigrees; once a line was established in the public eye in this way, many were led to pay fancy prices for descendants in the hope of putting their own herds and flocks into the same favoured class.

The chemical analysis of plants and of manures begun by Sir Humphrey Davy (1778–1829) had given clues to the existence of elements common to both. Justus von Liebig (1803–1873) and other chemists had already calculated the amount of carbon, nitrogen, calcium, phosphorus, sodium and potash removed from the soil in the ordinary crop rotation of seeds used for hay, wheat, turnips and barley and therefore the theoretical replacements required. It was also known that plants could absorb carbon from the carbon dioxide in the air and that some plants, such as beans and clovers, could absorb nitrogen, presumably also from the air. Liebig therefore deduced that plants drew only minerals from the soil, and 'that crops in a field diminish or increase in exact proportion to the diminution or increase in the mineral substances conveyed to them in manure'. From the high phosphorus content of wheat and the low nitrogen content of turnips, he deduced that phosphatic manures were required for the former; and that Britain must be suffering from a progressive shortage of phosphate 'as is proved by the rapid extension of the cultivation of turnips and mangold-wurzel, plants which contain the least amount of the phosphates and therefore require the smallest quantity for their development'.[34] These gloomy conclusions were directly opposed to current practice, which applied nitrogenous manures

[34] J. von Liebig, *Letters on Chemistry*, 3rd edn., 1851, pp. 211, 522.

such as Peruvian guano to raise the yields of wheat, and phosphates to turnips and pastures. A young landowner, J. B. Lawes (1814–1900) and a young chemist, J. H. Gilbert (1817–1901) had already begun a long series of experiments on a farm at Rothamsted inherited by the former; preliminary results led them to the cautious conclusion that differences in the mineral content of soils were less important than the availability of those minerals to the growing plants which seemed to depend on the presence of nitrogen and of lime.[35] Experiments by J. Thomas Way and H. S. Thompson also demonstrated that soils could absorb and retain substantial quantities of ammonia (in an undetermined form) from the various fertilisers supplied; and that clay soils retained the highest proportion while sandy soils were easily leached of their nitrogen by water.[36]

By 1850, therefore, the chemists had done little more than confirm the practices of the best farmers who fed their fattening animals with some variety of pulse or oilseed to supplement the bulky fodder in the form of turnips, hay and straw; who fed their lands with Peruvian guano, powdered bones or Lawes's superphosphate to supplement their farmyard manure; who kept the rain off their dung-heaps; who manured light lands frequently and broke up the sub-soil to deepen their cultivations. More farmers might have followed these examples had the price of purchased supplements borne a constant relation to their value. Unfortunately, the composition of oilcake and of such natural products as Peruvian guano varied greatly; the chemists were uncertain which of the various ingredients contained the most valuable component; and adulteration was so common as to be universally expected. 'I got a ton and a half [of guano] at Bradley's in High Street', said the Archdeacon, 'and it was a complete take-in. I don't believe there was five hundred-weight of guano in it.'[37] But contemporary chemical analysis could be useful in the

[35] J. B. Lawes and J. H. Gilbert, 'On Agricultural Chemistry', *J.R.A.S.E.*, vol. 12.i, 1851, p. 33.

[36] H. S. Thompson, 'On the Absorbent Power of Soils', *J.R.A.S.E.*, vol. 11.i, 1850, pp. 68–74.

[37] A. Trollope, *Barchester Towers*, 1857.

detection of fraudulent mixtures of sand with fertiliser and saw-dust with oilcake. The two national societies had already appointed consulting chemists to advise their members on the composition of these purchased requisites: Dr Thomas Anderson worked in Edinburgh for the Highland and Agricultural Society from 1849 to his death in 1874; and first Leon Playfair and then J. Thomas Way performed similar functions for the Royal Agricultural Society. Anderson at Edinburgh, Way in London, Voelcker newly appointed to succeed Way at the Royal Agricultural College at Cirencester, Lawes and Gilbert at Rothamsted, were almost the only professional workers at this time in the field of agricultural chemistry, which included not only the analysis of fertilisers and feeding stuffs but also the chemistry of soils and the physiology of plants and animals.

Agricultural chemistry had thus proved itself to be of some value to farmers, firstly in detecting adulteration, and secondly through Lawes's invention of superphosphate, the treatment of bones or mineral phosphates with sulphuric acid to produce a valuable 'patent fertiliser' for arable or grassland. But the mid-nineteenth century was no more successful than earlier ages in combating plant disease; indeed, the potato blight of 1845 and 1846 had been a recent and tragic demonstration of the ignorance of man in the face of destruction of a staple crop which supported the peasant communities of Ireland and of the western islands of Scotland. Johnson, in his *British Husbandry* published in 1847, commented that 'much has been written, to very little purpose, regarding the diseases of corn'. Most farmers, he thought, looked upon rust, mildew and blight as distinct disorders which never-theless arose solely from the influence of the atmosphere, disorders which could be mitigated, though not prevented, by steeping the seed in limewater or in urine in accordance with ancient custom. But solutions of arsenic and of sulphate of ammonia had been proved more satisfactory by recent experiments of French chem-ists, though by no means without risk.[38]

Veterinary science had reached a somewhat comparable stage

[38] *Gardeners' Chronicle and Agricultural Gazette,* 1849, p. 10.

of utility. The experience of generations of animal doctors had developed various methods of repairing damage to bones, joints or muscles in farm animals, but farmers could expect little assistance in preventing or curing diseases. That some types of disease were infectious was obvious to all, in the disastrous epidemics that periodically swept through the cattle herds in Europe and in Britain; but there was no agreement on how this infection spread. Was it contained in discharges from sick animals, or in their breath, or by a generally unfavourable combination of weather or diet which affected many animals simultaneously? How was it that one or two animals might remain obstinately unaffected in the midst of general sickness, or alternatively, that individual cows might slip their calves without provoking an epidemic of abortion? Liver rot in sheep was known to follow grazing on wet ground and to be associated with the presence of flukes in the liver, but were these flukes the cause of the disease, or merely the symptoms of an advanced stage of a condition originated by noxious marsh air? For all such diseases, the remedies of the eighteenth century were still commonly used in the nineteenth. Bleeding was still the general prescription for all inflammatory diseases; sheep scab was countered by flowers of sulphur, tobacco juice, soap or turpentine; liver rot mitigated by pasturing on dry ground and by the provision of salt licks. But there were neither cures nor preventives for the major epidemics which could eliminate hundreds of herds and flocks and reduce flourishing and experienced farmers to bankruptcy. The town dairies were peculiarly liable to these disasters, but the continuous movement of cows, cattle and sheep from the rearing districts through a complex system of markets to the fattening farms and the dairying districts brought almost all farmers within range of general epidemics.

The prosecution of scientific research and the dissemination of its results was the affair of individuals, either singly or in co-operation. The Highland and Agricultural Society supported in Edinburgh the lectures on agriculture given by Professor David Low from 1831 to 1854, and then by John Wilson, as well as those on veterinary science given by William Dick from 1823 to 1866; it held examinations on this latter subject until the founding in 1844 of the Royal College of Veterinary Surgeons which gave a recognised status to this profession. The Society's first advisory chemist, Anderson, took up his post in 1849 and plunged into innumerable analyses for the 2,707 members, of whom only 239 were tenant farmers. It was therefore primarily an association of landowners but many of them were active farmers, or active supervisors of their farming tenants, as well as encouragers of the local farming clubs which could be affiliated to the central Society [39]; these clubs were often the centres of mutual education by the farming members. South of the Border, there were three national societies in London, the Smithfield Club founded in 1798, concerned solely with fat stock; the Farmers' Club, founded in 1844, whose members read papers on various agricultural topics at the monthly meetings; and the Royal Agricultural Society, which published a journal and provided the services of an advisory chemist for its members. Outside London, there were many local farming clubs which held shows each summer and monthly meetings for discussion in the winter, at which members recounted their experiments with guano or linseed or the new drill. A group of landowners, almost all members of these societies, had just founded the Royal Agricultural College at Cirencester, where systematic instruction in the current principles of agricultural science was combined with practical work in the management of a large mixed farm on land leased from Lord Bathurst, and with independent research by the teaching staff. All these institutions depended for their finance on the support of landowners and farmers, together with the fees obtained from those who attended the courses of lectures or availed themselves of the chemical analyses.

If good farming could be learnt from books, there should have been no medieval farming in the British agriculture of 1850. Under Philip Pusey as editor, the bi-annual *Journal of the Royal Agricultural Society* provided full reports of the Society's shows and

[39] A. Ramsay, *op. cit.*, pp. 447–51.

of the scientific lectures given to general meetings; there were also descriptions of farming practice in a series of prize essays and short notes on practical matters, some contributed by Pusey himself from his experience in farming about 350 acres of his family estate at Pusey in Berkshire. Lawes and Gilbert were prompt in publishing the results of their experiments either in the *Journal* or in the *Rothamsted Memoirs on Agricultural Science* which they began in 1847. The new knowledge was also discussed by such periodicals as the *Quarterly Journal of Agriculture* published in Edinburgh from 1828 for the northern farmers and the *Journal of the Bath and West of England Agricultural Society* from 1853. At a more popular level, there was the *Agricultural Gazette*, a monthly publication edited by J. C. Morton who had been a pupil of Low at Edinburgh; its rival the *Farmers' Magazine* ran (with breaks) from 1832 to 1890; the *Mark Lane Express* was established in 1832; and the oldest of them all was *Bell's Weekly Messenger*.[40] 'I means to take a hundred or a hundred and fifty acres in hand, and try all the new experiments on a liberal scale – guano, nitrate o' soder, bone manure, hashes and manure mexed, soot, salt, sand, everything in fact; shall lector on agricultur, and correspond with the Royal Society, and so on – Mr Jorrocks on buck wheat – Mr Jorrocks on clover – Mr Jorrocks on long 'orns – Mr Jorrocks on short 'orns',[41] as the most famous of sporting writers caricatured the urban magnate turned into reforming squire.

THE PROFITS OF FARMING

This wide range of periodical literature could be supplemented by a number of substantial text books, such as Henry Stephens' *Book of the Farm*, describing the management of large mixed farms in south Scotland. Youatt's *The Complete Grazier* had run through eight editions by 1846, and Low's *Elements of Practical Agriculture* had reached a fourth edition by 1843, showing that many graziers and farmers were at least book buyers. These various textbooks

[40] F. A. Buttress, *Agricultural Periodicals of the British Isles, 1681–1900*, Cambridge, 1950.
[41] R. S. Surtees, *Hillingdon Hall, or the Cockney Squire*, London, 1845.

and the observations of contemporaries like James Caird give us some clues to the level of output, profits and expenses which were customary in the agriculture of 1850. The tenant of a mixed farm, with an intensive four- or five-course cropping and the necessary livestock, was thought to require about £10 per acre of farming capital. High farming with oilcake, guano, pedigree stock, steam power, would need more, especially if local custom required an incoming tenant to pay his predecessor the agreed value of his last year's cultivations and manures. Many farmers managed their farms not too badly on £6–£8 per acre of capital, but it was the general opinion that the lower the capital, the lower the output and the income; lack of tenant's capital was commonly quoted as the chief reason for inefficient farming. On the normal level of capital, a farmer of average ability and luck might hope, on the average of years, to obtain a cash return of about 10 per cent or a little more, say round about £1 per acre.[42]

Caird calculated that rents for the large arable farms in the eastern and southern districts of England averaged some 20*s*–25*s* per acre; in the western districts, with smaller farms and the emphasis on livestock, he thought that rents were some 10*s* per acre more. The cost of labour was commonly put at 25*s* or so per acre of arable land; the cost of horse power, with a pair of plough horses to every fifty acres, at about £25 per pair per year, or some 10*s* per acre. If to these sums are added another 20*s*–30*s* per acre for miscellaneous expenditure, we arrive at a total cost of £4–£4½ per acre, which is a rough average of the range of costs collected by Caird (p. 320). Costs in this sense included only those items paid in cash; they excluded the farmer's own income though they included the costs of producing the food grown on the farm for use in the households of the farmer and his men. An average profit of £1 per acre suggests an average gross output valued at £5–£5½ per acre from the well managed arable farm worked on some variant of the corn-roots-grass rotation which obtained its grain yields from a combination of manure, guano

[42] D. Low, *Elements of Practical Agriculture*, 4th edn., Edinburgh, 1843, p. 772; *Agricultural Gazette*, 1849, p. 58; 1850, pp. 44, 57; C. W. Johnson, *op. cit.*, pp. 43, 49.

and crushed bones or superphosphate. What are these figures worth? How many farms would approximate to these averages of costs and profits, output and inputs?

Such accounts as we have of this period relate to large arable farms run by outstanding tenant farmers or by experimentally-minded landowners; neither of these classes can be regarded as typical of the general run of arable farming, and still less as typical of the 190,000 farms recorded in 1851 as being less than 100 acres in size. Even among the bigger arable farms, there were note-worthy differences in cropping systems, in methods of employing and paying labour, in the use of fertilisers and bought feeds, as well as the inevitable differences in the efficiency of management. It was commonly observed, for instance, that the Lothian farmers used fewer horses and therefore required fewer ploughmen in proportion to their arable area than did the farmers in Lincoln-shire or Norfolk. On the light land each side of the Border, it was reckoned that there should be one man and two horses to every 70–90 acres where the land was moderately level, in contrast to the accepted standard in the south of a plough team and plough-man to every fifty acres of arable land.[43]

This economy in horse-power was attributed to the two-year ley, the larger and more regularly shaped fields, and the better man-agement of the Lothian farmers. The northern farms also seem to have paid a higher proportion of their wages in farm produce and in the keep of livestock, a practice which reduced both their sale-able output and their money costs of labour in comparison with ·the practice common in the south of paying wages almost wholly in cash.

Of the mainly grassland farms, whether dairy or fattening or stock rearing, we have still less in the way of reliable accounts, whether financial or physical. The output of the dairy farms took the form of butter and cheese, except in the immediate neighbour-hood of towns with a market for liquid milk, and there is only fragmentary evidence on average milk yields. Contemporary opinion recorded that a herd of good dairy cows properly man-

[43] J. Haxton, 'Light Land Farming', *J.R.A.S.E.*, vol. 15.i, 1854, p. 105.

aged might give 3–3½ cwt of cheese each in a season, a milk yield for this purpose of some 400 gallons. Sewell Read assumed that the Buckinghamshire dairies had an average yield per cow of some 200 lb of butter in nine months, all destined for the London market.[44] But there must have been many farms where under-fed cows reared a calf and provided no more than a couple of hundred gallons of milk in the summer grazing season.

To this summary of the scanty data on milk yields, there can be added some indirect evidence on profits from those districts where it was common for the farmers on large holdings to sublet their herd of cows, as in Dorset, whose butter commanded the best reputation and the highest price on the London market. The farmers supplied the cows and all the food required at the rate of about 2½–3 acres per cow, partly for summer grazing, partly for hay in winter; the dairymen paid a rent ranging from £8 10s to £10 per cow per year, from the proceeds of the butter, cheese and pigs, while calves were usually sold back to the farm. Over and above this rent, the dairymen must have obtained enough to keep themselves and their families, on whom fell the work of milking the cows, making and selling the dairy produce and rearing the calves.[45] Caird recorded a similar level of rents in Devon for a similar type of 'share-milking', to use the modern terminology; and Acland noted that on the north Somerset marshes three acres would keep a cow whose produce from summer grazing would yield 3–4 cwt of cheese selling at 50s–65s per cwt, the middle range about paying the rent of the land.[46] Presumably, therefore, these West Country dairies, using only summer grass and winter hay, could expect a gross return of, say, £15 per cow and upwards, depending on the quality of the pasture, the skill of the dairy-women and the price level in local markets.

[44] C. Sewell Read, 'Farming of Buckinghamshire', *J.R.A.S.E.*, vol. 16.i, 1855, p. 299.

[45] L. H. Ruegg, 'On the Production of Butter', *J.R.A.S.E.*, vol. 14.i, 1853, p. 74.

[46] J. Caird (1), p. 54; T. D. Acland and W. Sturge, *Farming of Somerset*, London, 1851, p. 51.

Of the fattening and rearing farms, no generalisations can safely be made. From the natural pastures that fattened a bullock to the acre, there was all the variation that led to the Blackface ewes on the lower slopes of the Cairngorms. As always, the profits of these stock farms would vary with the ravages of disease, with the variability of the season, and with the range of prices obtained for a few commodities – wool, or store stock or fattened beasts. But it seems likely that these grassland farmers bought little from the industrial world of that time; that they relied almost entirely on home-grown feeds, without help from fertilisers or oilcake; and that if the proceeds from the sale of their main product paid the rent and the haymakers and left them with a little cash in hand, they would not bother about accounts.

PROGRESS AND PRICES

The lack of information on agricultural output was greatly deplored by Porter in his famous work *The Progress of the Nation*. He had no doubt that there had been marked progress in the production from British agriculture in the half-century before 1850, but in the absence of any statistics on crops and livestock it could only be measured indirectly. There had been the steady enclosure of waste lands under private Acts of Parliament and under the recent General Inclosure Act of 1845; the output from the arable fields was also rising with the greater use of field drains, guano, superphosphate and steam ploughs.[47] More conclusively, there ·was the rise in the population of Great Britain from $10\frac{3}{4}$ million in 1801 to the 20·9 million to be recorded at the census of 1851, fed very largely from British agriculture. Imports into the United Kingdom of wheat and flour in the early 1840s amounted to less than 3 million quarters annually in years of fairly high prices at home, falling to almost nothing in years of good harvests such as 1845, when home prices were low and the import duties high. The famine year of 1847, when wheat was scarce all over Europe,

[47] G. R. Porter, *The Progress of the Nation*, London, 1851, pp. 138–66; see Ch. iv, p. 125.

brought imports of wheat not much more than the normal level, but imports of maize for Ireland rose from almost nothing to 3–4 million quarters, while nearly 2 million quarters of flour and meal were also brought into the country. Porter calculated that, on the average of the nine years 1841 to 1849, and assuming an average consumption in Britain of 6 bushels of wheat per head per year, the import of grain would then have supplied about 3·5 million persons, compared with 16·1 million fed from British wheat; if the average consumption was judged to be 8 bushels, then the imports sufficed for only 2·6 million people, against 17 million supported by British agriculture.

Until 1847, the imports of grain followed the price trends in the British market, rather than induced them. Grain imports increased when prices in this country rose above those in the other European countries that were the chief suppliers, and rose above the level at which heavy duties were imposed; imports fell when good harvests at home brought low prices to British farmers and high duties to importers. But the Corn Laws had been swept away and past experience was therefore no guide to the future of the grain market. From the two years 1848 and 1849, however, farmers could note a new and ominous pattern in prices and imports. Both these harvests, and that also of 1850, were good, yet the imports of wheat, wheat flour and maize had considerably exceeded the level of all previous years, except that of the famine itself; prices of wheat on British markets had fallen steadily from the 50–60*s* per quarter common in the early years of the decade to below 40*s* per quarter in the autumn of 1849 and the spring of 1850. Wheat at less than 40*s* per quarter could not return the costs of production on many farms whose low yields implied high costs per quarter for ploughing, cultivating, weeding and cutting. Either yields must be increased by better drainage and more fertilisers, or costs reduced by steam power and other economies in labour and horses.

Nor was it only the grain market whose future was so uncertain. In spite of heavy import duties, there had always been a regular import from the Low Countries and northern France of live cattle and pigs, of butter, cheese and eggs, destined mainly for the London market. Friesland butter was regularly quoted in London, in competition with butter from Dorset and Buckinghamshire and with the salt butter from Ireland; and many of the urban dairies filled some of their stalls with imported cows. In repealing the Corn Laws, Peel's government had also repealed the duties on the import of live animals, meat and hams, and also substantially reduced those on bacon, dairy produce and eggs; these last survivals of the food taxes were again reduced in 1853 and eliminated in 1860. Imports of all these products showed increases after 1847 and livestock farmers suffered from unusually low meat prices from 1848 to 1852.

It is not surprising, therefore, that most farmers and landowners faced the 1850s with anxiety. Caird, Peel and other educated and moneyed men might write encouragingly of the growing demand for meat and milk and beer from the great expanding towns in the newly industrialised areas; they might preach the virtues of fertilisers, the greater profits of milk or meat over wheat, the greater efficiency of steam power and of reapers. But the application of these new ideas meant money, money either from the tenant farmers for machinery or superphosphate, or from the landowners for tile drains and new buildings. With markets wide open to imports from all countries and continents, would tenants and landowners be willing to invest their money and their work in the capital structure of their farms? To what extent could British agriculture share in that industrial revolution of the last half of the nineteenth century whose symbols were the steam-engine on land and the steam-ship on the high seas?

2

The Preponderance of the
Landed Interest

*Political Power – Local Government – Sport – Social Position – Philip Pusey – Wales –
Scotland – Corporate Owners – Encumbered Estates and Family Settlements*

THE predominant partner who would have to take the lead in
the application of these new ideas to agriculture was the landowner. The great territorial magnate in the mid-nineteenth century had inherited immense prestige from the eighteenth century
and Regency period when agricultural wealth had been the
principal support of gracious building and the cultivation of the
art of living to its highest point. Britain's heritage of beauty, its
country houses and gardens, its private art collections and libra-
ries, are evidence of the taste and wealth applied to the encouragement of the architects, artists, authors and musicians in whom
those periods were so rich. The social position and political power
of the group, comparatively small, of aristocratic families, both
Whig and Tory, went unchallenged. They regarded themselves
as belonging to an order different from that of the general run of
mankind, and were accepted at their own valuation without
question until the French Revolution demonstrated how easily an
aristocracy could be eliminated. But the English aristocracy,
rooted in the land, and living much on their own estates, were
in a position far stronger than that of their opposite numbers across
the Channel. Thus they weathered all the storms of the early
nineteenth century – its growing industrialism, the awakening
of the political consciousness of the middle classes culminating in
the Reform Act of 1832, the agricultural depression, the Chartist
movement and the Repeal of the Corn Laws.[1]

[1] This subject is covered more fully by F. M. L. Thompson in his book, *English
Landed Society in the Nineteenth Century*, London, 1963.

POLITICAL POWER

The Reform Act shook their political power by abolishing the pocket boroughs, but they retained their hold on the county seats, which were increased in number, with little difficulty. The two-member seats which the Act set up made possible family compacts to divide them, constituencies returning one Whig and one Tory at the behest of the leading landowners. On many of the smaller boroughs, too, they kept a stranglehold. Moreover, the Act gave the vote to tenant farmers paying over £40 a year in rent, and as many of these could be turned out at six months' notice, he was a bold man who, before the days of the secret ballot, would vote against his landlord's nominee. Eviction or threats of eviction, for political reasons, were by no means uncommon for many years after the passing of the Act. Lady Charlotte Guest has left the following account of a contest during the election of 1837: 'The Tory landlords brought their tenants up themselves like flocks of sheep, and made them break their pledge-words. They absolutely dragged them to the Poll, threatening to turn them out of their farms unless they voted plumpers for Lord Adare. One man shed tears on being forced to this.'[2] At the same election, a member of the great Whig family of Grosvenor complained of Mr Gladstone, at that time still an unrepentant Tory, for violating the sacred canons of electioneering etiquette by canvassing the Westminster tenants. 'I did think', he wrote, 'that interference between a landlord with whose opinions you were acquainted and his tenants was not justifiable according to those laws of delicacy and propriety which I considered binding in such cases.'[3]

There was a considerable scandal over the 1837 election in West Wales, when Lord Cawdor was accused of unduly influencing his tenants to vote for the candidate he supported, the Earl himself having changed sides since the last election. His agent had instructed all the tenants to vote for his nominee, and there was a debate on the subject in the House of Commons in

[2] Lady Charlotte Guest; extracts from her *Journal, 1833–1852*, ed. by The Earl of Bessborough, London, 1950, p. 54.

[3] John Morley, *Life of Gladstone*, London, 1903, vol. i, p. 239.

June 1838. Sir James Graham argued 'that landlords might appropriately guide the judgment of their tenants', and Lord John Russell joked about tenants 'wandering about in search of information as to which way their landlord was going to vote'.[4] Putting pressure upon tenants in this way was the general practice among landowners, as everybody knew, so no action was taken. This sort of political intimidation was to become a burning question later in the century, particularly in Wales, as men became more politically conscious and the franchise was extended. The introduction of the ballot in 1872 safeguarded the secrecy of the actual vote, but for long years after that tenants dared not openly support a candidate of a different colour to the landlord. In fact it was not until farmers had attained real security of tenure that they could afford to be politically independent – on those estates where politics loomed large.

Political parties in the middle years of the nineteenth century were highly fluid and there were as many landlords among the Whigs as among the Tories. Although the agitation for the repeal of the Corn Laws was organised and carried through by industrialists of the north, many landowners were free traders, and did not share the belief that without protection agriculture was doomed. What they were all united in believing was that good government stood for sound administration and the protection of property in all its forms, but that the less it interfered with private life the better. The country must be ruled by gentlemen, who were its natural leaders, and the social structure was accepted by all classes as part of the natural order of things.

LOCAL GOVERNMENT

After the aristocratic families, owning vast estates, came the great mass of smaller landowners, some of them owning considerable areas, others single parishes, others again only a few farms. Most of these lived on their estates, taking an active part in

[4] David Williams, *The Rebecca Riots*, Cardiff, 1955, p. 32.

management, and being the acknowledged leaders in society and in local government.

'The Justices of the Peace, drawn from the landed gentry and embodying that spirit of autocratic dilettantism which marked the internal government of England from 1800 to 1830',[5] were still the organ of administration in the mid-nineteenth century. The Municipal Reform Act of 1835 had put the government of towns into the hands of elected representatives, but in the country the old parish organisation by manor court or vestry had mostly broken down and the Justices were the only authority. They were appointed directly by the Crown, on the recommendation of the Lord Lieutenant of the county, himself a leading landowner, and to be on the Bench was considered part of the normal pattern of life of a country gentleman. The amount of time and energy they gave varied according to individual taste and capacity; the great nobleman with estates in several counties took little part in purely local affairs, but for the smaller squires Quarter Sessions was a sort of club where they met their fellows and felt their importance increase as they directed the affairs of the county. As well as administering justice at Quarter and Petty Sessions, they were responsible for highways and bridges, prisons, licensing of public houses, the raising of rates and many other matters. The New Poor Law seemed to have brought a new element into local government with its elected Guardians of the Poor, but all J.P.s were *ex officio* Guardians, and their meetings were generally held on the same day and in the same place as the Petty Sessions, so that in ·one capacity or another the landed interest retained its supremacy.

Another important function of the J.P.s was the direction of the County Police, for the adoption of a County Police Force in place of the old Parish Constables, at first optional, was made compulsory in 1856. All this work was done voluntarily, with practically no paid staff, and though no doubt it satisfied their sense of power, there was also a real sense of obligation among many landowners, a feeling that property had its duties as well as its rights.

[5] J. Redlich and F. W. Hirst, *The History of Local Government in England*, 1958, p. 107.

SPORT

Sport played a large part in the lives of English landowners. Hunting and shooting had been recognised occupations of a country gentleman for many centuries, and in the nineteenth century both became more highly organised and elaborate. Stag hunting, hare hunting and coursing were traditional sports, but fox hunting predominated, and all of them carried a tacit recognition of the right of hunting folk to commit trespass. Trollope's *American Senator* found this very hard to understand.

> I know it will be impossible [he said in his lecture] to make my countrymen believe that a hundred harum-scarum tomboys may ride at their pleasure over every man's land, destroying crops and trampling down fences, if their vermin leads them there, going with reckless violence into the sweet domestic gardens of your country residences; – and that no one can either stop them or punish them. An American will believe much about the wonderful ways of his British cousin, but no American will be got to believe that till he sees it.

Until the end of Queen Victoria's reign, a royal pack was maintained at Windsor, and the office of Master of the Buckhounds was a Cabinet appointment, changing with the Government. On a famous north Midland estate, where the noble owners have maintained a pack of foxhounds for more than two hundred years, the revenues of two farms are said to have been included in the family settlement upon the condition that hounds should go out during the season on no fewer than two days a week. Hunting was part of the serious business of life, and many writers of Victorian fiction have made abundantly clear the place the sport held in the lives of the squires about whom they wrote. But the pleasure was shared by all classes in the English countryside. Farmers and tradesmen rode to hounds when they could afford it, and sometimes when they could not, for social as well as for sporting reasons. The first action of a *nouveau riche* on buying a country estate was to send a subscription to the local Hunt. To farm workers the passage of the pack through the fields in which they were working provided a welcome break and distraction, a chance to show which way the fox had gone, to open a gate, or to help a casualty at a jump. In the villages the meet was a colourful spectacle and an excitement for young and old, and many would follow on foot. To shoot a fox was an unthinkable crime, and if the Hunt were generous over poultry losses and other damage, there was nothing about hunting to engender bad feeling such as extensive game preserving produced.

The social effects of shooting were very different, because it was essentially a class sport and the landowners were protected by the Game Laws. Probably more time was spent by J.P.s in rural areas on cases of breaches of these laws than on any other kind of offence. The whole subject of who should be allowed to kill wild animals and birds goes far back into history, to the Norman Conquest and earlier, but by the beginning of the nineteenth century it was well established that shooting was the prerogative of landowners and that heavy penalties were the lot of anyone found trespassing with intent to kill game. Certain wild creatures were no longer regarded as a source of food, or as vermin to be destroyed; they were for sport and were jealously preserved, though the practice and intensity of preserving varied widely from estate to estate and from county to county, according to the taste and fancy of the landowner and the sort of country in which the estate was situated. Only those who had a landed inheritance amounting to £100 a year, eldest sons of men of rank and esquires, and persons authorised by a lord of the manor, such as gamekeepers, were allowed to shoot. Moreover no game might be sold. For a time, mantraps and spring guns were allowed to be put in the game covers and the penalty for being caught trespassing with a gun was transportation for seven years; but these more brutal manifestations were abolished shortly before our period opens, for the loss of life and limb and liberty had aroused the public conscience. But poaching went on, both by individuals who wanted something for the pot, and by gangs both within the villages or from nearby towns.

As the century advanced, shooting became more and more fashionable, keepering and rearing of game birds more elaborate and the scale of shooting parties larger. This meant greatly increased expense for the landowner, even when much of the game was sold. The saying was 'Up goes a guinea, bang goes a penny and down comes half-a-crown'. In parts of England such as the Brecklands of Norfolk, admittedly not country of high agricultural value, farming was completely secondary to sport. A striking example of this is the Elveden estate of some 5,000 acres, which changed hands three times in the course of the century, each time going to a wealthy man not dependent upon his agricultural rents for an income. Here the shooting was organised to the highest pitch, thousands of birds were artificially reared and crops grown for them, enormous bags were taken at the great shooting parties held at intervals through the season, and most of the land was kept in hand to avoid disputes with tenants over game damage.[6]

To farmers excessive preserving was a real grievance, because of the damage done to crops by pheasants, and by hares and rabbits, and it was aggravated by the prohibition of shooting trespassing game. To watch your best wheat being devoured and to be powerless to do anything about it must have been exacerbating in the extreme. Some landlords made an allowance in the rent to farmers whose fields adjoined game covers; of course the bitterness varied from estate to estate, according to the vigilance of the keepers and the personal relations of landlord and tenant.

During the Anti-Corn-Law League campaign, John Bright tried to use the Game Laws to drive a wedge between landlords and farmers. When he entered Parliament in 1845 he began to get up a case, interviewing many farmers, poulterers, poachers and others to get his facts, and trying to estimate the amount of corn lost to the nation by game depredations. Then he rose in a House of Commons full of sportsmen and demanded a Select Committee to enquire into the whole question. They listened to him and he was granted his Committee (no small triumph), but there the matter rested, and Bright admitted a few years later that he had been forced to drop the agitation, 'not having received

6 G. Martelli, *The Elveden Enterprise*, London, 1952.

that aid from farmers which their private representations had induced me to expect'.[7]

It was too soon; another generation was to pass before any substantial alteration of the Game Laws could be made. Much of the evidence Bright collected was embodied in Harriet Martineau's *Game Law Tales*.

SOCIAL POSITION

Though many country estates had been held by the same families for centuries, and their owners were proud of their long descent, their ranks since the days of the Tudors had been invaded by the monied men, the wealthy merchants of the city, the bankers and successful lawyers. To invest in land was the common practice when it could be acquired, and the old hereditary nobility and gentry had absorbed and intermarried with the newcomers, to their material advantage, in a way that would have been impossible in continental countries such as France and Germany. But in the nineteenth century a new class was beginning to invade the countryside, the rich manufacturers from the Midlands and North, wanting to get away from the vicinity of mill or factory and to make their sons into gentlemen on their new country estates. These in their turn were duly accepted and absorbed, not without some laughter at their uncouth manners, and the countryside benefited by the money they brought into it.

It must be remembered, too, that many of the smaller squires in the 1830s and 1840s were themselves ill-educated. The aristocracy sent their sons to Eton, Winchester and the like, and then to the University, but other boys went to the local endowed Grammar Schools, and the quality of these, completely independent and uninspected as they were, varied enormously and was often very bad. But the squires' sons rubbed shoulders with the farmers' sons, often to their mutual advantage. Sometimes they did not go to school at all, but to a clergyman who took a few pupils in his own house. The reform and growth of many Gram-

[7] G. M. Trevelyan, *Life of John Bright*, London, 1913, pp. 124–28.

mar Schools, and the rise of new foundations such as Marlborough, Wellington, and Clifton in the middle part of the century, together with the coming of the railways, making it possible for boys easily to travel to schools in other parts of the country, changed the outlook of the landed gentry in many ways. Instead of mixing with their tenants' sons and rarely leaving their own county, they went away to be better taught and to mix with the growing middle and professional classes. This may have broadened their minds and deepened their sense of responsibility, but it also widened the social gulf between them and their country neighbours when they came home.

But the foremost duty of a rural landlord, in a period when knowledge of agricultural science and technique was growing fast, was the care and improvement of his estate and the encouragement of better farming by his tenants. The great days of Turnip Townshend and Coke of Norfolk were not forgotten, and some of the landlords of the Victorian era showed their capacity for leadership in the founding of the Royal Agricultural Society of England in 1839. Earl Spencer was its first President, and its object was to further the improvement of English agriculture by the application of science to practice. It was founded during the agitation for the repeal of the Corn Laws, and, with great wisdom, its sponsors agreed to ban all political discussion, so that both Whig and Tory landowners and others might be able to work together for the promotion of knowledge and the dissemination of information, by means of shows, experiments, demonstrations, prizes, an annual journal, and so on. By 1844 its membership had risen to over 6,000 and its influence grew steadily as the century advanced.[8]

But this is not to say that all landowners were concerned with the promotion of better farming among their tenants. As Mr Villiers put it in the Debate on the Address in 1850:

Land is not regarded by many of its owners as a means of producing the greatest quantity of produce at the least possible cost. Land has a value to

[8] J. A. Scott Watson, *The History of the Royal Agricultural Society of England, 1839–1939*, London, n.d.

many people quite independent of that consideration. Accordingly, we find that it depends much upon the taste and objects of the proprietor what will generally be the tenure or circumstance of the farmer or cultivator of the soil. One man is a sportsman, and preserves game on his land, which destroys much of the produce. Another man is a politician, and cares more for the vote than the skill of his farmers. Another charges his estate with debt, and has nothing left, after paying the interest, for improvements. Another looks to influence from the possession of territory; while many like to tie up the land or limit the interest of the owner, for the sake of perpetuating the same property in one line of descent; while there are few only who are very ardent agriculturists.[9]

Politics, administration, sport, estate improvement, the home farm, one or other, in greater or lesser degree, were the chief interests of country landowners in the middle of the century. Occasionally there might be found among them a student, like the one in Tennyson's *The Village Wife*, who was 'a Varsity scholard and niver lookt arter the land', who bought books and statues and got heavily in debt. Some were really learned men making their contribution to the intellectual life of the time; some bogus, like Mr Brooke in *Middlemarch*. There were occasional eccentrics, but by and large English landlords were outdoor men without much real interest in culture – Matthew Arnold's 'Barbarians'. Many were moved by the religious awakening in the Church, both Evangelical and Tractarian, but their religion expressed itself practically, in charity, in the building of schools and cottages for their dependants, and in church restoration. Of course there were black sheep who ran through their patrimonies in various forms of folly or vice, but the grosser hedonism of the upper classes in Regency times was no longer tolerated. The practice of duelling had died out, and by the middle of the century respectability and a growing social conscience were more the marks of the English country squire. The Duke of Omnium had been succeeded by Plantagenet Palliser.

[9] *Hansard*, 31 Jan. 1850.

The Preponderance of the Landed Interest

PHILIP PUSEY

There were notable leaders of agricultural improvement in this period, and the most outstanding was Philip Pusey. He was not a man of great wealth or vast acreage, but the owner of a small estate of 5,000 acres in Berkshire. Born in 1799, he inherited the estate in 1830, and sat in Parliament from 1833 to 1852, following the fortunes of Sir Robert Peel. He was a highly versatile man, cultured and literary (one of the founders of the London Library), and also very practical and interested in all branches of science. He was a founder member of the Royal Agricultural Society of England, and gave it its motto, 'Practice with Science'. From the beginning he was Chairman of the Society's Journal Committee and virtually its editor, writing in it regularly and collecting material for it. His conviction that modern scientific knowledge must be applied to farming if agriculture was to flourish led him to cultivate the men of science, and to break down the social barrier which divided them from the landed gentry. He would invite men like Josiah Parkes, the land drainage expert, Liebig, the great German chemist, Dr Daubeny, the botanist, and other eminent men, to stay with him and to lecture and discuss with local landowners and farmers, and he was always ready to try experiments on his own home farm. New machinery interested him immensely, and he was in charge of the agricultural implements section of the Great Exhibition. Caird remarked in his *English Agriculture*: 'The benefit which Mr Pusey does to the district around him, by introducing new agricultural implements, is readily recognised by the farmers, who profit by adopting those which he finds successful, while they, of course, avoid his failures.'[10]

Pusey believed firmly that British agriculture could flourish without protection if it took advantage of the new knowledge available to it, as he showed in his valedictory address to his constituents in 1852: 'Protection has this year fallen ridiculously, not by the assault of its enemies but the desertion of its supporters. . . .

[10] James Caird (1), p. 111.

Improvement has more resources than ever to offer, and its loudest opponents, stepping from the heights of their eloquence, must soon pay it a silent tribute by consenting to purchase new manures and less uncouth implements. Chemistry and mechanism have beaten politics and protection.'[11]

He saw that farmers must have security of tenure and compensation for disturbance of their tenancy if they were to give of their best to the land. He brought up the question in Parliament, and in 1848 got a select Committee of the House to consider it, with himself as Chairman; its Report became the basis of later legislation.[12] He was an extremely enlightened landlord of his own estate, rebuilding his cottages and caring for the welfare of his labourers in every way. His untimely death in 1855 was a sad loss to the country, and twenty years later Disraeli said of him in the House of Commons: 'Mr. Pusey was, both by his lineage, his estate, his rare accomplishments, and fine abilities, one of the most distinguished country Gentlemen who ever sat in the House of Commons.'[13]

WALES

In both Wales and Scotland the position of landlords differed from that in England in various ways. In rural Wales, in the 1840s, the class barrier between owners and tenants was very strong, accentuated as it was by the strength of the Methodist revival in the early part of the century, and by the acute poverty of both farmers and farm workers. As in Scotland, the old basis of landowning had been tribal, and there was still the feeling among dependants of loyalty and deference towards the head of the family.

But much land had changed hands. Some of the large estates had passed to Englishmen who had married Welsh heiresses; others had been bought by wealthy industrialists such as the Guests. Others were held by old Welsh families who also had

---

[11] Sir Ernest Clarke, 'Philip Pusey', *J.R.A.S.E.*, vol. 11.iii, 1900.

[12] See p. 170.

[13] *Hansard*, 24 June 1875.

estates in England or Scotland, so there was much absenteeism, and the estates were run by agents, though the mansions were lived in for part of the year. The smaller estates were often heavily mortgaged, and their owners, though Welshmen and proud of their descent from ancient Welsh kings, had ceased to speak Welsh, and showed little interest in estate improvement, or in anything except sport and getting their rents in full. In an impoverished countryside where Methodism was the prevailing religion, they represented an alien Church and an oppressive oligarchy quite out of touch with those who depended upon them. Sir James Graham, when he was Home Secretary, wrote to Sir Robert Peel in 1843: 'I grieve to say that South Wales bids fair to rival Ireland. Poverty and the misconduct of landlords are at the root of crime in both countries. . . . This is a truth not the less dangerous because it cannot be openly declared.'

When the Rebecca Riots in the 1840s brought to a head the acute social unrest in South Wales, it became clear that the landlords were not able to take the lead in maintaining order and redressing the many grievances from which their tenants suffered. There was actually a shortage of magistrates, for though there were plenty of names on the list, few of them ever functioned on the Bench. Yet when the Home Office, during the riots, urged the appointment of more magistrates, the answer was that it was not possible 'without descending to a grade of persons who have not usually been included in the commission of the peace'.[14]

The situation in South Wales was summed up by *The Times* thus:

It cannot be denied that the people look upon the landlords and gentry and magistrates, as a *class*, with hatred and suspicion, and if one quarter of the stories are true which I have heard, not without just cause. That this arises from no Chartist or political feeling, but solely from oppressive and insulting, haughty, offensive demeanour I am convinced, from the fact that whenever an individual of the gentry has pursued an opposite course, he is beloved and idolised.[15]

[14] D. Williams, op. cit, pp. 18, 37.
[15] *The Times* 30 Sept. 1843. Quoted in *Royal Commission on Land in Wales and Monmouth*, 1896 (C-8221).

SCOTLAND

Conditions of Scottish landowners after the repeal of the Corn Laws were different from those in England, and can only be understood in the light of the history of that country. In England, 'the power of the overmighty subject' had been put down by the end of the fifteenth century, and since that time Englishmen had lived in (comparative) peace and security, broken only by the Civil War which finally established the rule of law more firmly than ever. But Scotland, until the Act of Union in 1707, had never, except for brief periods, had a strong central government, nor been free from civil or external war and violence and the recurring fear of famine. There had been little opportunity to cultivate the arts of peace. Yet in spite of her troubled history, inclement climate and general poverty, when peace and stability had been secured, agriculture and industry were to develop with amazing rapidity, and in this some of her landowners in both the Highlands and the Lowlands took part.

In the Highlands, after the rising of 1745, the clan system under which society was organised was broken up, the 'Heritable Jurisdictions' were abolished, and the hereditary chieftains who had exercised such absolute power had to adapt themselves to a totally new way of life. Formerly what they asked of their estates was the largest possible number of men ready to take arms when called upon. After the '45 they began to realise that it was not men that they needed, but money, and that if their estates were to yield them an income, agriculture would have to be improved, and some of the surplus population living at starvation level in the Highland glens and the Islands would have to go. As the Duke of Argyll put it: 'Disembarrassed on the one hand of powers which had outlived their time, and emancipated on the other hand, from liabilities which discouraged the use of capital, the Ownership of Land in Scotland was ready to go forward faster, and with redoubled energy, on a career which indeed was by no means new, but which was now to be pursued under more favourable conditions and with an immense development of industrial results.'[16]

The ancient feudal dues and services exacted from tenants and sub-tenants by their overlord were superseded by a system of tenure by leases in which the mutual obligations of landlord and tenant were exactly defined. Leases had long been the practice in other parts of Scotland – the Duke of Argyll refers to one in his possession dated 1631 – and there is no doubt that the Scottish habit of giving a clear legal basis to their land tenure was more conducive to agricultural improvement than the loose system of tenancy at will which prevailed over much of England. This is not the place to tell the story of the various attempts to reorganise the Highlands – the raising of the Highland Regiments; the teaching of better methods of farming; the founding of the Highland and Agricultural Society in 1784; the promotion of industries such as fishing and kelp-gathering; the encouragement of emigration overseas; the bringing in of sheep; the Highland Clearances.

The Highlands were for the most part owned in very large estates (reckoned in acreage not in wealth) by noble families. No doubt there was still a sentimental tie of loyalty to the head of the clan, but the Highlanders did not know their landlords as English farmers knew theirs. The noble owners did not live on their estates all the year round, they came north for the shooting and fishing, and the technical estate management was carried on by commissioners, generally lawyers, who would have several stewards or factors under them. Some landlords were interested in schemes for improvement, particularly in forestry. Much planting and experiments in the introduction of new species were carried on in the nineteenth century. But it was all remote from the ordinary life of the Gaelic-speaking crofter who was still living in extreme poverty, but who did not take kindly to efforts to make him change his way of living.

In the Lowlands, though there were many large estates, there were also many small ones which the owners managed themselves. This they regarded as both an art and a business, and in the

[16] Duke of Argyll, *Scotland as it was and as it is*, Edinburgh, 1887, 2nd ed., p. 280.

improvement of agriculture and forestry they associated their sons. 'Ae be sticking in a tree; it will be growing while you are sleeping' was the advice of one of them to his grandson. Scottish landowners did not have the political influence nor the consuming interest in politics of English ones; nor did they have such exclusive power in local government. Administration was more centralised in some matters, and in minor local affairs the chief social force and censor of morals was the Kirk Session, consisting of the elders of the Kirk and chief heritors (i.e. farmers). Scotland, like Wales, had lately been deeply shaken by a religious revival which had resulted in the Disruption, the splitting of the Established Church and the foundation of the new Free Church of Scotland. The split turned largely on the relations of Church and State, and as the landowners were mainly on the side of the Establishment, and had threatened to withhold sites for the new churches the Free Churchmen wished to build, they were further estranged from the people. Thus the general social pattern in rural areas was utterly different from that in most English villages, where the squire and parson usually pulled together, and the aim of the Church of England was to put a gentleman in every parish of the country. In rural Scotland communities were smaller and much more scattered, and the domination of the great house over a docile village rarely to be found.

CORPORATE OWNERS

Not all the agricultural land of Britain was owned by individuals, for the Crown, the Church, and charitable institutions of all kinds were also landowners. The Royal Forests, the estates of the Duchies of Cornwall and Lancaster, and other land formerly the personal property of the Crown, had been made over to the State in the eighteenth century in return for a Civil List, and were managed by the Commissioners of Crown Lands. The Church of England was a considerable landowner, from the Cathedral Chapters to the parish priests. In some parishes the parson still farmed his glebe land himself, while in others it was let to tenants.

Then there were the estates of charitable trusts, of which the most extensive were those owned by the Colleges of Oxford and Cambridge[17]; but a large number of landowners came into this category, down to the trustees of small village charities owning a few acres. The total amount of land in corporate ownership in the middle of the nineteenth century was about a million and half acres.[18]

ENCUMBERED ESTATES AND FAMILY SETTLEMENTS

Such then is the general picture of British landowners in the middle of the nineteenth century – their political and social supremacy apparently unquestioned, with a magnificent opportunity before them to lead the agricultural industry to new heights of prosperity in a rapidly increasing industrial country. Enterprise, knowledge and capital were needed if they were to respond to this challenge.

By their way of life, the great landlords must have seemed to the rest of the community to be secure and wealthy. Rents had risen sharply during the Napoleonic Wars and had not fallen proportionately in the subsequent depression. Many landowners were not dependent solely upon their agricultural rents for their incomes, but were profiting immensely by the growing industrialisation of the country. The Percys in Northumberland, for example, could exploit great deposits of coal underlying their properties; the Dukes of Bedford, Westminster, Grafton and others of the nobility could lay out building estates in growing London; while there were many others who found more profitable uses than agriculture for their landed estates, through coal and ironstone for industry, building land for the new towns, factories and docks, together with the development of railways.

On the other hand, there were properties which were heavily encumbered with debts and mortgages. The eighteenth century had been a period of magnificent building, when many old country houses were pulled down and replaced by splendid mansions,

---

[17] See p. 160.
[18] J. Caird (2), *The Landed Interest and the Supply of Food,* Ch. 10.

while the new art of landscape gardening was given full scope. All this cost money and made for a more expansive way of life. Moreover, the fashionable pastime, especially in Regency times, was gambling, and that on an exceedingly lavish scale, and fortunes were sometimes staked and lost in a single night. Estate improvement could be expensive too, for Thomas Johnes of Hafod, one of the few improving landlords of Wales, had to sell his estate and died in debt for £50,000.[19]

The classic example in England of aristocratic indebtedness is that of the second Duke of Buckingham and Chandos, who succeeded to the dukedom in 1834. His income from the rents of his estates was about £67,000. He had four mansions, including Stowe, with its magnificent art collections, and was active politically, being the author of the 'Chandos Clause' in the Reform Act which gave tenant farmers a vote. When his son, the Marquis of Chandos, came of age in 1844, the Duke had debts of over £1½ million. Various efforts were made to reduce them, but in 1848 bankruptcy threatened him, and much of the estates had to be sold, as well as the contents of Stowe, a nine days' wonder to London society, while the Duke himself went to live in the Great Western Hotel at Paddington.[20] So by the middle of the nineteenth century there were landowners still trying to pay off the debts incurred by their grandfathers, while continuing to live on their properties and to keep up their social position with all the expenditure which that entailed. On the Ailesbury estate in Wiltshire, the first Marquis of Ailesbury, after building Tottenham House in Savernake Forest, found himself in debt to the tune of about £260,000, and in 1832, to avoid bankruptcy, handed the estate over to trustees.[21]

How many estates had wealth and capital to spare for estate improvement when the challenge of free trade came, and how many were encumbered with debt we do not know. But James

[19] D. Williams, *op. cit.*, pp. 70, 78.

[20] F. M. L. Thompson, 'The End of a Great Estate', *Econ. Hist. Rev.*, vol. 8.ii, 1955, pp. 36–52.

[21] F. M. L. Thompson, 'English Landownership: The Ailesbury Trust, 1832–56', *Econ. Hist. Rev.*, vol. 11.ii, 1958, pp. 121–33.

Caird found an amazing diversity in the efficiency of estate management, and in discussing the landlords' responsibilities, he concluded:

> But there is one great barrier to improvement, which the present state of agriculture must force on the attention of the legislature, – the great extent to which landed property is incumbered. In every county where we found an estate more than usually neglected, the reason assigned was the inability of the proprietor to make improvements, on account of his incumbrances. We have not data by which to estimate with accuracy the proportion of land in each county in this position, but our information satisfies us that it is much greater than is generally supposed. Even where estates are not hopelessly embarrassed, landlords are often pinched by debt, which they could clear off if they were enabled to sell a portion, or if that portion could be sold without the difficulties and expense which must now be submitted to. . . . [22]

These encumbrances to which Caird refers, and which were hampering the proper development of estates, arose from the practice of family settlement. Most landowners at all times in the history of landed estate have striven to preserve their heritage intact from generation to generation. 'The rooted propensity of Englishmen, once possessed of land, to found and keep up a family'[23] had shown itself in the system of primogeniture and family settlement, to prevent the dissipation of the property by any reckless member who succeeded to it. The creation of a perpetual entail of an estate – passing always to the eldest son – had been abolished in England some centuries before, and no land could be tied up for longer than the lives of living persons and for twenty-one years after the death of the longest survivor. But the intentions of the law were defeated by the lawyers through the device of resettlement. Thus a landowner, John, could leave his estate to his eldest son, Robert, and to Robert's son, Charles. But in order to secure provision for his widow and younger children, John would execute a deed of settlement, charging the estate with certain sums for this purpose, and appointing trustees to see that it was carried out. John then became the tenant-for-life, no longer the absolute owner, and Robert the tenant-in-tail, with reversion

[22] J. Caird (1), p. 495.
[23] G. C. Brodrick, *English Land and English Landlords*, London, 1881, p. 332.

to his next brother if he died without issue, and so on through the family. When Robert came of age, the entail could be broken, by agreement between him and his father, but nearly always a fresh settlement would be made. Thus Robert would be provided with an allowance out of the estate, to enable him to marry, and his eldest son would be named the tenant-in-tail in remainder. The opportunity might be taken, when the entail was broken, to sell off some outlying portion of the property to pay off some old debts, and to make any other necessary adjustments in the family settlement, which could not be altered again until Robert's son Charles came of age, when the process of resettlement would begin all over again. There were strong inducements to both parties to agree to a fresh settlement; to the father, so that he could ensure a certain provision for his widow and younger children, without leaving them to the tender mercies of the eldest son, like Mr Dashwood in *Sense and Sensibility*; to the son, so that he might get an allowance independent of his father's caprice and make sure of his own succession to the property. When it is added that the family lawyer was usually a trustee to the settlement, and had the business of drawing it up, it is obvious that a continuance of the practice seemed to be in the interests of everyone.

The system certainly succeeded in its object of building up and keeping intact the family estates of the country. Accurate figures, of course, are not available, but it was estimated in 1847, in evidence given before the Pusey Committee on Agricultural Customs, that some two-thirds of the land of England and at least half the land of Scotland was held under settlement.

The limited owner, as the tenant-for-life was called, with all the social and political prestige with which his property endowed him, might often find himself seriously short of ready money for efficient estate maintenance, much less for improvements. He could not sell any of the land, nor grant leases for longer than his own life, nor raise money on mortgage, nor do anything to prejudice the estate to which his son must succeed. Out of the rental he received, he had to keep up the family mansion and park, pay the jointure of his mother, and allowances to his brothers and sisters charged on the estate by the settlement made on his own coming of age, and any other charges incurred by his father. He might represent the county in Parliament, with all the attendant expenses for elections, a house in London, and so on. If he himself had a large family, their education, a start in life for younger sons and dowries for daughters, had likewise to come out of the estate; and although agricultural rents had risen substantially in the early part of the century, he might have but little left of them for farmhouse and cottage building, for drainage, road-making and all the other improvements which modern agricultural development required. If he had access to other free capital, through marriage with an heiress, compensation paid by railway companies for compulsory purchase of land, successful speculation and so on, he was in a better position; but without any such outside sources of income he was often a seriously embarrassed man.

The heir to a settled estate might seem to be a fortunate young man with an assured future of rights and duties in pleasant surroundings; but here again there were drawbacks. He was less free than his younger brothers. Whatever his tastes and abilities, it was unthinkable that he should enter any profession except the Army, though if he were heir to a peerage, he might go into politics and sit in the House of Commons for some years before proceeding to 'another place'. When he turned twenty-one, the estate provided him with an allowance, but he might be a man of middle age before his father's death gave him control of the property and allowed him to take his rightful place in the county. Victorian fiction is full of examples of such men, spending their time in amusing themselves, hunting, racing, loafing about town, getting into debt, often on bad terms with their fathers, finally going to the money-lenders to borrow, on the expectation of the properties to which they would succeed eventually, at exorbitant interest which would be a charge upon the estate for years to come. Lord Chiltern, George Vavasour, Ralph Newton, Adolphus Longstaffe, Osborne Hamley and many others come to mind from the pages of Anthony Trollope, George Eliot, Mrs Gaskell and other novelists, and the theme occurs also in family memoirs and biographies of the period. Undoubtedly the position of heir to a settled estate was one full of temptation to a young man, and though many passed through it unscathed, many more added further encumbrances to already encumbered properties.

When Lord Shaftesbury succeeded to his father's estate in Dorset in 1851, he was a man of fifty with a large family. He and his father had quarrelled, and he had received only a meagre allowance from the estate, so that for long years while he was in Parliament and working for the improvement of factory conditions, he had been living on borrowed money. He found the estate in a shocking state of neglect and longed to set about improving it, but, as he wrote in his diary: 'Inspected a few cottages – filthy, close, indecent, unwholesome. But what can I do? I am half pauperised; the debts are endless; no money is payable for a whole year, and I am not a young man. Every sixpence I expend – and spend I must on many things – is *borrowed*! . . . Oh, if instead of one hundred thousand pounds to pay in debt, I had that sum to expend, what good I might do!'[24]

In Scotland the problem of settled estates differed somewhat from that in England and Wales. There was the same desire to keep the land in the family at all costs, and deeds of entail or tailzie were drawn up, settling the estate on the eldest son and his heirs in perpetuity, not, as in England, limited to three lives. They were regulated by a statute of 1695 (before the Act of Union with England), under which all who possessed land under entail were prohibited from selling, from contracting debts which might affect the estate, and from altering or defeating the order of succession. The deeds of tailzie, guarded by 'irritant and resolutive clauses', were recorded in a central register, and any disputes were interpreted by the Supreme Court in Edinburgh. There being no possibility of breaking the entail, Scottish landlords, throughout the eighteenth century, were even more restricted than their fellows in England, who could break it on the heir's coming of age. In 1770, however, the Montgomery Act, provided that any proprietor of an entailed estate who laid out

[24] Quoted by J. L. and B. Hammond, *Lord Shaftesbury*, London, 1923, p. 173.

money in enclosing, draining, planting or erecting farmhouses might charge the estate with three-quarters of the money so laid out, provided the amount did not exceed four years' rent. He might also grant leases for thirty-one years, or for fourteen years and one life, or for two existing lives, and might grant building leases of not more than five acres for up to ninety-nine years. This was far in advance of what an English limited owner could do at that date, and coming as it did at a time when knowledge of new methods of farming was spreading, Scottish landowners were able in many ways to collaborate with their tenants in land improvement. Sir John Sinclair's *Agricultural Report on Scotland*, published in 1814, gives a picture of a vigorous community, with much improvement going on. Scottish landowners, except for the very large ones, usually managed their estates themselves, keeping their home farms in their own hands, and associating their heirs with the management. For them, landowning was a business for which knowledge and training were necessary, and Edinburgh University had had a Chair of Agriculture since 1790. The amateur way in which many English landlords managed their estates, or left them to agents or solicitors, was not so often to be seen north of the Border.

Nevertheless, contemporary writers agree about the bad effects of settled estates upon the individuals concerned and upon the development of farming.

The proprietor of an entailed estate, being a mere life-renter, is deprived of the means, and in a great measure of all motive for the improvement of his estate. As a life-renter, his means are necessarily narrowed, and burdened, (on his entry) by the provisions made for the widow and children of the former proprietor, his powers are still further narrowed. A proprietor so situated, and prohibited to give long leases, must be incapacitated from attempting any of the more important improvements, ... and equally incapable of enabling his tenant to undertake such operations. The effect of this, on the productive powers of the estate, and the general improvement of the country, must be very obvious; and in so far, the interest of the community is concerned. But, thus entangled by the fetters of his entail, the heir in possession is unable to support the appearance of a great proprietor, and at the same time to provide for the establishment of his family. The effect of this on the female branches of the family must be peculiarly severe. Bred up with ideas inseparable from the style in which they have lived, their situation, when reduced to the mere pittance the entailed estate can afford, must necessarily produce scenes of deepest domestic misery.[25]

The last sentiment would certainly have been echoed by Mrs Bennet in *Pride and Prejudice*.

In 1848, a Bill, the Law of Entail (Scotland), was introduced into the Commons by the Lord Advocate, Sir Andrew Rutherford, who said that 'its object was to get rid of an absurd and preposterous system which had been a curse to the country for 160 years'.[26] The Bill set out to abolish perpetuity and to enable entails to be broken (as in English law) by the consent of the parties concerned on the heir's coming-of-age, and to allow portions of the estate to be sold for the benefit of younger children. Some of the Scottish peers, while agreeing that reform was needed, felt that the Bill was too sweeping and that it trampled on vested rights; but the Lord Chancellor remarked rather complacently that 'long experience had proved that the [English] law of entail ... was satisfactory, and that they would have a safe precedent to guide them in respect to Scotland'.[27] The Bill passed the Commons without opposition and became law in August 1848.

The only way in which a limited owner could get release from the shackles of a family settlement was by a Private Act of Parliament, setting aside its terms and allowing him to sell or exchange portions of land or to grant long leases. But a Private Act was a slow business, which might cost anything up to £1,500, so that unless the advantages to be gained were very great, the process was not to be lightly undertaken. Nevertheless, in the middle of the century, an average of about fourteen or fifteen Private Bills varying the terms of family settlements were introduced into Parliament every year.

[25] Sir John Sinclair, *Agricultural Report on Scotland*, 1814, vol. 4. Appendix No 1, by Robert Bell, p. 207.

[26] *Hansard*, 24 Feb. 1848.

[27] *Hansard*, 29 June 1848.

In 1855 the Lord Chancellor, Lord Cranworth, brought in the Leases and Sales of Settled Estates Bill, which allowed the tenant-for-life to grant agricultural leases for fourteen years, as well as long building and mining leases, the terms of which would be binding on his successor: and also, under careful safeguards, allowed him to sell outlying portions of his estate. Instead of an expensive Private Act of Parliament, the approval of the Court of Chancery would be sufficient, after approval of the application by a judge.

This was a great advance for the owners of settled estates, who, as Lord St Leonards said, 'did not possess all the powers they desired, and nine-tenths of their Lordships were probably in that position'.[28] But the Bill had a rough passage through the House of Commons, not so much because there were serious objections to its principles, but because a certain Sir Thomas Meryon Wilson, who owned part of Hampstead Heath under a settled estate, wanted to sell this 'playground of London' for building development. He had applied for a Private Act of Parliament, which had been refused, and the Commons were afraid he would try again under the new Act and that the Court of Chancery might over-rule a decision of Parliament. However, the Leases and Sales of Settled Estates Bill became law on 29 July 1856, and by an Amending Act of 1864 limited owners were allowed to grant leases without even applying to the Court of Chancery.

This amount of freedom did not go far enough to enable limited owners to do much in improving their estates. Long agricultural leases were not popular in England, and the process of selling any land was slow and cumbersome. The initiative had to be taken by the trustees, not by the owner himself; the trustees were generally conservative in their outlook and more concerned to safeguard the rights of the heirs than to help the tenant-for-life. Before they would consider any application for the sale of any land, they had to be convinced that it would be for the ultimate benefit of the property and that the money so realised would be spent upon improvement. Moreover, the settlement could be so

[28] *Hansard*, 10 March 1856.

drawn up as expressly to forbid any sale in any circumstances, thus defeating one purpose of the Act.

It is curious that legislation was needed to 'free' landowners from restrictions which each generation imposed on the next, though the settlement need not have been renewed when each eldest son came of age. It appears that the economic development of a landed estate was regarded as of less importance than the continued association of the family and the land throughout successive generations. Sir Walter Elliot's feelings about Kellynch in Jane Austen's *Persuasion* are typical of his class: 'There was only a small part of the estate that Sir Walter could dispose of: but had every acre been alienable, it would have made no difference. He had condescended to mortgage as far as he had the power, but he would never condescend to sell. No; he would never disgrace his name so far. The Kellynch estate should be transmitted whole and entire, as he had received it.'

Further, family settlement gave each limited owner the opportunity of providing for his widow and younger children independently of his heir. Money is the most fruitful source of family quarrels, and a settlement was one way of avoiding any uncertainty. Frederic Knight of Exmoor was much embarrassed for ready money for his improvements by the heavy costs of a Chancery suit about his father's will, brought by other members of the family, so he might have been better off under a settlement.[29] As the family lawyer put it, in George Meredith's *Celt and Saxon*, 'Where estates are not entailed . . . the expectations of the family are undisciplined and certain not to be satisfied'.

Thus the general opinion among the old landed families was that settlement was necessary and desirable, and that estate improvement must be financed out of current estate revenue, without seriously committing the heir. It was the Repeal of the Corn Laws which brought general recognition of the need for long term expenditure on estate improvement, and Sir Robert Peel's state loans for land drainage specifically provided for limited

[29] C. S. Orwin, *The Reclamation of Exmoor Forest*, Oxford, 1929, p. 71.

owners.[30] There was considerable expenditure on estate improvement going on slowly all through the decades of prosperous farming, on estates both settled and unsettled, for such expenditure looked like being a profitable investment as well as a gratifying hobby. The prestige of the landed gentry, both political, social and economic, was still largely unchallenged.

[30] See p. 195.

3

The Condition of the Farm Workers
in 1850

The New Poor Law – Conditions of Life and Work: Scotland, North of England, the Eastern Counties, Wales, Midlands and South of England – Crafts and Skills – Help and Self-Help – Education – Health and Housing – The Coming of the Railways

THE condition of agricultural workers in the generation before the Repeal of the Corn Laws must be seen against the background of the country as a whole, a country becoming more and more industrialised, with agriculture, still the largest industry, going through its own revolution which was affecting in greater or lesser degree the lives of all who lived by it. One consequence of this revolution was the emergence of a class of wage earners with no direct interest in the land. There had, of course, been workers for wages in agriculture for centuries, but many had had common rights, the chance of keeping a few stock or of getting a few strips in the open fields, opportunities for getting on and maintaining some independence. Poor they were, no doubt, but not with the hopeless and grinding poverty of the early nineteenth century, nor was there the social gulf between them and the farmers which was to come later. By becoming workers for wages and nothing else, labourers lost status, and the whole character of the English village community was changed. The high corn prices during the French wars, which enriched landowners and farmers, only impoverished farm workers still more by raising the price of their basic food; and the depression following the peace led farmers to cut their wage bills, and thus intensified unemployment and poverty.

THE NEW POOR LAW

The shadow which lay over the life of the English farm worker in this period was the new Poor Law of 1834. For a generation before it agricultural wages were being subsidised out of the Poor Rates in many parishes under the Speenhamland system, a benevolent scheme begun when prices were rising rapidly during the French war and when current wages were often inadequate to keep families from starvation. A scale was worked out linking the price of bread and the size of families, and wages paid by farmers were made up to this out of the Poor Rates. The system was continued after the war, and its long-term effect upon the workers was to take away all self-respect and incentive to improve their lot, and to put a premium on early marriages and immorality, for they got an additional allowance for every child and for bastards too. Some of the young men got away to the towns, but this was not easy, for under the Laws of Settlement then operating, they were liable to be caught and sent back to their own parish, in case they should come on the rates of the new one. For the farmers also it was a degrading business. So long as wages could be supplemented by parish relief, they were not going to raise them. True, they were rate-payers, but so were the small farmers who employed no hired men, the local landowners, shopkeepers and village tradesmen. So they shared the available labour of the parish between them, passing men from one farm to another, and feeling no responsibility for their well-being nor for providing work all the year round. Their main method of meeting low prices was to reduce their permanent labour force, often to the detriment of good farming. The Overseers of the Poor who administered the doles, farmers or tradesmen elected by the Vestry to hold office for a year, seldom learnt the job properly. Generally ill-educated themselves, their accounts were often badly kept, the administration fluctuated between harshness and weakness according to the character of the overseer; and everywhere the poor rates continued to rise.

The demoralisation of the countryside, as the years went on, had come to such a pitch that it was clear a new approach was required to the whole question of poverty and relief. The principle embodied in the Poor Law Amendment Act of 1834 was that of 'less eligibility'. Subsidies to wages out of the poor rates were stopped; a free labour market was therefore established in rural areas, and wages found their economic level on the 'laissez faire' principle of the time. Able-bodied persons who became destitute were relieved in such a way that 'the condition of the recipient should not on the whole be more eligible than that of any labourer living on the fruits of his own industry.'[1]

'Less eligibility' was achieved by the 'workhouse test'. Parishes were grouped in Unions, with a workhouse in each Union administered by the Guardians of the Poor, and to this all the destitute poor were sent, instead of receiving relief in their own houses, as had hitherto been the common practice. The 'workhouse test' was not originally designed to be applied to the aged, the infirm or the widows and children who might come under the care of the guardians, and for whom other institutions were proposed. But few parishes made any effort to provide such alternatives, or to classify their paupers and to provide different standards for their needs. As a result, the sick, the aged, the infirm, lunatics, orphans and unwanted children, illegitimate babies and their mothers, the unemployed with their wives and families, were all housed in the same grim and barracklike building, with the sexes separated, and all subjected to the same regime designed as a deterrent. The old parish workhouses for the destitute had been squalid enough, and the treatment of paupers in them often cruel and degrading, but they were smaller, there was more freedom within them, and they do not seem to have aroused the deep resentment which the labouring poor felt towards the new Unions. Perhaps the separation of families was the thing they feared and resented most of all. George Edwards, son of a farm worker, gives a vivid picture of one incident in his early life:

It was in the year 1855 when I had my first experience of real distress. On my father's return home from work one night he was stopped by a policeman

[1] Edwin Chadwick, quoted by S. R. Finer, *Life and Times of Sir Edwin Chadwick*, London, 1952, p. 74.

who searched his bag and took from it five turnips, which he was taking home to make his children an evening meal. There was no bread in the house. His wife and children were waiting for him to come home, but he was not allowed to do so. He was arrested, taken before the magistrate next day, and committed to fourteen days' hard labour for the crime of attempting to feed his children! The experience of that night I shall never forget.

The next morning we were taken into the workhouse, where we were kept all the winter. Although only five years old, I was not allowed to be with my mother. On my father's release from prison, he, of course, had also to come into the workhouse. Being branded as a thief, no farmer would employ him. . . .[2]

This hatred of 'The House' by the rural poor persisted right through the century and beyond. Thomas Hood, in 'The Lay of the Labourer', part of which is quoted below, expressed it from the point of view of a farm worker:

'A spade! a rake! a hoe!
  A pickaxe, or a bill!
A hook to reap, or a scythe to mow,
  A flail, or what ye will –
The corn to thrash, or the hedge to plash,
  The market team to drive,
Or mend the fence by the cover side,
  And leave the game alive.

Wherever Nature needs,
  Wherever Labour calls,
No job I'll shirk of the hardest work,
  To shun the workhouse walls;
Where savage laws begrudge
  The pauper babe its breath,
And doom a wife to a widow's life,
  Before her partner's death.

My only claim is this,
  With labour stiff and stark,
By lawful turn, my living to earn,
  Between the light and the dark;
My daily bread, and nightly bed,
  My bacon, and drop of beer –
But all from the hand that holds the land,
  And none from the overseer!'

[2] George Edwards, M.P., *From Crow-Scaring to Westminster*, London, 1922, p. 22.

Wages were generally so low that agricultural workers could never really save for their old age, so that when it came, unless their children could keep them, the workhouse was their dread and often their fate. In some villages there were one or two alms-houses for the aged poor, charitable foundations of former centuries, with a tiny pension attached to them; but these were few and far between, and were generally earmarked for the 'deserving poor', which in practice meant those who kept on the right side of the vicar and churchwardens.

The Poor Law of 1834 took some years to get into operation all over the country. The rules of the Commissioners had to be digested, the unions of parishes designated, the new workhouses built, the Boards of Guardians elected from those with the appropriate property qualifications. The new Commissioners began their reforms in the south of England, but soon ran into trouble when they turned their attention to the north. The new Act had been designed primarily to do away with the scandals which had developed under the outdoor allowance system to agricultural labourers; the attempt to apply it in the manufacturing towns, where large numbers of men might be unemployed simultaneously for short or long periods, broke down altogether, and the granting of outdoor relief had to continue. The Act was naturally hated by the unrepresented workers, but it was unpopular too with many of those who had to administer it; these objected to the remote control from London, and felt that the distant and autocratic Commissioners, who were not at first responsible to Parliament, did not understand local needs and conditions – that perennial problem which confronts democracy everywhere. The result was that the strict letter of the Act was not carried out universally, more latitude was gradually allowed to local authorities, and in 1847 the Commission was transformed into the Poor Law Board, answerable to Parliament. So although the principle remained that outdoor relief was to be withheld from the able-bodied, administration varied very much from one district to another.

After the introduction of the new Poor Law the employment of women and children in agriculture increased in many parts of

England. Under the old system of subsidising wages from the rates, allowances were received for children; but when this practice was superseded, a large family was no longer an asset in this way, and the father's wage could not feed them unless it was supplemented by children's work as soon as they were able to earn.

The extent of employment of women and children has most wonderfully increased since the Poor Law came into operation. It has had that effect by rendering it necessary that the children should be so employed in order to adjust the wages to the wants of the family. The expedient adopted by all the employers of labour in getting rid of the allowance in aid of wages consists in affording such employment to the women and children, especially in large families.[3]

Dr Kay was perhaps optimistic about the disinterestedness of the employers, for the result of this was to keep down the wages of the men. If farmers could get much of the work done by the cheaper labour of women and children, why should they take on more men at a higher rate? The wives and children were competing in an overstocked labour market, and if their wages brought a little more cash into the straitened household, it was at the expense of the man's status and opportunity.

Scottish farm servants did not suffer from the shadow of the 'workhouse test' as did their brothers in the south. The new Poor Law of 1834 did not apply to Scotland, where the system of poor relief was different. The poor in Scotland were supported by weekly collections made at the parish churches, and by charitable donations to the church-session. When these fell short, assessments for the poor were paid, one-half by the landholder, and the other half by the farmer, or occupier of land in the country, or of houses in towns. They were rarely levied except in populous towns.[4]

Thus the great difference between the Scottish and English attitude was that the Scots had never lost the sense of communal

[3] Dr Kay's evidence before the Lords' Committee on the Poor Law Amendment Act, 1837–8, p. 467. Quoted by Hasbach, W., *History of the English Agricultural Labourer*, London, 1908, p. 225.

[4] Sir John Sinclair, *op. cit.*, vol. 3, sect. viii; Sir George Nicholls, *A History of the Scotch Poor Law*, London, 1856.

responsibility towards poverty, and the Church had led the way in raising and administering relief. There was a distinction between the 'ordinary' poor – the aged, chronic sick, widows and so on, whose names were on a roll and who received regular small allowances – and the 'occasional' poor, able-bodied people temporarily out of work, or sick, who might be helped at the discretion of the Kirk Session. There were also many authorised beggars, but the Speenhamland system with its deplorable results was never applied to Scotland, and a new Poor Law was necessitated by the remarkable growth in population and the distress in the towns rather than in the rural areas. The Poor Law Amendment (Scotland) Act was passed in 1845. Administration was put into the hands of a Board of Supervision, a body of nine very eminent persons; parochial boards consisting of the Kirk Session and heritors (i.e. landholders) were established in each parish, who in their turn appointed an Inspector of the Poor to administer relief; and paupers could appeal to the Board of Supervision if they felt that the relief granted to them was insufficient. The attempt to impose the 'workhouse test' on rural Scotland under this Act never really succeeded. Workhouses were built, very slowly, in the towns, and slowly, also, the parishes adopted the system of raising a compulsory poor rate instead of relying on voluntary contributions. But in the areas of small, scattered communities in the Highlands and Islands, where everyone was poor, the old system went on, though the terrible potato famine of the late 1840s produced such distress as could only be alleviated by collections from outside, and by emigration overseas or to areas where there was work to be had.

In Chapter 8 will be found an account of changes in the earnings of farm workers in the middle years of the nineteenth century. Here it suffices to say that their wages were very low, and to quote the words of one of their friends, the Rev. J. Guthrie, a Wiltshire parson: 'Much is done to relieve their distresses by many, and is done with judgment and discrimination; but when all is done, I never could make out how they live upon their present earnings; for after examining with all the accuracy that much local knowledge both of persons and places can supply, the accounts of their necessary weekly expenditure, and trying to compare it with their weekly earnings, in all cases that I have tried, without exception, their expenditure seems to exceed their earnings. . . .'[5]

CONDITIONS OF LIFE AND WORK

Scotland

In the Highlands and Islands the farm worker for wages was rarely to be found at all. Rural society consisted of small isolated communities of crofters settled in the narrow valleys, living in a state of chronic poverty upon holdings too small to support their families and employing no paid labour. They and their sons and daughters might go as farm servants to Lowland farms for a time, coming home at intervals to help on the family farm.[6]

The drovers who collected the cattle from the Islands and remote parts of the Highlands and drove them down to the great trysting fairs at Falkirk and elsewhere were a race apart. Their job was skilful, arduous and hazardous, for the journey would take weeks and even months. They had to know the route thoroughly; to be prepared for dangers by storm, flood and theft; to know the cattle and their powers of endurance, so as not to overdrive them; to get the whole bunch safely and in good condition to the Fair; and sometimes to carry through their sale to the English dealers there assembled to buy them. Some of them might also be engaged to drive the cattle on to their new homes in England. It was a highly responsible job requiring a long training, and the drovers were well paid; but by the time our period begins the trade in that form was declining.[7]

In the Lowlands there were few villages in the English sense, and the farms were scattered and isolated, so it had long been the practice to board the unmarried labourers in the farmhouses.

[5] *Report of the Special Poor Law Commissioners on the Employment of Women and Children in Agriculture*, 1843 (510), p. 57.

[6] See pp. 21-23.

[7] See p. 27.

Where only two or three men were employed, they lived on the 'chaumer' system, having their meals in the farmhouse and sleeping in a loft over the stable. On larger farms, with perhaps six or eight single men, they were accommodated in a bothy, and cooked their own food, which consisted almost entirely of oatmeal in one form or another, with milk and potatoes. When they married and lived in a cottage on the farm, they still often received the greater part of their wages in kind. Men were normally engaged on a yearly or six-monthly contract at the hiring-fair in the nearest town; thus they were sure of regular work throughout the year. It was an austere and comfortless life, but, as a recent writer has pointed out,[8] it was an excellent training for the hardships of pioneer life in the new countries, where many Scottish farm workers proved so successful. But they had their recreations – at Hogmanay, in the initiation ceremonies of the young horsemen (in which whisky played a part), in practical joking, singing and telling stories. Some of the bothy ballads of these times give vivid pictures of life on these farms, generally uncomplimentary to the farmer.

A married farm worker was often required to provide and house a woman worker for field work on the farm – it might be a wife, daughter or sister, but if a relative were not available, some other single woman. As might be expected, this 'bondager' system was unpopular and led either to quarrels or immorality or both, and it gradually died out as the century advanced. Though women worked on the land as a matter of course, it would seem that children were not put regularly to work at such an early age as they were in England. They went to school and stayed there longer, though they were, no doubt, called in to help with the harvest or in particularly busy times.

Without villages to draw on for casual labour, Scottish farmers on the newly-improved farms with large arable acreages were sometimes hard put to it to get their harvest in. Many Highlanders, men and women, as well as unemployed weavers and others from the towns, came down to the Lowlands for the harvest. From

[8] J. A. Symon, *Scottish Farming Past and Present*, London, 1959, p. 162.

early in the nineteenth century, the native force was steadily augmented by itinerant Irish labour. In the 1820s steamboats began to ply between Ireland and Scotland, and from that time onwards Irish peasants, with little work to do on their own tiny holdings, came in their thousands during the summer months to hire themselves out to farmers for hay-making and corn harvest. They were generally men between sixteen and sixty-five, practically destitute when they arrived, but they made their way as best they could to Edinburgh and other towns, and stood at the market cross, to which farmers came to hire them, and to bargain about their rates of pay. It was cheap labour, for they were splendid workers, living on such oatmeal and potatoes as they were given and sleeping where they could in sheds or barns. They were cheerful and gay, delighted if they could take £3 or £4 back with them at the end of the summer, to pay their rent at home. They were not very popular with the Scottish farm workers, for they were dirty and noisy and pugnacious, and fights were frequent. But the harvest could not be got without them, and their gaiety and wit and the songs they brought with them must have provided a little light relief in the life on Scottish farms.[9]

Though Scottish farm servants were tied by their contract for the year, it was customary for them to move at the end of it. The Laws of Settlement which tied English workers to their own parish did not apply in Scotland; men could move about freely, and by moving to a new master they got a more varied experience of farming methods, which made them more useful workers. In some respects, however, the yearly contract pressed hard upon Scottish farm servants. The agreement as to wages and hours was only a verbal one, and the wages were not usually paid until the end of the term of service, though small advances might be given from time to time. If the servant found himself with a bad master, he could not get away, for under the Law of Master and Servant the breach of contract was a criminal offence for which he could be sent to prison. But if a farmer broke his side of the contract and dismissed the servant, this was only a civil offence.

[9] J. E. Handley, *The Irish in Scotland, 1798–1845*, Cork, 1943.

He could be sued for wrongful dismissal or the witholding of wages earned, but it was extremely difficult for a servant to establish these breaches of the law. The commonest disputes which appeared in courts were about hours of work, which were very long, or about non-agricultural jobs for which servants did not consider they had been engaged, such as cleaning the church, or carting a neighbour's furniture. But in nearly all the cases coming up, the farmers' actions were upheld by the local justices and there was no redress for the dismissed servants.[10] The Law of Master and Servant applied also in England and Wales, but as yearly contracts were less common, breaches of them among farm workers did not often occur.

North of England

Conditions in the Border counties of Northumberland, Cumberland and Durham approximated very much to those of the Scottish Border – yearly contracts, unmarried men boarded on farms, much of the wage in kind, the 'bondager' system, and so on. In the mountain areas of Cumberland, Westmorland and the West Riding of Yorkshire, where small family farms prevailed and there was less opportunity for hired labour, a boy or girl would be boarded in the farmhouse when needed. In Lancashire, Yorkshire and Staffordshire men could easily get away to the industrial towns, where there was generally work of some kind to be had, and it was this pull which kept wages higher than in the south.

In the Yorkshire and Lincolnshire Wolds, areas of large farms often recently reclaimed and laid out, there was a sharp distinction between the 'confined' men and the ordinary day labourers. The former lived on the farms, single men boarding with the foreman, and married men in cottages. They were the stockmen and horsemen, men with skill and responsibility, receiving much of their wage in kind and on yearly contracts. They felt themselves in a much superior position to that of the day labourers, who were less skilled, liable to be stood off at any moment, and who often

[10] G. Houston, 'Labour Relations in Scottish Agriculture before 1870', *Agric. Hist. Rev.*, vol. vi, Part 1, 1958, pp. 27–41.

lived long distances from their work. This distinction was also to be found in other parts of England.

The Eastern Counties

This great dry corn-growing area consisted in the main of large farms, and the number of workers to a farm was high when nearly all the processes were manual. Some of the extra labour required at harvest time was supplied by immigrant Irish, and through the year gangs of women and children were employed, a practice which was to be the subject of enquiry and legislation later in the century. Here (though also in other parts of the country) were to be found the 'open' and 'closed' villages. A 'closed' village was one in which all the land was owned by one landlord, who might refuse to allow any more cottage building and might even pull down such cottages as there were. The reasons for this were partly aesthetic – if he didn't wish to see the squalor of labourers' dwellings near the big house and park – and partly economic, because any increase in the number of labourers with a settlement in the parish might put up the poor rates. 'Open' villages were ones in which there were a number of landlords, and in which cottages were owned by small tradesmen, or had been built by squatters on the waste, or by speculators charging rack rents. The difference between the two types of village may be seen in Trollope's *Framley Parsonage*, where Lady Lufton's tidy and well-conducted village of Framley, nestling under the shadow of Framley Court, is contrasted with the rough and straggling parish of Hogglestock, where there was a brickfield as well as farms.

One result of the 'closed' village was that labourers had much further to travel to their work. Caird notes one farm on the Duke of Grafton's estate in Norfolk where two regular labourers had to walk nine miles a day to and fro, while in Lincolnshire some farmers provided donkeys for their men to ride, to save them from arriving too exhausted to do their work properly.[11] How many of the footpaths which country ramblers are concerned to

[11] J. Caird (1), pp. 161, 197.

preserve today were first trodden out by farm workers seeking short cuts through the fields on their weary tramp homewards?

Wales

In Wales, a country of small family farms, the social gulf between farmers and labourers was not nearly so wide as in England. South Wales in the 1840s went through a period of acute social unrest culminating in the Rebecca Riots, in which farmers, labourers and others collaborated in the burning of toll-gates in protest against high toll charges. Though the tolls were the immediate and practical grievance, the underlying causes were deeper and less tangible – agrarian depression, land hunger, high rents and rates, the new Poor Law, Chartist agitation – but chiefly the prevailing poverty. It was not a farm labourers' movement, though many of them became involved in it.[12]

The rise in population through the first half of the century had intensified the poverty, for the development of the heavy industry of South Wales was only just beginning and people were chiefly dependent upon agriculture for a living. So the competition for farms was fierce, and fresh land was being taken into cultivation higher up the hillsides, where it was still more difficult to wring a scanty living. But poor though the farmers were themselves, they did employ labour, both male and female, the women servants sleeping in the farmhouse and the lads in the out-buildings. They were engaged by the year at autumn hiring fairs and their wages were a few pounds a year and their keep. Married labourers were also hired by the year and paid fortnightly, sometimes having potato ground on the farm. There were a few small local industries, and domestic spinning and weaving sometimes helped the narrow budget, but for the most part at this period there was little employment alternative to agriculture.

Midlands and South of England

The lot of the labourers in the south and south Midlands of England was probably the hardest of all at this period. It was here

[12] See D. Williams, *op. cit.* Ch. iv.

that the 'Labourers' Revolt' of the 1830s, the rick-burnings and Captain Swing, the savage sentences and transportations, the case of the Tolpuddle Martyrs, had left a heritage of hopeless bitterness, and where the new Poor Law seemed most oppressive. There were fewer alternative occupations open to farm labour, and periods of unemployment were almost inevitable. In Dorset, annual contracts at the hiring fairs were usual, but wages were paid by the week, with nothing on wet days; much of the pay was in kind and the whole family was expected to work on the farm. In Wiltshire and Devon, too, wages were very low, but in Cornwall they were rather higher, for there was other work to be had. No part of Cornwall is very far from the coast with its many little ports, and fishing was a major industry, while there was also tin-mining and slate-quarrying.

The standard of housing was almost uniformly low, and the status of farm workers may best be summed up in the words of Sidney Godolphin Osborne, the Rector of Bryanston, in his evidence before the Commission on the Employment of Women and Children in Agriculture in 1843:

With regard to the general condition of the agricultural labourer, I believe the public to be less informed, or worse informed, than about that of any other class of society. His most common vices are, it is true, pretty well known . . . but the hardships of his life at best, its temptations, the hindrances to its improvement, the scanty remuneration afforded for his hardest labour, the ingenious methods used to hold him in thraldom, permitting him neither to work where he likes, at the wages he could obtain, or to spend those he does obtain where he chooses; the manner in which he often sees the welfare of the beast he drives more valued than his own, and his own welfare often sacrificed to some caprice of his employer – threatened with the 'Union House' if he refuses them, his wages are settled by the combined interest or opinion of the employers around him, forced to pay an exorbitant rent for a dwelling in which he cannot decently rear his family; if he is single he is to receive less for the sweat of his brow than if he was married; if he does marry, every ingenuity is used to make him feel that he is regarded as one about to increase the burdens of his parish, to say nothing of the ingenuity used to shift him into some other parish – these are parts of his condition on which the public are not so well informed.[13]

[13] Poor Law Commissioners, 1843, *op. cit.*, p. 76.

CRAFTS AND SKILLS

These lowly-paid men were craftsmen and skilled workers. Practically every process in farming at that time was done by manual or horse labour, and skill in the use of tools was essential to every farm worker. The laying out of a field for ploughing, the accurate setting of the plough, the ploughing of a straight furrow at the right depth, the cunning use of a scythe, the laying of a hedge, the swinging of a flail, were all jobs calling for intelligence, exactness and training, while the proper care of animals called for patience, observation and understanding only achieved after considerable experience. Of course much farm work was monotonous and toilsome, but it was never so mechanical as much work in factories. There was always some variety; no one field is exactly like another, and soil conditions vary within the same field, calling for adjustment on the part of the worker. Neither is one beast exactly like the next; each cow and horse has its own idiosyncrasies and needs different treatment. And the alternations of seasons and weather, the different crops grown and stock kept, all combined to make what could have been a richly varied working life, if only the conditions and status of the labourer had been such as to make him feel this. But instead he was given starvation wages, overlong hours of work, disgraceful housing, little or no education, and was generally treated as of lowly estate and a being of no account, an object of charity, perhaps, but with no prospect of improving his lot. There was always 'that hateful chasm that lies too broad and forbidding between employer and employed, in civilised England'.[14] Farmers, perhaps with memories of the bad old days of pauper labour, drove the hardest bargain they could in this as in all other branches of farming.

But there was, of course, another side to the picture. On large farms the head horseman, the head cowman and the shepherd held positions of real responsibility, often stayed on the same farm for most of their lives, and identified themselves completely with its fortunes. Their knowledge of and pride in their charges were

[14] C. Wren Hoskyns, *op. cit.*, p. 92.

such that they would refer to '*my* sheep', '*my* horses', and so on. Their wages were constant throughout the year, and they had opportunities, which the day labourers did not have, of picking up a little extra cash. A horseman would get an extra shilling for carting or fetching goods away from the farm, a shepherd a shilling for every pair of twin lambs raised, and various other bonuses might come their way.[15] Moreover, they paid nothing, or a very nominal rent, for their cottages. In parts of Lincolnshire, also, where large upland farms had outlying portions in the marsh below, separated from the main holdings, the regular workers had to be responsible and trustworthy men, able to work without supervision. This was reflected in their wages, and they were generally allowed land for their own cow or pigs, and potato ground.[16]

Even the day labourers were not always in a state of abject poverty. A family with two or three stalwart sons living at home and all contributing, would be very comfortable, and the mother would not need to go out to work. If they had a good allotment and could grow part of their own food, and crops for sale, they were better off still; but it was a precarious existence. The sons would marry, or go off to work elsewhere, and the lot of the elderly farm worker was often very hard. Some farmers would keep their old men on as long as they could, finding them light jobs they could do about the farm; but others would turn them off, and unless their children were prepared to support them, they had to 'go on the parish' and eventually to the workhouse.

Then again, certain types of work were paid at piece rates which enabled the quick and skilled workers to earn more than the average. The farmers claimed that the men worked harder and quicker when on piece rates, and there were many complaints of the idleness of labourers working in a gang on time rates, when the pace was accommodated to that of the slowest and every opportunity taken of shirking. In the eastern counties the rate for getting in the harvest was a matter of bargain between

[15] George Ewart Evans, *The Horse in the Furrow*, London, 1960, p. 73.
[16] Joan Thirsk, *English Peasant Farming*, London, 1957, pp. 252-3

the farmer and his men, a subject of earnest discussion for weeks beforehand. It was always a gamble, for bad weather might prolong the harvest period, or a hot, dry spell speed it up. It was generally reckoned to last from three to four weeks, at the end of which the men would get their agreed sum, anything from £8 to £10, with beer thrown in, or malt and hops for them to brew it themselves. But it was to the advantage of everyone to get the work done quickly, so the Lord of the Harvest, the worker chosen to lead the team, had to set a good but steady pace, fast enough to satisfy the young and strong workers, but not too fast for the weaklings to keep up with all day.

The classification of farm workers into skilled men on an annual wage and day labourers still does not give the whole picture. There were also the specialist piece workers of many kinds and skills – the drainers, thatchers, stallion leaders, drovers, engine men on steam tackle, dowsers, rat and mole catchers, and others. These were independent people who were called into the farm when needed, and who covered areas beyond their own villages. Then in English villages, especially those in which the great house did not dominate everything, one or more men might be found, owning their own cottages, with perhaps a little bit of land and a horse; men who were independent and called no man master, who picked up a living in all sorts of ways by turning their hands to anything that came along. They might do a bit of dealing or higgling; they could be relied upon to take down an old tree, to cart goods to and from the station, to pick fruit, to mend a gate, dig out a ditch, etc. They were the hobjobbers, the men people went to in an emergency. Farmers would take them on in rush times, or when one of their men fell sick, but they never stayed long on one farm nor allowed themselves to be tied down. What they did was by favour, in their own time and in their own way. Sometimes they were the salt of the earth, like Joseph Ashby of Tysoe, natural leaders who made a place for themselves in the village community and beyond it. Sometimes they were disreputable enough, poachers and scroungers, the despair of the parson, men who only worked when they felt inclined, like John

Darbeyfield in Hardy's *Tess of the D'Urbervilles*. But they and all those between these two extremes were alike in their love of independence, and as such they were a valuable ingredient in a village life full of docile labourers. How many there were and how distributed it is impossible to say, but their counterparts can still be found in villages up and down the country.

Then there were the women workers, in many areas vital to the work of the farm. There are some unforgettable pictures of them in *Tess of the D'Urbervilles*. The first is of the harvest field, when the young Tess works with a gang of women and girls, binding sheaves and stooking, and during the midday break suckling her baby. Then there is the picture of a large dairy farm in a fertile vale of South Dorset, a dairy of 100 cows, selling milk and butter. The whole rhythm of the life is shown, the dairymaids rising at 3 a.m. to skim the cream, the early morning milking, the cooling, scouring and churning, the afternoon milking in the fields, the fun and companionship in a big household under a good master. In strong contrast is the third picture, of the roughest field work on an upland arable farm – 'a starve-acre place' of poor and flinty land under a bullying farmer. Here Tess pulled and hacked swedes through the winter in wind and rain, and when the weather was too bad was put to reed-drawing in the barn (i.e. drawing out straw from the carried corn and cutting off the ears). 'Reed-drawing is fearful hard work, worse than swede-hacking', her companion told her. Then there is a description of threshing in March with a steam threshing machine, the women handing, untying and feeding the sheaves on to the drum of the insatiable monster from dawn to late evening, going on by moonlight to finish the stack. The dusty monotony of the job, the noise and vibration of the machinery, and the utter weariness of the workers are brought out vividly.

One class of woman worker who got little notice from Royal Commissions was the dairymaid, for this indoor work was done by the farmer's wife and daughters with the help of indoor servants. Just as poultry-keeping, until well into the present century, was considered the prerogative of the farmer's wife and not really part of the legitimate business of the farm, so in the nineteenth century the produce of the cow was also her affair, except in certain specialist areas. It was on the small family farms that the bulk of the butter and cheese was made.

The dairymaid was so often the heroine of folksong and story that she is still seen through a romantic haze, like Marie Antoinette at the Petit Trianon. The setting of her work, too, was attractive, as described by George Eliot in *Adam Bede*:

> The dairy was certainly worth looking at ... such colours, such coolness, such purity, such fresh fragrance of new-pressed cheese, of farm butter, of wooden vessels perpetually bathed in pure water; such soft colouring of red earthenware and creamy surfaces, brown wood and polished tin, grey limestone and rich orange-red rust on the iron weights and hooks and hinges. But one gets only a confused notion of these details when they surround a distractingly pretty girl of seventeen, standing on little pattens and rounding her dimpled arm to lift a pound of butter out of the scale.

The reality must often have been different. There is ample evidence that the small farmers and their families worked harder and for longer hours than many labourers. The little girls who went to live on a farm for their keep and a few pounds a year were kept hard at it, first at the routine jobs of scouring and cleaning and polishing, before they were admitted to the mysteries of skimming, churning, curd-cutting, pressing and turning the heavy cheeses, as well as milking and the feeding and rearing of calves. Butter- and cheese-making were not only heavy physical work, but highly skilled, calling for long experience and accurate judgment, in the days before mechanical devices came in to lighten toil, and scientific ones to give accuracy to the old empirical methods. The skill, particularly in cheese-making, was an intimate and personal one, which some might never acquire, hence the extraordinary variety in the quality of farmhouse cheese and butter sold. Happy was the farmer whose wife had inherited the skill and who could pass it on to her daughters. These women needed great toughness and stamina, and if they worked hard themselves, they drove those whom they employed even harder. To quote George Eliot again, according to Mrs Poyser, 'Wi' them three gells in the house, I'd need have twice the strength to keep 'em up to their work. It's like having roast-meat at three fires; as soon as you've basted one, another's burnin'.'

If life was hard in the villages, the poor, though denied outdoor parish relief, undoubtedly received much help in the form of private charity, both in money and in kind. Here again conditions varied enormously, according to the motives of the squires, the parsons and their ladies. Some were moved by genuine compassion, others by a desire for popularity, others by a sort of medieval conception of the duty of a lord to his dependants. But to many more it was a religious duty. The parents of Philip Pusey, living in Berkshire in the early part of the century, used to set aside £100 every Christmas for gifts to the poor in their small village.

Distribution of coals and blankets, and beef at Christmas, was quite usual, and soup in times of particular distress. In some places the 'gooding', a gift of 6d or 1s on St Thomas's Day to every family towards the cost of a Christmas dinner, was the practice. Sometimes there were old endowed charities – bread for poor widows, outfits for children leaving school, coal for the aged, etc. But the distribution of all these good things was apt to be capricious, and might be withdrawn from those whose behaviour or opinions did not find favour with the powers that be. Joseph Arch in his *Autobiography* tells a graphic story of how his family never received any of the available soup even when his father was out of work for eighteen weeks, because of the battles between his mother and the parson's wife. In the places where there was no big house or resident squire, nor even a resident parson, the agricultural workers fared worse, even if they kept their independence. But some of the farmers and their wives were kind, and there was much mutual help between neighbour and neighbour among the poor themselves. This was particularly true in Wales.

Nor were farm workers entirely without self-help even in the bleak days of the 1840s. The Friendly Society movement was beginning to spread to the countryside. Many a little village was organising its Sickness Benefit Club, under which small weekly payments were collected and members given financial aid in times of illness or to help with funeral expenses. These clubs were run by the members themselves, not imposed from above, and so were very popular; as the century advanced they became a characteristic feature of village social life, with a definite ritual. According to Joseph Arch, the squires and clergy disapproved of them because they made the labourers feel less dependent upon charity; but the clubs had come to stay and were soon accepted. Their Annual Meeting Day, Whit Monday, was a popular holiday. It began with a procession through the village to the church, with the band and the club banners, the labourers wearing their best smock frocks and club badges. After a short service and sermon from the Vicar, members repaired to the village inn for dinner, for the publican was generally the Club Treasurer. The accounts were read and the rest of the day was spent in drinking the balance. But the benefits which such clubs could provide were pitifully small, and perhaps their values were more moral and social than practical at that time.

Another form of self-help by which a farm worker might add to his income was by poaching. The more savage parts of the Game Laws had been repealed in the 1830s; man traps and spring guns were no longer legal, nor was transportation the penalty paid by the poacher. But sentences were still severe, imprisonment up to seven years was possible, and the reputation of being a poacher damned a man in the eyes of authority more surely than any other offence. The risks were great, but so also was the temptation. A rabbit or a hare made a welcome addition to the table of a family who could rarely afford fresh meat. Then in many areas, especially in those near large towns, there was a ready sale for game, and poaching gangs which came out to get it relied to a certain extent upon local knowledge, for which they would pay cash. An out-of-work farm labourer with a hungry family did not feel that poaching was wrong, and no villager would ever turn informer. The keeper was the best hated man in the neighbourhood, and good luck to those who could outwit him and the squire.

The self-help which authority approved for the farm worker was the growing of some of his own food in his cottage garden or allotment. Chadwick wished to make the provision of allotments a corollary to the New Poor Law of 1834, but the Poor Law Commission considered that since allotments would be beneficial both to those who let the land at increased rents and to those who cultivated it, their provision might be left to self-interest. In 1843 a Report on them by a Select Committee found that in places where allotments had been let to farm workers through the initiative of local landlords or farmers, there was less distress. A man with a quarter of an acre could make a net profit of £4 a year, and the moral effect of having a healthy occupation for leisure time, in which the family could participate, kept men from the public house and gave them a sense of independence and self-respect. But they must not have too much land, according to the Report: 'As it is desirable that the profits of an allotment should be viewed by the holder of it in the light of an aid, and not of a substitute for his ordinary income accruing from wages, and that they should not become an inducement to neglect his usual paid labour, the allotment should be of no greater extent than can be cultivated during the leisure moments of the labourer and his family.'[17]

But self-interest was not working fast enough, and the Committee recommended legislative action to increase the number of allotments. The Inclosure Act of 1845 contained a provision that wherever an inclosure of common land was carried out under the Act, allotments 'for the labouring poor' should be laid out if there were a demand for them. According to John Stuart Mill, this was a contrivance to supplement farm workers' far too low wages instead of doing it from the rates – in fact, to 'make people grow their own poor rates'.

Another method of self-help recognised both by custom and by

[17] *Report of the Select Committee on the Labouring Poor* (*Allotments of Land*), 1843 (402), p. iv. See also p. 189.

authority was that of gleaning in the stubble of the cornfields after harvest. This was done by women and children, and a large family might gather enough dropped ears to keep them in flour for several months, when threshed and ground at the local mill. Gleaning, or leasing as some called it, must be one of the oldest and most universal of farming customs (witness the story of Ruth and Boaz). There were fears that the poor would lose this right of gleaning upon the inclosure of open fields, but it appears that through the nineteenth century most farmers did not object to the invasion of their stubbles, and gleaning went on till the rise in the workers' standard of living made it unnecessary. In the Second World War, countrywomen used to go gleaning, not for their families but for their severely rationed domestic hens.

EDUCATION

The educational opportunities for English farm labourers' children in the early part of the century were scanty, and varied from place to place. In some villages there might be an old endowed school 'for the deserving poor'; in others a dame's school where an old woman in a cottage gave some very elementary instruction; in others, nothing at all. But the nineteenth century was a time of religious revival, and both the Church of England and the Non-conformist Churches were beginning to have a wider concern for education. The 'National Society for the Education of the Poor according to the principles of the Church of England' started early in the century, and this body made grants for school buildings, while in 1833 the State set aside the sum of £20,000 annually for grants to voluntary schools, the first tentative step towards universal education. But the usual fee of 1*d* or 2*d* a week was sometimes hard to find out of a father's wage of 7*s* or 8*s*, and in the 1840s rural children's schooling was often intermittent even when it was available. George Edwards says that the only schooling he ever had was at Sunday School, and it was his wife who taught him to read.

However, the effects on the Church of England of the Oxford

Movement were soon to be reflected in the villages, wherever there were active parsons. Sometimes they prevailed upon the resident landowner to build a school at his own charges; sometimes they would get a grant from the National Society or raise subscriptions in the neighbourhood; but whatever the source, Church schools began to rise in the villages from the 1840s onwards. Many of them are still here today, close to the church, with their Gothic porches, high windows so that the children could not see out while at work, and little asphalt playgrounds. The teachers were at first quite untrained; the parson would undertake the whole of the Scripture teaching, and if the squire's wife and daughters were interested, they would contribute enthusiastic if unscientific instruction, as many novels of the period testify, particularly those of Charlotte M. Yonge. The chief object of the Church schools was to save the souls of the children and to teach them their religious duties, and the amount and standard of secular teaching they gave was not very great; but they were a beginning of better things and a civilising influence in the villages.

Scottish farm workers were far in advance of the English in education. Before the Union, an Act had been passed directing the heritors and the Kirk Session to set up and maintain Parish Schools; and the Schoolmasters' Act of 1803 directed that poor children should be taught free if their parents could not afford the fees. Thus no child was denied schooling, and the moral and social effects of this are quite incalculable. While most English farm workers were still sunk in ignorance and brutishness, the Scottish, though they may have lived in even greater poverty, were literate and awake. In Scotland, and in Wales, too, the farmers' and the labourers' children attended the same schools, so the social gulf between them when they grew up was never so great as in parts of England. George Hope of Fenton Barns said of his workers, 'I have people who have been with me all my life; we were brought up as boys together, and they are still upon the place.'[18]

[18] Evidence before Select Committee of House of Lords on Improvement of Land, 1873 (326), p. 248.

In Wales the schools were increasing, and here too the impulse came from the religious bodies. The Methodists were to the fore, but there were Anglican schools too, and bitter was the rivalry between them. But the Welsh valued education, and the Sunday School movement, promoted by the Methodist Church and attended by adults as well as children, was a weekly intellectual stimulus of great significance, partly because it was conducted in Welsh, not in the alien English.[19]

HEALTH AND HOUSING

The Whit Monday Club procession, the annual mop or village feast, the harvest home supper and the mummers at Christmas were the principal village amusements in England. Farm workers had little leisure for recreation in the modern sense; but their lives were not without interest, with their pride in their work, their gardens, their pigs, their neighbours' affairs, and the village inn or beershop in which they spent their evenings. Their housing at that time was almost uniformly bad. One room with a sort of lean-to kitchen and one bedroom above was the normal accommodation, though housing varied from county to county and from estate to estate, and often two and occasionally three bedrooms were provided. Proper water supply and sanitation were very rare. Though the subject of housing received some publicity from the writings of Cobbett, Sidney Godolphin Osborne and others, there was little improvement until much later. One notable exception was on the Bedford estate. Francis, the seventh Duke, who succeeded in 1839, set himself to build substantial cottages with two or three bedrooms, a kitchen range and copper, and a garden. His views on housing set the tone for the more enlightened landowners during the rest of the century, when he said: 'To improve the dwellings of the labouring class, and afford them the means of greater cleanliness, health and comfort, in their own homes, to extend education, and thus raise the social and moral habits of those most valuable members of the community, are among the

[19] D. Parry-Jones, *Welsh Country Upbringing*, London, 1948.

first duties, and ought to be among the truest pleasures, of every landlord.'[20]

In Scotland and Wales, housing standards were even lower than in England. In Scotland the 'but-and-ben', the two-roomed house, was usual, but many of the farm cottages had only one room. The bothies for single men were cheerless sort of dormitories, used for cooking, eating and sleeping; or the lads might sleep in lofts over the stables.

In Wales, cottages had often been built by squatters on waste ground on the mountain sides, the tradition being that if some sort of building could be put up in one day, so that smoke could be seen coming out of the top in the morning, the right of the squatter was established. Afterwards the house could be made more habitable, but many of them were little more than hovels. But the occupier could not be evicted, and this gave the married Welsh farm worker a measure of independence which the Englishman lacked. Moreover, he and his family might cultivate some of the waste land round them, keep a few hens, and eventually work it up into a little smallholding and get their feet on the agricultural ladder.

Bad and shockingly overcrowded as was most rural housing, it was no worse than that in many manufacturing towns and mining villages, or in the slums of London and Glasgow. In the country at least there was fresh air, the children could play out of doors, and the dangers of infectious diseases such as typhoid and cholera, which were becoming a nightmare in the cities, were very much less – though epidemics of 'fever' did occur. If the water supply were often contaminated, it mattered less when most of the men drank beer and the women and children tea. Tuberculosis, spread by overcrowding, carried off many, and rheumatism, aggravated by damp houses and clothing, was the normal burden of most older farm workers. Many of the cottages had gardens, so fresh vegetables were not lacking in their diet, but they rarely tasted fresh meat and were undernourished by all modern standards.

[20] *J.R.A.S.E.*, vol. x.i, 1849, p. 187.

THE COMING OF THE RAILWAYS

The coming of the railways was one of the prime factors making for the improvement of the farm worker's lot. In the first place, their construction offered alternative work to strong young men, who joined the armies of 'navigators' as they moved over the countryside building the permanent ways. This helped to diminish competition for farm jobs; when the lines were completed, there was still work available for linesmen, porters, signalmen and so on in the rural areas through which they passed. Secondly, the coming of the railways began to break down the isolation in which the villagers lived. Goods arrived by train; coal, a luxury for the rural poor in areas remote from coalfields, began to replace wood and turf on their cottage fires; all sorts of new and strange things appeared in the shops of the country towns; farm produce was sent away by train; new people arrived, and though farm workers may rarely have travelled by train themselves, they could not fail to be conscious of a larger world outside their village. The Penny Post, too, which came in 1840, was another extending and unifying factor, making it possible for them to communicate with sons and daughters who had gone away.

Farm workers were hardly touched by the campaign for the Repeal of the Corn Laws, Chartism, or the movements for factory inspection, shorter working hours and trade union recognition which loomed so large in the 1840s. Their isolation from the main stream of working-class life concentrated in the towns was the result of their geographical separation and their dispersal in small scattered groups under the eyes of their employers. It must be remembered, too, that the labour force in agriculture has always contained a number of farmers' relatives, whose incomes and aspirations depended on the general level of farm profits rather than on wages.

4

Markets and Crops
1851–1875

PRICES, RAILWAYS AND MARKETS

THE prices of almost all the main farm products were unduly low in the first three years of the new half-century, unduly low as measured by the experience of the previous decade. Sauerbeck's prices, derived from the London market, showed wheat selling for annual average prices of about 40s per quarter, oats well below 20s and barley oscillating between 23s and 29s. Prime beef fetched 36d to 38d per stone of 8 lb in these years, against more than 40d in 1846, 1847 and 1848; mutton prices fell by nearly 10d per stone (of 8 lb) to round 44d; butter prices, as represented by quotations for supplies from Friesland, fell from more than 100s to less than 90s per cwt, the lowest prices known in the forty years after 1850 in this important market. Nor was agricultural despondency likely to be cheered by the weather. Although in the early 1850s the winters were unusually mild, the autumns were unusually wet, and 1852 was one of the wettest years on record in England, being rivalled only by the disastrous season of 1879. 'A long season of the most appalling distress' was the verdict on 1852,[1] and it was followed by two years with rainfall somewhat above the average, especially in the autumns.

These wet years not only produced poor crops of hay, and heavy losses to vale farmers in the path of the floods; they also led to a severe epidemic of liver rot in sheep in the southern half

---

[1] C. Sewell Read, 'Farming of Oxfordshire', *J.R.A.S.E.*, vol. 15.i, 1854, p. 200.

of England, and they involved the heavy land arable farms in grave and expensive difficulties. It was impossible to get on to many fields after harvest for the autumn cultivations, with the result that less winter wheat could be sown; the turnip lands could not be brought to a proper tilth in the spring, and the crop was weedy and poor; the rush of spring work was more than the horses could manage and the corn and bean crops went in late, with a consequent fall in yields. The worst result from inadequate cultivations was such a multiplication of weeds in general, and twitch or couch grass in particular, as could only be controlled by a summer fallow, with the consequent loss of a corn crop or of a fodder crop to be turned into muck for the next season's turnips. Even the well-drained lands suffered in these ways from the rain of 1852 and from the subsequent wet autumns; the vast expanse of undrained lands were virtually put out of action each year until they had benefited from a long period of drying winds and warming sun throughout the spring. The combination of low prices and wet weather must have imposed a severe strain on the resources of many arable farmers at this time.

But the outbreak of war in the Crimea in the winter of 1853–4 brought the usual improvement in prospects to those who sold the basic necessities of food and power to Governments engaging in hostilities. From the autumn of 1853, prices of all grains and provisions rose sharply. Wheat sold for an average price of more than 50*s* per quarter in that year, and at more than 70*s* in 1854 and 1855. There was a smaller rise in barley and oat prices, but a recrudes-·cence of blight pushed up wholesale potato prices to more than 130*s* per ton in 1853 and to 120*s* in 1854. Wholesale beef prices rose by a third between the average of 1850–2 and the years 1854 and 1855, and those for mutton, pork and butter followed the same trend, though not to the same extent. The end of the war and the commercial crisis of 1857 brought a break in most prices which was quickly checked; wheat prices were to remain between 44*s* and 55*s* per quarter for the next six years, and the general level of most prices remained substantially higher than in the early years of the decade. It is noteworthy that this period of rising prices from 1853 coincided with a temporary fall in the import of grains, but imports of butter, cheese and eggs were stimulated by the reduction in import duties made in 1853 on these products.

By the end of 1848, nearly 5,000 miles of railway were in operation in Britain; virtually all the main lines of the modern structure had been established, from Perth in the north, Truro in the south-west, Shrewsbury in the west and Norwich in the east. But the next decade brought the construction of many subsidiary and alternative routes covering Britain with a network of rail transport totalling 8,350 miles by 1858 and 14,500 by 1875.[2] Apart from the central block of Wales, north Scotland and the Border hills, there could have been few farms which by 1875 could not get their cattle or their carts to the nearest railway station within a day; in the north, there was still the droving of animals from the islands and the north-western counties to the railheads at Lairg and Oban.

All over the country, therefore, in the decade after 1850 the prices received by farmers were changing as this new form of transport altered the costs of marketing. For livestock, the superiority of railways over road was measured not so much by the comparative money costs as by the indirect costs avoided, the loss of weight and the difficulties of finding fodder and water. Caird noted that sheep driven to London by road from Norfolk might lose 7 lb in weight and a bullock 28 lb. Sewell Read emphasised the same point in 1858. Before the railway

... cattle and sheep for the Smithfield Monday market had to leave their homes on the previous Wednesday or Thursday week. Such a long drift, particularly in hot weather, caused a great waste of meat. The heavy stall-fed cattle of East Norfolk suffered severely. The average loss on such bullocks was considered to be 4 stones of 14 lb, while the best yearling sheep are proved to have lost 6 lb of mutton and 4 lb of tallow; but beasts from the open yards and old sheep with careful drovers did not waste in like manner. Stock now leave on the Saturday and are in the salesmen's layers that evening, fresh for the metropolitan market on Monday morning. The cost of the rail is considerably more than the old droving charges, but against that there is the gain of 20*s* a head on every bullock a Norfolk farmer sends to town, to say nothing of being able to take immediate advantage of a dear market.

[2] *A.B.H.S.*, p. 225.

Farmers and dealers were quick to realise the advantages for livestock transport of the railways, and before 1845, the Liverpool and Manchester Railway was carrying more than 100,000 animals annually.[3]

In every county, the direction of trade in agricultural products was shifting towards the towns well served by the railways, or even created by them. The Great North of Scotland Railway reached Aberdeenshire in the 1860s, and in the succeeding decade, weekly or monthly auction sales at the stations of Inverurie, Insch, Huntly, Rothienorman and Turriff took the place of the old cattle fairs at Warthill, Rayne, Clatt and Lumsden. Further south, Echt, on the plateau between the Rivers Dee and Don, had eleven fairs annually in the early nineteenth century, and seems to have served as a collecting centre for the dispatch of produce to Aberdeen by the turnpike road.[4] With the construction of railways, the markets moved to Inverurie and Alford on the Don valley line, and to Aboyne on the Dee line, with Aberdeen as the major market for the whole region drained by these two rivers and served by the railways along each.

In the north of the county, the junction of the two branch lines running from Aberdeen to Fraserburgh and to Peterhead created an entirely new market at Maud. This name is not mentioned in the Statistical Accounts of the eighteenth and mid-nineteenth centuries; the principal market in that district was then Aikey Fair, held periodically three miles to the east outside the village of Old Deer. The siting of the railway junction at Maud led to its rapid development at the expense of the villages of New and Old Deer on either side. Auction marts for livestock were established at Maud soon after the junction; a poorhouse was built there in 1866 to serve a number of adjacent parishes; the North of Scotland Bank opened a branch there in 1867; and by the end of the century, Maud, an ugly huddle of auction marts, temporary

[3] J. Caird (1), p. 169; C. Sewell Read, 'Recent Improvements in Norfolk Farming', *J.R.A.S.E.*, vol. 19.i, 1858, p. 296; C. R. Porter, *Progress of the Nation*, London, 1851, p. 329.

[4] *New Statistical Account, Aberdeenshire*, 1843, p. 742.

offices, shops and a few houses, was an important market for live-stock and a general meeting place for farmers from every part of Buchan. Aikey Fair gradually dwindled to become an annual sale of horses combined with a circus, an occasion of amusement rather than a place of business. And all over the country, similar changes were taking place in the structure of agricultural markets, regular auction marts held near railways gradually absorbing the trade formerly carried on at periodic fairs along the old droving routes.

If the first effect of the railways was to cheapen and remodel the marketing of livestock, two further changes followed rapidly. Areas distant from the main consuming markets could develop their own trade in fat beasts, instead of consigning them as stores to the drovers to be fattened nearer the towns. And it became possible to avoid altogether the cost of transporting live animals by developing the trade in dead meat, with the further advantage that the different parts of the same carcase could be marketed in different areas in accordance with local prices. From the end of the 1850s, farmers in Aberdeen and Banff, who had up till then been stock-rearers, were able to produce fatstock, sold to the growing industrial towns between Edinburgh and London either direct or through the slaughterhouses in and near Aberdeen. Other lowland areas also became importers of store stock from hill farms or from Ireland for fattening, as railways penetrated the northern dales.[5]

When wholesale prices began to rise from 1853 onwards, there-fore, most farmers also benefited from a fall in the costs of getting their produce into market and of getting their requirements on to their farms; some farmers were also able to adopt more profitable enterprises. From the early 1860s onwards, a new pattern de-veloped in store sheep prices in the northern markets, a pattern of wider fluctuations from a generally higher level of prices, which reflected the increased demand from lowland farms for stock to turn into muck and money the larger crops of turnips

[5] J. Black, 'Agriculture of Aberdeenshire and Banffshire', *Tr. H.A.S.*, vol. 3.iv, 1870/1, p. 12; J. Wilson, 'Half a Century as a Border Farmer', *Tr. H.A.S.*, vol. 14.v, 1902, p. 37.

produced by guano, superphosphates and drainage. The autumn demand for store sheep was regulated by the size of the turnip crop, that staple winter fodder whose yield could be drastically cut by a dry summer or by a bad attack of 'the fly'. Thus the two dry years of 1867 and 1868, the latter with one of the worst droughts of the century, brought down store sheep prices to not much more than half the level ruling in 1864, and the drought of 1874 had a similar though less severe effect. But in spite of these variations, the arable farmers of the east and south of Britain usually provided ready markets for the greater number of sheep and cattle reared among the hills, with the railways as the essential link between the buyers and the sellers.[6]

FIELD DRAINAGE

In Britain's moist climate, the removal of surplus water from the soil had long been recognised as a basic necessity for higher output. From times immemorial, clay land had been laid up in high 'stetches', separated by the double water-furrow; and many landowners and farmers before 1846 had drained their fields either by the use of the 'mole' plough, cutting a narrow slit ending in a round tunnel, or by digging trenches to be filled with brushwood, stones or an inverted sod of turf under the ordinary soil. But such practices were both costly and temporary in their effects, since the drains silted up; often the outlets were inadequate and the lay-out ineffective. A most important development of the 1840s was the cylindrical agricultural pipe made by machinery, for it offered drains that were cheap, durable and available in standard sizes. Tile drainage was approved by Parliament in 1846–8 as justifying the loan of public moneys, so great was the benefit expected, and often obtained, from properly planned schemes. It was generally agreed that thorough drainage almost always paid its cost within a few years, provided it was followed up by subsoiling so that surface water could percolate to the new

[6] E. H. Whetham, 'Livestock Prices in Britain, 1851–1893', *Agric. Hist. Rev.*, vol. xi, 1963, p. 30.

drains, by the proper maintenance of outfalls and ditches and by appropriate changes in cropping and stocking. There was often, however, a conflict between the existing stetches and the desirable runs for a more carefully calculated system of drainage, which might cut across both stetches and furrows, giving an awkward variability in the depth of soil above the pipes. Farmers might then have to plough out the ridges, exposing successive surfaces of subsoil to the weather until the field was again level, but such a process was costly and slow. Field drains were therefore sometimes run down the old furrows, leaving the ridges to plague another generation of farmers whose drills and reapers were not adapted to undulating surfaces.

Within twenty-five years, the Inclosure Commissioners had approved drainage schemes involving an expenditure of about £8 million; as the cost was generally reckoned at not less than £4 per acre, and often more, this sum could not have benefited more than two million acres, but a considerable volume of drainage was executed outside the somewhat stringent conditions laid down by the Inclosure Commissioners as a qualification for a loan from public funds. Scottish tenants holding long leases from landowners who were willing to supply the pipes often laid them at their own expense, as did George Hope and his father at East Dirleton (p. 17); many of the large estates employed professional drainers to devise and execute comprehensive schemes, whose costs might be recouped in higher rents. Where tile drainage was skilfully and thoroughly done, the improvement in the clay soils was striking. The land lay drier in autumn and spring, giving more time for cultivations; the ridges could gradually be eliminated and the crops were easily sown by drill; with the help of guano or bone meal, a bigger range of higher yielding crops and fewer fallows increased the gross output and the profits. Before draining, the clays of Holderness had commonly supported two white crops and a fallow; after draining, the bare fallow gave way to turnips and seeds. Before draining, the Carse of Gowrie in Perthshire grew wheat, beans, clover and potatoes, but a well worked and expensive fallow at frequent intervals was necessary to keep down the weeds and to maintain tilth; the combination of drainage and the potato blight eliminated both the fallow and the potatoes between 1846 and 1850, in favour of turnips well dressed with manure, guano and nitrate of soda, and the farmers fattened more stock, especially sheep.

Yet Caird considered that barely one-fifth of the farm land in England and Wales which ought to be drained had received that benefit by 1873. Apart from the cost, an obvious deterrent to many encumbered estates, there were often legal and administrative difficulties, for geological strata and the flow of water had little reference to the pattern of ownership; the efficient operation of field drains might depend on other people's ditches, streams, rivers and outfalls, for whose maintenance or improvement there might be no administrative mechanism. The Land Drainage Act, 1861, encouraged landowners to combine in setting up Drainage Boards to deal with larger areas on a comprehensive basis, but the difficulties remained formidable throughout the nineteenth century.[7]

FARM IMPLEMENTS

In the development of farm machinery and implements, an important part was played by the agricultural societies through the demonstrations and tests made at the annual shows and through the reports of the judges and consulting engineers, such as C. E. Amos, who served the Royal Agricultural Society in this capacity from 1848 to 1871. In spite of occasional complaints, the general satisfaction of the makers with the tests was shown by the continuing rise in the number of implements submitted; from 1856, the Royal Agricultural Society instituted a three-year rota for the main classes, and from 1869 a five-year rota, in order to limit the volume of work falling on its judges. By this latter date, the major implements had become more uniform in their basic

[7] B. W. Adkin, *Land Drainage*, London, 1933; S.C. (H.L.) (Lands) 1873, pp. 344–52; S.C. 1848, Customs, p. 145; J. Dickson, 'Agriculture of Perthshire', *Tr. H.A.S.*, 1869, p. 168; see also pp. 194, 195.

principles, after a period in which manufacturers had experimented with a wide variety of methods and devices; it was becoming increasingly difficult for the judges to distinguish sufficiently between the various makes for the award of prizes, or to find a sufficiently substantial innovation to justify the award of the Society's medals, so that a five-year interval between tests for each class of implements was not thought to be any hardship for the manufacturers. But in the years immediately after 1850, there was variety enough in the implement section of the agricultural shows, with the greatest interest concentrated on the machinery designed to be used with steam power.

By 1850, it had been demonstrated that steam was an economic source of power for the many stationary jobs in the steading of the large arable farm and especially for threshing. The succeeding decades confirmed that fact, as steam engines became more efficient converters of coal into power, and as improvements in methods and materials were applied to the gearing and belting of the unit that transmitted the power. The Royal Agricultural Society and the Highland and Agricultural Society both held regular tests of steam threshers, taking into account both the efficiency with which the coal was used in providing power and the efficiency of the threshing mechanism. At Chester in 1858, the judges of the Royal Agricultural Society had no less than eighty-nine threshers on test; there was 'an avenue of steam engines neatly arranged at equal distances, their fly-wheels in perpetual motion, presenting a very animated scene; but what would have been the effect produced on the visitor's nerves had he known that three of these steam-engines were liable to burst at any moment?'[8] Fortunately, the stewards were at hand to order the fires to be drawn and to disqualify the offenders from further competition, but such risks had to be taken by the users of steam power in its early days.

These early steam engines could be made 'portable', in the sense that, with empty boilers and hearths, they could be drawn

---

[8] Report on ... Implements at Chester Meeting, *J.R.A.S.E.*, vol. 19.i, 1858, p. 313.

by a team of horses from one farm to the next. But even empty, they were heavy loads and it was only logical to use their own power to propel themselves; by the time of the Carlisle show in 1855 the judges could comment favourably on the mobility of most of the engines on test. More durable disabilities were public opinion which regarded steam engines on the roads as highly dangerous to the occupants of horse-drawn carriages, and the state of those roads themselves, with their soft patches, steep gradients and weak bridges and culverts. By legislation in 1861, the speed of mechanically propelled vehicles on public roads was limited to two miles per hour, and each was to be preceded by a man with a red flag sixty yards in front, in order to warn on-coming traffic; as a further safeguard, local officials could restrict the movement of steam engines to the hours of darkness, when there was the minimum of ordinary traffic.

As soon as steam engines became mobile, ingenious farmers and agriculturally-minded engineers saw the advantages of a com-pact, mobile power unit which could perform the ploughing and cultivating that so severely taxed the working horses on heavy land. The three basic methods which were tried out were the direct draught with the implement being towed by the steam engine; the engine with implements directly mounted; and the use of cables to convey power from a stationary engine to the implement in the field.

The prime difficulty with the first two methods was the weight of the engine, which either bogged down in the field to be culti-vated, or so heavily packed the land that the result was worse than no cultivation at all. The more hopeful answer lay in the technically less efficient method of operating at a distance by cable. At the Great Exhibition in 1851, Lord Willoughby de Eresby exhibited steam ploughing on this model, as he had developed it for his estate at Grimsthorpe in Lincolnshire; a single engine, mounted on rails in the centre of the field, pulled two ploughs towards itself by means of ropes wound on cables, but they had to be drawn empty away from the machine to the edges of the field by the usual horses. Fowler of Leeds and the Fisken brothers of Northumberland seem to have developed almost at the same time the principle of a single engine operating a plough or cultivator through cables attached to a windlass on the opposite side of the field to the engine. Both the engine and the windlass had to be moved forward along the headlands as each furrow was completed; the wire rope was held off the ground by porters which had to be lifted and replaced to allow the plough to pass, and it therefore required three men and three boys to operate the whole mechanism. In spite of these disadvantages, Fowler's steam ploughing did effective work and in 1851 it won the prize of £200 offered by the Highland and Agricultural Society, and in 1858, at Chester, the prize of £500 offered by the Royal Agricultural Society. But there were severe difficulties in any system which involved long lengths of wire rope to be manipulated through windlasses and drums and porters, and a number of firms, including Fowler again, decided that efficiency was best secured by the use of two engines moving slowly along opposite sides of a field and hauling between them the plough or other cultivator, on a comparatively short length of cable.

In his reviews of the use of steam power for cultivation in the *Journal of the Royal Agricultural Society* in 1859, and again in 1863, J. A. Clarke decided that power from such steam engines gave greater depth of cultivation, faster work and less pressure on the land than horse work; it therefore enabled more cultivations to be done in the autumn and eased the pressure on the horses at the peak periods of autumn and spring. With large fields of regular shape, steam cultivation could be cheaper than the equivalent horse-power, but its two main advantages were its speed, and the greater depth to which the plough could be taken. It was therefore most suitable for use with a subsoil plough to break through an old established pan, and it could also be used to open trenches for drainage work. Only a few landowners grubbed up hedges, filled in ditches, straightened their boundaries, enlarged their fields, hardened their roads, widened their gates and drained their land so that steam-drawn implements could be freely used. This was the policy adopted by Mr Smith of Woolston in Buckingham on his property – 'the first whole farm ever tilled by a steam engine'; he thereby reduced his six horses to three, cultivated more deeply and raised his yields. But the majority of arable farmers decided that steam cultivation was best kept for occasional use, for difficult work such as subsoiling or draining, and for these purposes they preferred to hire the tackle and the experts. By 1863, it was estimated that there were possibly some 600 sets of steam cultivators in regular use, operated either by contractors or by local companies formed expressly for this purpose, but not many of these companies survived the next decade of wet seasons and falling prices. A few contractors managed to build up success-ful businesses in the arable areas of the country; sixteen double-engine sets were used for reclamation work on the Scottish estates of the Duke of Sutherland between 1871 and 1892; but generally speaking, steam power was of service to British agriculture chiefly for threshing on the farms and for pumping in the fenland.[9]

A variety of cultivators, grubbers and scarifiers were also de-signed to be used either with a steam engine or with horses. Their advocates argued that these tools broke up the 'plough pan', the layer of soil just beneath the normal depth of ploughing which had been compressed by the weight of generations of ploughs and plough horses; a greater depth of soil was thus opened up for plant roots, and the effect of drought and of excessive rain was alike reduced. The use of steam to draw a heavy plough or a cultivator became indeed an essential part of successful draining on the heavy soils; unless the clay was well broken between the drains, and especially beneath the ridges, the drains might be only partially effective. Steam power also facilitated the use of mole ploughs to drain clay and loamy soils without the use of tiles.

There still remained, however, the conventional implements used with horses, of which the most important was the plough. The recent invention of the dynamometer enabled Amos and other

[9] On the use of steam, see C. C. Spence, *God Speed the Plow*, Illinois, 1959; P. A. Wright, *Traction Engines*, London, 1959; J. A. Clarke, *J.R.A.S.E.*, vol. 20.i, 1859 and vol. 24.i, 1863; P. H. Frere, 'On the Moveable Steam-Engine', *J.R.A.S.E.*, vol. 21.i, 1860; G. E. Fussell, *The Farmer's Tools*, London, 1952.

engineers to measure the draught on the horses of dragging various types of plough through various soils. It thus became possible to measure quantitatively the effect of changes in shape and design when used for various tasks – for skim-ploughing a weedy fallow before burning, for setting a clay stubble on edge for winter mellowing, or for ploughing under a clover ley for immediate sowing. Much of the variety found also in shares and mouldboards reflected ancient customs which were by no means correlated with technical efficiency as measured by the dynamometer; the regular testing of ploughs at the shows of the national and local societies gradually eliminated some of the less efficient variants in favour of the more standardised productions of the large manufacturers. Wooden-framed ploughs were in use until the end of the century but the progressive cheapening of metal and the improvement in its quality increasingly favoured the products of a few large firms offering wrought iron ploughs to which could be bolted working parts of chilled iron or steel. Stephens' *Book of Farm Implements and Machines*, published at Edinburgh in 1858 as a textbook for agricultural engineers, gave details of a popular two-wheeled plough made by Howards of Bedford with a mouldboard of cast iron, a steel plate, a sock of chilled cast iron and wheels of unequal size, so that the frame of the plough ran level with a minimum of friction (p. 184). Such ploughs when adapted to take a barred mouldboard could be used to loosen potatoes from the ridges, shaking them free of earth and so easing the work of the potato lifters (p. 202). In the next decade, hand-forged wrought iron gave way to cast iron and then to steel. Ploughs with patent steel axles were shown at Leicester in 1868 and the judges recorded that this improvement facilitated changes in the setting of ploughs to suit varied working conditions, and also greatly reduced the friction on wheels and axles.[10]

The use of these new materials to reduce friction also made it possible on lighter soils to use a double-furrow plough, thus performing twice as much work for the same distance travelled by the ploughman and his team. At Leicester in 1868, Piries showed

[10] Wm. Sanday, *J.R.A.S.E.*, vol. 4.ii, 1868, pp. 448–50.

a three-wheeled, two-furrow plough; the difficulty of turning such an implement was met by adding a second pair of wheels to the centre of the frame lowered by a ratchet at the end of each furrow; after minor improvements it became a popular model among light-land farmers. The single furrow plough, with many variants in mouldboards and shares, remained however the normal tool for arable farmers; the ploughing matches regularly held by local agricultural societies up and down the country encouraged a high standard of skill in manipulating a plough and plough team to produce straight, perfectly uniform furrows set up at the required angle, irrespective of irregularities in the soil surface. No plough-man can hide his work from the inquisitive eye of his neighbours, and the numerous teams on the large arable farms in the eastern districts maintained the traditions of skilled craftsmanship.[11]

Seed drills were regularly submitted for tests at the shows of the national societies. There are considerable mechanical diffi-culties in the way of securing an even flow of seed from the hopper to the soil, especially in a machine passing over uneven ground. The apertures through which the seed fell had to be adjustable either in size or in speed of rotation, in order to accommodate seeds of different sizes and a variety of seeding rates; the tubes down which they passed had to be both rigid, to secure straight lines suitable for the subsequent use of the horse-hoe, and yet flexible, to avoid breakages and blockages. The machines available in the 1850s normally employed either a cup feed, or a grooved cylinder for the smaller root seeds, and these remained the standard methods with only minor modifications brought about by better materials and easier gearing from the driving wheels. The second problem led to the use of telescopic tubes held loosely in place with small chains; the firm of Hornsby attempted to reduce the frequent breakages by using india-rubber tubes[12]; during the next decade these problems of breakages and blockages were met

[11] D. Pigeon, 'Evolution of Agricultural Implements', *J.R.A.S.E.*, vol. 3.iii, 1892, p. 50; G. E. Evans, *The Horse in the Furrow*, London, 1960.

[12] G. E. Fussell, *The Farmer's Tools*, London, 1952, p. 112; 'General Report on the Exhibition of Implements', *J.R.A.S.E.*, vol. 1.ii, 1865, p. 376.

by the use of steel, either in springs or in ball-and-socket joints, which kept the coulters and telescopic tubes to their job with less weight and more efficiency. Improvements in gearing also reduced the draught by a quarter to a third of that demanded by the older models, and the larger drills were often equipped with a fore-carriage for easier steering and draught. It is noteworthy that the drills exhibited in the 1850s were but little modified in subsequent years; the basic principles of the machines were found to be satisfactory in practice and the variety in size and price put the farmer with a small acreage on an equality with the largest unit, in this respect.[13] There were also the broadcast sowers, regularly used until the end of the century on farms where stones and slopes impeded the efficient working of the drill mechanism. Broadcast sowers were available with a width of about 18 feet, the two ends of which could be folded inwards on a central portion when travelling between fields; this greater width and the simpler mechanism of the broadcaster were its advantages over the ordinary drill, but the crop could not of course be horse-hoed.[14]

The same problem of providing flexibility with rigidity arose to a lesser degree with horse-hoes, whose tines also required adjustment laterally to suit different widths between drills. Here again, the main improvements adopted after 1850 arose from the use of the better materials provided by the metal trades, which combined greater durability with less weight. Cambridge's flexible disc roller was already in use by the middle of the century; its revolving iron discs were both more effective on the clods and less likely to choke than the older stone or solid iron rollers. Similarly, there was little change in the design of the zigzag iron harrows used both on arable land and on grassland; but there were minor improvements in jointing and folding and again a gradual improvement in the materials used.[15]

[13] *J.R.A.S.E.*, vol. 22.i, 1861, pp. 453–5; vol. 1.ii, 1865, p. 374.

[14] S. Copland, *Agriculture, Ancient and Modern*, London, 1866, p. 624; H. Stephens, *The Book of Farm Implements and Machines*, Edinburgh, 1858, p. 271.

[15] D. Pigeon, 'Evolution of Agricultural Implements', *J.R.A.S.E.*, vol. 3.iii, 1892, p. 59.

MOWERS AND REAPERS

The interest shown in the 1850s in the problems of harnessing steam to cultivate land was only equalled by that shown in the development of an effective mechanical reaper, whether for grain or for hay. The simplest form, a horse-drawn mower for natural or sown grass, was already in existence by 1850, though its use must have been insignificant compared with the work annually performed by gangs of mowers. The great difficulty was that of keeping the cutting knives at work at a predetermined height without blockages or breaking, irrespective of the irregularities in the surface traversed and in the density of the crop. *The Journal of Agriculture* in July 1855 could illustrate thirty-one different cutting mechanisms found on reaping machines but in the course of the next decade experience eliminated most of them in favour of that shown in Bell's reaper – triangular knives oscillating between fixed finger plates which guided the grass to the cutting edges and acted as one half of the scissor. At the Leeds exhibition in 1861, the judges were impressed by the mechanical ingenuity being applied to these problems; at the Manchester exhibition in 1869 they were able to report that the mowers 'attained a degree of practical efficiency equal to that of any other agricultural implement'. Improvements in gearing gradually reduced the draught to an extent which made it feasible for a two-horse team to cut a four-foot swathe. At the time of the Manchester show, the average cost of the two-horse mowers was a trifle under £20 and they could cut an acre or so every hour, compared with the acre per day of the skilled scythesman.

The horse-mower left the hay in continuous strips along the field, while the scythesmen left a line of discontinuous swathes each easily turned by a hayfork, and eventually pitched into a cock. The haytedders praised by Wren Hoskyns (p. 7) performed the first operation by picking up the swathes and turning them over, to dry the underside; but their simple gearing did not give them enough flexibility in adjusting the revolving speed of the tines to suit the variable character of the crop and the density of the swathes. The haytedders were given in the 1860s alternative motions, a simple forward motion to turn the swathes or a backward toss for spreading swathes that had caught the rain; by 1869, the prize-winning tedders had acquired steel axles and gearing which allowed for a considerable variety in revolving speeds to be derived from the normal walking pace of a farm horse. They had thus largely eliminated the heavy work of turning swathes by hand two or three times on successive days, or even more often, if the weather was unfavourable.

The haytedder, labour-saving though it was, left the hay scattered and it could not be pitched into cocks or into the haycart without gathering back into swathes or bundles suitable for the hayfork. The tedder, therefore, logically required the horse-drawn rake, fitted with a delivery pedal controlled by the driver, which raked up the hay and left it in swathes for pitching. This comparatively simple machine was almost fully developed by the time of the Plymouth show in 1865, when the horse rake by Howards was awarded first prize; it cost £8 10s, had a central axle of steel and sickle-shaped steel tines.

The mechanical cutting of corn was a more complicated operation. The crop was stiffer to cut than hay and could not be left lying loose on the ground; it had to be bound for stooking, and there was therefore a great advantage for subsequent operations if the reaper left the corn in convenient bundles. An efficient cutting mechanism had already been found in the oscillating knife bar working between finger plates, but wide-angled triangular knives with saw edges were found to be least liable to choke in grain crops, compared with the smooth-edged sharp-pointed knives that worked best on grass. Starting with this basic mechanism, manufacturers tried a variety of inventions designed to regulate the flow of cut corn, without making the draught too heavy for the usual two- or three-horse team. The simplest and cheapest of the machines used in the 1850s and 1860s was that developed by Hussey; two horses pulled an iron-framed implement with a cutter bar at the right delivering the swathe backwards on to a low platform from which it was raked off by a second man. In the absence of any device for holding the standing corn to the knives, the machine did not work well with bent or wet straw. In a heavy crop very hard work was required of the raker and of the horses to keep the knives working at the proper speed, and there had to be enough workers to bind the sheaves and clear them from the path of the horses before they came on the following round. This type of machine was popular with farmers in the north of England and south Scotland; it won many prizes at local and national shows, including the first prize medal at the International Show of 1862. It was cheap, costing between £20 and £30; in favourable circumstances it was light in draught, it had comparatively simple mechanisms, and it was adapted in the 1860s to take a sloping platform offering a side-delivery of the swathe, to the rear of the main frame.

Bell's reaper, with a revolving reel holding the corn against a forward-mounted cutting bar, with horses pushing from the rear, avoided this problem of backward delivery into the working path for the next cut; delivery was always effected by a tipped endless band which shot the corn well on to the land side of the reapers. The firm of Crosskill, which developed these patents, used rubber for the bands in 1856, which reduced both the friction and the draught, and obtained the largest prize from the Royal Agricultural Society in that year and again in 1861. But the length of this machine meant that it did not work well on rough ground and the operating parts were placed so far forward of the main driving wheels that it was difficult to secure an efficient mechanism.

McCormick's reaper had combined the main principles of Bell's reaper (oscillàting knives and a holding reel) with a side-mounted cutter bar, over which was placed a platform to catch the cut swathe, as in Hussey's reaper. The same problems arose of regulating the flow of the cut corn to secure periodic delivery of the unbound sheaves to the landward side of the cutting bar. Burgess and Key, the principal makers of this type of reaper, showed in 1855 a machine with a screw delivery which was highly praised and won many prizes, but the most effective mechanism was found to be a periodic rake, worked from the driving wheel by means of a cam, which swept the platform clear either at pre-determined intervals, or as controlled by the driver through a foot pedal; at the Manchester show of the Royal Agricultural Society in 1869, the Grantham firm of Hornsby and Sons won the main prizes for reapers with this type of delivery. The trials here were enlivened by the appearance of a light American reaper, made of wood (except for the cutting mechanism) and 'drawn by a pair of light thoroughbred horses adorned with carriage harness and small American and English flags at the horses' ears', but this machine could not manage the heavy crop of half-ripe rye which was being used for the tests. The judges recorded that 'the reaper trials excited much interest, and during the first few days it was necessary to employ both horse and foot police, and retaining ropes, to keep the crowd back'.

By the time of the Manchester show, most of the large arable farms cut their corn and hay with one or other of these machines, and were therefore 'no longer subjected to the supercilious and intolerant behaviour of bands of unscrupulous reapers'; it was recorded one year from Worcestershire that 'mowers were so scarce that they not only had 5s per acre for mowing, but insisted on being conveyed in a fly to their work'.[16] Such horrors could only be inflicted on farmers by skilled men conscious of their in-dispensability at a crucial moment in the seasonal work; the great advantage of the mechanical mowers was the liberty it gave farmers to perform the cutting by their own staff, assisted as before by the women and children who made the straw bands, bound and stooked the corn, or helped to pitch the hay into cocks or stacks. Jacob Wilson deduced from his own experience in the north of England that the machines available in the 1860s reduced the cost of corn harvesting by 30 to 40 per cent, but that their full benefits would only be obtained on land properly prepared by thorough drainage and levelling, by the abolition of water-cuts and furrows, by the removal of large stones and the frequent use

[16] Jacob Wilson, 'Reaping Machines', *Tr. H.A.S.*, 1864, p. 149; C. Cadle, 'Agriculture of Worcestershire', *J.R.A.S.E.*, vol. 3.ii, 1867, p. 449.

of rollers.[17] The many small farms that could not meet these requirements continued to rely on the scythesmen for grain harvesting and the mowers for the hay crop throughout these two decades until the machines became sufficiently cheap, reliable and efficient to make hand labour uneconomic even in the smallest fields.

WEEDS AND WORK

The cutting and subsequent management of the hay and grain crops by human labour had left the farm horses comparatively idle until they began the work of carting to the yards the haycocks and corn stooks. The mechanical mowers, haytedders and reapers brought the horses into full use at these seasons of pressure, thus saving much heavy human toil; a reaping machine might save the labours of ten to thirty mowers or reapers, using instead the work of two men with two or three horses, together with the normal complement of haypitchers, bandsters and stookers.[18] As a result, the big arable farm with its lands lying some distance from its stackyard found its horses fully employed in June, both in the hayfields and among the root crops, and from the middle of August in the cornfields. If the weather was favourable and long hours possible, a mechanised reaper might be used with a double shift of two or three horses. The work was severe, because a minimum speed had to be continuously maintained in order to operate the cutting and delivery mechanism. The bringing home of the sheaves overlapped with the lifting and carting of potatoes and mangolds, while horses also had to be made available for the ploughing, harrowing and sowing of the fields for the next year's crop of wheat and beans, and for hauling out the dung and spreading it in front of the plough. The Scottish figures given in Table 1 show a rise of nearly one-third in the number of horses employed on farms between 1856–7 and 1869, although the total area of arable land remained virtually unchanged.

This shift from man to horse power in harvesting on the large

[17] Jacob Wilson, *op. cit.*, pp. 148, 149.
[18] Jacob Wilson, *op. cit.*, p. 148.

arable farms was being made simultaneously with other changes in the seasonal distribution of work. On the farms which had been efficiently drained with tiles and perhaps subsoiled by steam power, the harvested fields lay so much drier in the autumn that it became possible to execute a greater volume of cultivations before winter. 'Much more ploughing and weeding done in the autumn than formerly' was a frequent comment in the prize essays on the agriculture of various counties written for the Royal Agricultural Society after 1850, and this earlier and more thorough cultivation of the heavier soils itself led to better crops in each succeeding year. It was also an essential part of that control of weeds which made possible the gradual reduction in the area of fallow, and the increase in catch cropping. The best time to attack the perennial weeds, and especially twitch, was directly after harvest, before the plants had time to grow away from the competition of the grain crop. 'In clearing a field of twitch, I should first plough it up, then drag it, then harrow and roll it, then fork it with men. . . . Then I should drag it over again and then have girls and boys to pick it over. Fen land would want to be cleared like this every fourth year' one witness told the Commission on Children's Employment of 1862 (*Sixth Report*, p. 22). If such work was not done in the autumn, then a similar attack had to be mounted as early in the spring as possible, before the root crop was planted, but by then the twitch would have a firmer hold and require still greater efforts. Annuals, such as charlock or poppy, were weeded out in the fens by sending women or children through the standing corn in the summer.

This trend towards more autumn cultivations intensified the pressure on the horses in those months. One writer calculated that a large arable farm required in September three times and in October and November twice as many horse-days of work as were needed in the winter months, while the spring peak in March, April, May and June was only about 30 per cent above the winter level.[19] The number of horses maintained throughout the year

[19] J. C. Morton, *J. Bath and West Sc.*, vol. viii, 1860, p. 303. This pattern would apply to the southern half of Britain; in the North, where winters were longer and

was necessarily determined by the peak load; the more horses to be fed, the fewer the cattle or the smaller the volume of crops available for sale. But the more cultivations that could be done in the autumn, the better the control of weeds and the bigger the crops that could be expected in the subsequent season.

A second consequence therefore was the growing employment of gang labour for the weeding. The routine in the Lincolnshire fens was described by a witness to the 1867 Commission. A few women and children were employed in January and February on sorting potatoes for market or picking stones on fields to be drilled. In March gangs would be hired for picking twitch, spreading manure, hoeing generally and in planting potatoes. The spring work was mainly weeding by hand or hoe and picking twitch from the root fields or fallows. In July there was hay-making and turnip-singling as well as weeding the corn crops by hand. Employment rose to a peak in August and September with gangs making ties for the reapers or the reaping machines, stooking, pulling flax and gleaning. In October the heavy work began of lifting potatoes and mangolds, and spreading manure while the young children would be back on twitch picking; the last two months of the year saw a few gangs still lifting carrots or picking twitch or stones. It was reckoned that some 6–7,000 women and children were commonly employed in these fenland areas in the so-called 'public' gangs, but there was an unknown number employed in smaller units by farmers direct, under the supervision of the regular farm staffs. George Hope, for instance, employed local women and also Highland girls for hoeing and turnip-singling, muck-spreading and root-lifting; the girls lived in bothies on the farm during the months they had employment there.[20]

The reports of these Commissions brought legislative control over the public gangs by the Gangs Act, 1867, but there remained the twin problems of weed control and the seasonal fluctuations

---

wheat less grown, the spring was normally the period with most pressure on the horses.

[20] R. C. Employment, 1867, *First Report*, p. 13; *Sixth Report*, p. xxiii: A. G. Bradley, *When Squires and Farmers Thrived*, London, 1927, p. 80. See also p. 15.

in work, to be dealt with by other methods than that of paying a gangmaster 14*s* or 15*s* a day for the work of twenty boys and girls. The advocates of steam ploughing urged the benefits of mechanical power for the heavy autumn work, thus freeing horses and men for the lighter work of harrowing, forking and twitch-burning; steam threshers also made it possible to thresh in the fields, and thus to postpone to a slacker time of year the carting home of the grain and straw, while sheep folded on the roots economised in the autumn work of carting, which was exceptionally heavy on the farms that fattened cattle over the winter. More use of horse-hoes both in drilled corn and in the root crops took the place of children kept longer at school by the Education Acts after 1872, while in all districts the growing unwillingness of women to go out to field work forced on farmers a re-organisation of their routine.

In the era before tractors and sprays, weed control on the large arable farm offered an intricate problem in crop rotations, crop yields and costs. Slovenly farming brought lowered yields and higher costs each year, and it also created an adverse item of depreciation in the costs that would have to be incurred over a term of years before the weeds were brought under control. A farmer taking over a weed-infested farm would need extra workers for twitch-picking and hoeing, and extra horses to drag and culti-vate more often each autumn and spring; he would lose the crops foregone on the bare fallow that might be required on the worst fields; and he might be limited in his crops for the first few years to those that could be regularly hoed for a long period of each season, thus ruling out, perhaps, wheat, rye, beans and even sown grasses. Conversely, farms once made clean of weeds by thorough cultivation and regular hoeing required fewer horses and less casual labour; they had therefore lower costs as well as higher yields and greater flexibility in cropping. Efficient weed control was thus an important part of a tenant's management; if weeds were not effectively controlled, the farm began to run down, but unless they were economically controlled, the costs of seasonal cultivations might absorb the farmer's own profits.

CROP ROTATIONS

From 1846 almost until his death in 1866, the Highland and Agricultural Society had as Secretary that energetic and efficient man John Hall Maxwell. He was a firm supporter of those who wanted more information about British agriculture, and in 1853 he and his Council decided to organise the collection of crop and livestock statistics from farmers in Scotland, using the officers of the many local agricultural associations for whose shows and ploughing matches the central society provided prizes and certificates. The final assembly and compilation of the returns was undertaken by Hall Maxwell's office, and the enterprise was blessed by the Treasury with a small grant in aid of the clerical work; the grant and the enterprise alike came to an abrupt end when a strait-minded official insisted that all who received Treasury money, for however short a period, must be properly appointed civil servants.

The returns, given in Table 1 for 1856 and 1857, indicated that there were some 3½ million acres of cultivated land in Scotland, farmed on a five-course rotation, two-fifths in corn, two-fifths in temporary grass and one-fifth in green crops. Oats were grown on 900,000 acres, more than twice as much as the other two corn crops taken together, and covered one-quarter of the arable land. There were nearly 150,000 acres of potatoes, mainly in Aberdeen, Fife, Forfar, Perth and Lanark, but some 470,000 acres of turnips and swedes provided the main winter food for the livestock. Some of these turnips were 'sheeped' in the fields, but the greater part was lifted in the autumn and stored alongside the stalls and yards; this usual Scottish practice made it possible to take the wheat crop, where it was grown, after the roots, where it could benefit from the dung applied the previous winter. South of the Tees, where a higher proportion of the turnips were fed off in the fields by sheep, wheat traditionally followed the ley and preceded the root crop.

The four successive censuses organised by the Highland and Agricultural Society showed a peak in the area under wheat in 1856 followed by a decline which was completed before the start of the official returns in 1866. From more than 250,000 acres in 1856, the area fell to barely 110,000 acres ten years later; it was to fluctuate between that level and 140,000 acres for another ten years. The fall was general in all counties but most marked in the north and west; by the 1860s, wheat was scarcely grown in Scot-

Table 1

Scottish Agricultural Statistics, 1856 and 1857

	1856	1857
	Thousand Acres	
Wheat	263	223
Barley and bere	181	220
Oats	919	939
Other Corn Crops	50	49
TOTAL Corn Crops	1,413	1,431
Potatoes	149	140
Roots	465	481
Cabbage, Vetches, etc.	21	25
TOTAL Green Crops	635	646
Other Crops and Fallow	19	19
TOTAL Tillage	2,067	2,096
Clover and Grasses in rotation	1,476	1,460
	Thousand Head	
Horses for Agric. Work	123	126
Cattle	967	974
Sheep	5,817	5,683
Pigs	127	146

Tr. H.A.S.

land except in the farms in the eastern arable belt from Forfar south to Berwick. Slightly more oats, potatoes and turnips showed where the greater profit lay – in feeding livestock and in growing the staple vegetable for the industrial towns. Since there was no comparable census taken in England and Wales until 1866, we have no evidence of similar trends there, but the price statistics of these years (given in Chart V) confirm that wheat became relatively less profitable, both in relation to the other grain crops and in relation to meat prices, after the dear years of 1854–6.[21]

In 1866 the Government was induced to collect returns from all the farmers of Great Britain on a uniform basis, using for this purpose the officers of the Inland Revenue. The figures for the first year were generally low because of omissions and evasions which progressively diminished as the census takers became more knowledgeable and the farmers less suspicious of their intentions[22]; Table 2 summarises the returns for the two years 1867 and 1870; and Charts I and II indicate the subsequent trends.

These figures showed that Scottish farmers still followed the five-course rotation, and showed also substantial differences in cropping between Scotland and Wales. Of the arable land in Wales, half was in cereals, mainly oats but with a proportion in both wheat and barley; more than one-third was under rotation grass, and barely twelve per cent under roots or green crops. The Welsh cattle were not wintered under cover on turnips, oats and straw; they wintered out with only a little help from oats and hay in hard weather, and were fattened mainly by the English graziers and eastern arable farmers who needed muck for their grain crops. There was thus little attempt at crop rotation on most Welsh farms in the second half of the nineteenth century; a couple of grain crops in succession were followed by two or three years under grass, with one or two fields in potatoes for the farm families and in roots for the milking cows and young sheep. There was twice as much grass, taking temporary and permanent together, as there was tillage in Wales, and a still greater area of moor and hill and mountain, grazed by 600,000 cattle, $2\frac{3}{4}$ million sheep and nearly 50,000 mares and young horses, which bred the power not only for the farms but also for the coal mines of South Wales and transport users everywhere.

[21] E. H. Whetham, 'Prices and Production in Scottish Farming 1850–1870', *Scot. J. of Pol. Econ.*, vol. ix, 1962, pp. 233–43.

[22] J. T. Coppock, 'The Statistical Assessment of British Agriculture', *Agric. Hist. Rev.*, vol. iv, 1956, pp. 4–21, 66–79.

Table 2

Crops and Livestock in England, Wales and Scotland, 1867, 1870

Thousand Acres	England		Wales		Scotland	
	1867	1870	1867	1870	1867	1870
Wheat	3,140	3,248	117	127	111	126
Barley	1,892	1,964	148	164	218	244
Oats	1,506	1,491	247	253	997	1,020
Pulse, etc.	861	868	9	10	38	35
TOTAL Corn	7,399	7,570	521	554	1,364	1,424
Potatoes	290	359	45	49	158	180
Root Crops	1,875	1,955	71	76	486	501
Green Crops	527	445	22	5	24	15
TOTAL Root and Green Crops	2,692	2,760	138	130	668	697
Other Crops	64	83	7	—	—	1
Bare Fallow	753	549	86	38	83	23
Rotation Grass	2,478	2,767	301	398	1,211	1,340
TOTAL Arable	13,386	13,729	1,046	1,120	3,326	3,485
Permanent Grass	9,546	9,680	1,368	1,428	1,053	965
Thousand Head						
Cows and Heifers in milk and calf	1,411	1,529	245	256	382	376
Other cattle:						
2 yrs and over	920	978	111	123	236	254
under 2 yrs	1,138	1,250	189	225	362	411
TOTAL Cattle	3,469	3,757	545	605	979	1,041
Sheep:						
1 yr and over	12,383	12,003	1,514	1,892	4,552	4,515
under 1 yr	7,415	6,937	713	815	2,342	2,236
TOTAL Sheep	19,798	18,940	2,227	2,706	6,894	6,751
Pigs	2,549	1,814	230	199	188	159

In addition to figures for each county, these early statistics gave a summary of the cropping for the two parts of England, the grazing counties and the arable counties; the dividing line was drawn along the western boundary of the East Riding of Yorkshire to meet the Channel at the eastern edge of Dorset (Table 3). To

Table 3

Cropping in Grazing and Arable Districts of England, 1870

Thousand Acres	*Grazing*	*Arable*
Wheat	1,212	2,036
Barley	738	1,226
Oats	781	710
Pulse, etc.	243	624
TOTAL Corn Crops	2,974	4,596
Potatoes	214	144
Root and Green Crops	981	1,421
Rotation Grass	1,517	1,250
Bare Fallow	268	281
TOTAL Arable*	5,954	7,692
Permanent Grass	6,352	3,329

* Excluding 'other crops'.

Grazing District: Chester, Cornwall, Cumberland, Derby, Devon, Dorset, Durham, Gloucester, Hereford, Lancaster, Leicester, Monmouth, Northumberland, Shropshire, Somerset, Stafford, Westmorland, Wiltshire, Worcester, Yorkshire, North and West Ridings.

Arable District: Bedford, Berkshire, Buckingham, Cambridge, Essex, Hampshire, Hertford, Huntingdon, Kent, Lincoln, Middlesex, Norfolk, Northampton, Nottingham, Oxford, Rutland, Suffolk, Surrey, Sussex, Warwick, Yorkshire, East Riding.

the north and west of this dividing line, there was more permanent grass than arable; the arable was cropped commonly in a four-course rotation of two years in grain, one in roots or bare fallow and one year in temporary grass. Wheat was the major corn crop in all the lowland counties in the grazing division; it was only along the extreme west from Cumberland to Cornwall that farmers planted less wheat than barley or oats. East and south of the dividing line, the arable counties had more than twice as much land under the plough as in permanent pasture; and the basic rotation on the arable was a five-course, with three years in grain, one in green crops and one in rotation grass or bare fallow. There were here just over two million acres in wheat, 1·2 million acres in barley, the second grain for the light land, and the same area in oats and pulse, taken together. A dozen counties took wheat twice in the rotation – the East Riding, Lincoln, Cambridge, Huntingdon, Essex, Surrey and Sussex in the east; across the Midlands, Nottingham, Shropshire, Hereford and Gloucester. Norfolk and Suffolk grew almost as much barley as wheat and seldom planted oats; but the south-eastern counties of Kent, Surrey and Sussex grew more oats than barley, for London had an insatiable appetite for horse fodder. The heavy lands that were predominantly under wheat had a comparatively high area of beans, of which more than half a million acres were grown in England and Wales; wherever soil was stiff, horse-work heavy and weeds difficult, beans were grown as fuel for the horses and as a cleaning crop in the rotation.

More potatoes were grown in the aggregate in the grazing counties than in the arable division; Chester, Lancashire, Cumberland, Somerset and Yorkshire supplied their neighbouring miners and factory workers, while on the arable side, Cambridge, Essex and Kent, each with about 10,000 acres, supplied the London market, as did the Scottish growers on the red soils round Dunbar. But there were fewer than 400,000 acres in England and Wales, for many landowners objected to commercial potato production on their farms and many farmers could not find the casual labour for the planting and lifting. All through the previous decades the potato crop had had a bad reputation for disease, low yields and widely fluctuating prices which made it more of a gamble than most crops; the Scottish census of 1854–7 recorded outputs of 3–4 tons per acre in most districts in most of these years, though on good soils and with no blight farmers might lift up to seven tons per acre. It had been noted that early varieties tended to be less affected by blight than the late, and the northern crops than the southern, which partly accounted for the intensity of potato production in Scotland. In Dunbar, William Paterson (1810–1870) imported stocks from all over the world in an attempt to breed disease resistant strains; he is said to have lost £7,000 on his experiments, but succeeded in putting on to the market in 1863 the variety 'Victoria' which for some years was highly successful. But the experience of the twenty-five years after the blight of 1845–6 destroyed the hopes of farmers for a potato that would be unaffected by this disease. The many 'new varieties' and 'improved strains' all succumbed to blight, if not immediately then within ten or fifteen years, and in spite of differing soils, climates and fertilisers. A warm spell with rain in the last half of July and the first half of August was certain to produce blight in varying degrees of severity up to the almost total loss experienced in Scotland in 1872 and in England in 1879.[23]

The traditional four-course rotation was only dominant in the north and west of England, though it was still often described in leases and was generally followed by some farmers in all parts of the country, as in its home county of Norfolk. But where it had been consistently followed for many years, two results were often visible. The first was a gradual building up of fertility, which was indeed the prime object of the rotation, but which eventually made it unsafe to take barley or oats after roots for fear of lodging, or to undersow the barley with seeds. Hence came the introduction of the second wheat crop on the better soils, extending the rotation to five years, with three in grain, or with two in grain and an extra course in potatoes. But the second and more disturbing result was the increasing risk of failure both of the turnips through finger-and-toe disease, and of clover from unknown causes. The first disease was known to be mitigated, if not prevented, by liming, an expensive remedy for tenant farmers without leases or agreements over compensation for improvements; mangolds, carrots, cabbages, kohlrabi, beet and Swedish turnips instead of the more susceptible globe variety were possible alternatives, together with two years in pasture, which also lengthened the

[23] R. N. Salaman, *The History . . . of The Potato*, Cambridge, 1949, p. 167; Report of the Select Committee on the Potato Crop, 1880 (274).

interval between the successive turnip crops. But clover sickness was a still more serious affliction on many soils, for which the only known remedy was not to grow clover for six or eight years. The disease could not be traced to any manurial deficiency; long experiments at Rothamsted showed that no variety or combination of fertilisers prevented red clover from failing on that soil after it had been grown twice in succession.[24] Lack of clover reduced the value of temporary pastures, where the dominant ryegrass was apt to fail in the months of late summer or in the second year. Sainfoin and lucerne were possible alternatives to red clover on the chalky soils of east and south England, but elsewhere clover sickness was a serious handicap for many farmers, forcing them to a greater dependence for their fodder on the more expensive crops of vetches or cabbage or turnips, and for their nitrogen on guano or nitrate of soda.

The note book of a Liverpool corn merchant has provided estimated wheat yields over a wide area of the Midlands and southern England, for the years from 1815 to 1859. From a range of 25–37 bushels per acre up to 1830, there was a remarkable rise to 45–50 bushels in the 1840s and a further rise thereafter to a peak of 58 bushels in the favourable years of 1857 and 1858. The merchant was clearly too sanguine, for the official estimates of yields begun in 1884–93 record a national average yield of only 30 bushels per acre. The absolute level is therefore less important than the fact of the large rise in estimated yields over these forty years, reflecting better drainage, better cultivations, a larger supply of minerals and nitrogen from guano and superphosphate, more manure from cake-fed animals. And these same factors must have had a similar effect on the yields of the other crops in the rotation, increasing both output and profit per acre, especially as prices rose in the mid-1850s.[25]

[24] J. B. Lawes and J. H. Gilbert, 'Report of Experiments on the Growth of Red Clover', *J.R.A.S.E.*, vol. 21.i, 1860, pp. 178–200.

[25] M. J. R. Healy and E. L. Jones, 'Wheat Yields in England, 1815–59', *J.R.S.S.*, vol. 125, 1962, pp. 574–7; J. B. Lawes and J. H. Gilbert, 'On the Home Produce, Imports and Consumption of Wheat', *J.R.A.S.E.*, vol. 4.ii, 1868, p. 368; *A.B.H.S.*, p. 90.

These general patterns of crop rotation indicate the routine of thousands of farmers, applying current knowledge of soils and of plant growth to the problem of making a profitable living out of their individual farms, at current levels of costs and prices. But the farms that were written about, visited, discussed, which became famous or notorious, were those of the innovators, of the exceptional men such as J. J. Mechi who were prepared to put new theories into practice and to test established customs in a new setting.

John Joseph Mechi (1802–1880), the son of an Italian immigrant, was born in London; as a young man he worked in a merchant house there before setting up in business as a cutler, and later he made a substantial fortune out of a patent razor strop. His wealth and talents brought him into office as sheriff of London and Middlesex in 1856 and alderman of the City of London in 1858, but this latter post he resigned in 1866, when two firms with which he was concerned were forced into liquidation by the financial panic of that year. But in 1844, he had bought 130 acres of poor, wet heath land at Tiptree in the Essex clays for £25 per acre; and with no inherited prejudices on how it ought to be farmed he applied his business ability and his capital to the problems of agriculture.

It appeared to him to be economically foolish to allow land to grow a minimum of water-logged crops and to support a few half-starved animals, especially when unemployed and half-starved men were asking for work at almost any wage. He therefore drained the farm with inch pipes at five feet depth and fifty feet apart, removed all hedges and trees, laid out square fields served with hard roads, and engaged as many men as applied for work to dig his land two spits deep at twopence per rod. Ten years later, when there were fewer unemployed and wages were rather higher, he subsoiled his fields by steam power. Mechi further decided that animals out in the wind and rain and sun wasted food and manure; he built well ventilated stalls and covered yards for his livestock, and after various experiments with bedding and dungheaps, he provided slatted floors covered with a minimum of straw, draining into a huge liquid manure tank. Periodically his steam engine pumped this manure on to his fields, and it also powered his thresher, grinding mills and feed cutters. By the application of liquid manure, lime, guano and superphosphate, he steadily raised the fertility of his land until it no longer responded to guano or lime. In the 1860s, he obtained average yields of 5–6 quarters of wheat, 7 quarters of barley and up to 40 tons of mangolds per acre. He normally kept 30–40 bullocks, about 200 sheep and large numbers of pigs and poultry; he considered that pigs were usually the most profitable producers of meat and manure, since in most years the price of 1lb of pork was considerably higher than the price of the 7 lb of barley or beans used in its production, while the manure paid for the labour. But in years when the ratio was unfavourable, he sold his corn and kept fewer pigs.

Perhaps Mechi's most startling innovation was the regular publication of his annual accounts, with explanations of his failures and occasional losses, as well as of the general profitability of his intensive farming. So few farmers kept any sort of accounts, let alone published them, that Mechi's yearly balance sheet became a regular news item of the farming press. Summaries of his accounts for the four years 1865 to 1868 are given below; he was fortunate in that he escaped the cattle plague of these years and was able to take advantage of the generally good prices. If Mechi had paid on the 130 acres that he owned the rent of £1 per acre that he paid for an adjacent area of 45 acres, he would have made over these years an average profit of £440, £2½–£3 per acre, or a return of about 18 per cent on his farming capital of £15–£16 per acre. From these accounts, he demonstrated the profitability of intensive farming, even on poor clay soils, in a flow of articles to newspapers and speeches to farmers' clubs which made him the centre of controversy and discussion. For two decades Tiptree Hall was one of the most famous of demonstration farms, attracting visitors from all over Britain as well as from overseas. Mechi was always keen to try anything new; he lent his fields for demonstrations of reaping machines and steam ploughing and adopted both these improvements at an early stage in their development. He had, of course, the advantage of being his own landlord, so that he could freely remodel his farm and its buildings and derive the

Table 4. *Tiptree Hall Farming Accounts, 1865–1869*

Expenditure	1865 £	1866 £	1867 £	1868 £
Valuation 1 Jan.	2,166	2,503	2,566	2,858
Feeds	384	460	487	824
Livestock	281	186	465	450
Horses	48	16	39	41
Labour and beer	409	375	478	504
Rent for 45 acres	45	45	45	45
Taxes and rates	82	84	83	93
Depreciation of machinery	25	25	25	25
Coals for engine	52	31	35	44
Tradesmen	57	41	74	99
Seeds and manures	160	111	180	124
Miscellaneous	29	22	31	52
	1,572	1,398	1,939	2,301
	3,738	3,901	4,508	5,159
Receipts				
Closing valuation	2,503	2,566	2,858	2,708
Corn	601	479	1,187	1,327
Peas for picking	44	2	41	68
Hay, straw, mangolds, seeds	113	102	131	146
Fatstock	813	1,123	873	1,265
Poultry and eggs	45	44	49	47
Wool	20	54	23	30
Cottage rents	16	16	16	16
Grinding for hire, etc.	85	45	58	78
	4,240	4,431	5,236	5,685
PROFIT	498	529	728	528

benefit from the rising fertility of his soil after the draining and manuring of the first decade.

The last years of Mechi's long life were clouded by illness and he gradually became unable to give his intensive farming the detailed supervision it required; like all clay-land farmers, he lost heavily in the run of wet seasons after 1875 and he was on the edge of bankruptcy when he died in December 1880, a tragic end to an active career as farmer, experimenter and publicist.[26]

Another controversial agriculturalist was the Rev. S. Smith of Lois Weeden near Towcester who experimented with a rotation of wheat and fallow in alternate strips. Using neither fertilisers nor manure, he sowed wheat in groups of three rows separated by a fallow strip of similar size which was dug two spits deep by hand as well as being ploughed and regularly horse-hoed; after each harvest, the fallow strip was planted with wheat and the wheat stubble dug up for the fallow treatment. He was able to show to his own satisfaction that with this rotation of wheat and fallow his soil was not exhausted and that each year he could obtain from the total area an amount of grain equal to an average yield of his neighbours in fields planted in the normal way. But Lawes could not obtain the same result on his lighter Rothamsted soils, though he did not work his land as thoroughly as Smith recommended; and the famous Broadbalk field, continuously cropped with wheat, showed yields markedly below the average, though some yield could always be obtained as long as weeds were kept under control.[27] The experiment at Lois Weeden seems to have had little practical result, though in the next decade John Prout began his long demonstration, at Blount's Farm, Sawbridgeworth, of growing successive grain crops without livestock. But few farmers were willing to follow these pioneers, nor were they willing to forgo the advantages provided by the normal crop rotations to grow fodder for animals. For even in the arable counties of England, the area devoted to animal fodder – oats,

[26] D. N. B. *Profitable Farming. Mr. Mechi's Latest Agricultural Sayings and Doings (with balance sheets)*, London, 1869.

[27] S. Smith, 'Lois Weeden Husbandry', *J.R.A.S.E.*, vol. 18.i, 1857; J. B. Lawes and J. H. Gilbert, 'On the Growth of Wheat by the Lois Weeden System', *J.R.A.S.E.*, vol. 17.i, 1856.

pulse, roots and green crops – was somewhat greater than that under the three crops grown primarily for human consumption – wheat, barley and potatoes; Mechi was probably following a normal pattern for an arable farmer in that he derived about half his gross receipts from the sale of livestock.

5

Livestock Farming
1851-1875

CATTLE BREEDS AND PEDIGREES

THE twenty years from 1850 to 1870 saw the dominance in British agriculture of the Shorthorn breed of cattle and the Leicester and Southdown breeds of sheep. That dominance was symbolised by their triumphs in the show rings of local and national agricultural societies, and demonstrated by the prices paid for stock with favoured pedigrees; but the glory of red rosettes and of silver cups derived basically from the importance of these breeds in providing the fatstock sold by British farmers and the meat eaten by British families.

On these matters, valuable evidence is provided by that agricultural and sporting journalist, H. H. Dixon (1822–1870), commonly known as 'The Druid', whose knowledge of pedigree and performance was unrivalled in his day. Summarising the evidence of experienced Smithfield salesmen, he thought 'that rather more than two-thirds of the average number of beasts (331,164) which came to the London market in 1863–4 were either pure shorthorns or shorthorn crosses.'[1] Shorthorns were bred primarily for the consumption of arable crops with some help from the manufacturers of the new oilseeds industry. Their early maturity enabled them, on a diet consisting mainly of roots, oats and straw, to be sold fat at $2\frac{1}{2}$–$3\frac{1}{2}$ years old, though most, being poorly fed when young, were not ready for the butcher

[1] H. H. Dixon, 'Rise and Progress of Shorthorns', *J.R.A.S.E.*, vol. i.ii, 1865, p. 324.

until a year older. Butchers found that their square frame covered with evenly laid flesh and fat gave a higher proportion of saleable meat than was obtained from the larger-boned animals with coarse-textured flesh. The pure-bred Shorthorn bulls were already renowned for their ability to transmit this beefing quality to their progeny, even when put to proletarian cows of other breeds. On the Scottish hills, Shorthorn bulls used on Highland and Galloway cows produced hardy animals that were sold at 2-2½ years old to lowland farmers for their yards and stalls; the blue-greys that resulted from white Shorthorn bulls and black Galloway cows were already noted as exceptionally good beef animals. All over Britain and Ireland, herds kept on poor land could be made to yield profitable beef stock through the use of Shorthorn bulls.

The ability to transmit this beefing quality was no doubt derived from the skilful judgment and careful in-breeding of the earliest Shorthorn breeders, Bates, the Collings and the Booths, Col. Towneley and Amos Cruikshank. The collection and publication of Shorthorn pedigrees by Coates from the year 1822 gave the breeders a long start over their competitors dealing with other types of cattle, for it enabled them to work with known material. In England, the dominant herds for nearly twenty years from the mid-1840s were those of the Booth family in Yorkshire. Thomas Booth (d. 1835) was succeeded by his two sons, John at Killerby, and Richard (d. 1864), the 'Wizard of Warlaby'. John Booth who died in 1857 also left two sons, J. B. Booth (d. 1886) who carried on his father's herd at Killerby, and T. C. Booth (d. 1878) who succeeded his uncle at Warlaby. The Booths not only bred and sold breeding stock, they also hired out some of their bulls for each season, and many enterprising landowners took advantage of this practice for the improvement of their own herds and those of their tenants, at comparatively little cost. A small number of animals thus had a marked effect in up-grading the cattle stock; the cattle in Ireland were in these decades bred from Booth bulls to such an extent that for many years few sires of any other strain of blood were used. The Warlaby herd suffered from repeated attacks of foot-and-mouth disease at the end of the 1860s;

it was reconstructed in 1875 from Booth-descended cattle bought at the dispersal sale of another famous breeder, William Torr of Aylesby, but it was then only one among a large number of herds which supplied pedigree stock for the British, Irish and overseas trade. Breeding stock had gone to the United States in 1853 from Col. Towneley's herd,[2] but the great expansion in the American demand developed after the close of the Civil War, and was concentrated for a time on the families bred from Bates's stock, dispersed at the Kirklevington sale in 1850. High prices were realised in the decade from 1870 to 1880 for a few animals inbred to the famous families of 'Duchesses' and 'Wild-Eyes', but this later inbreeding seems to have been less successful than that undertaken earlier in the history of the Shorthorn. Breeding for show and for fashionable lines was indeed a severe strain on the constitution of any stock, for the highly fat condition required to please the eye of many judges at important shows was destructive of fertility among both cows and bulls; both J. B. Booth and T. C. Booth eventually gave up showing for this reason. It was this emphasis on fat by the judges which gradually eliminated from many herds the dual function of the Shorthorn as a good milking animal which quickly fattened for the butcher. Dixon commented in 1865 that 'good milking pedigrees do not command an extra price, and, in fact, any allusion to them in a sale catalogue is rather regarded as an apology for doubtful or unfashionable blood.'[3] The concentration on beefing qualities was carried furthest by the Scottish breeders, and the 'Scotch Shorthorn' became another name for the animals bred both in Scotland and in north England for the butchers, while in the south the Shorthorn remained a dual-purpose animal found in both beef and dairy herds.

The early concentration of interest on pedigree Shorthorns forced their prices above the level of animals of the lesser known and less fashionable breeds. Dixon remarked that many of the London dairies relied on imported Dutch cows which could be

---

[2] R. Bruce, *Fifty Years Among Shorthorns*, London, 1907, p. 20; *Economist* 18 June, 1853, p. 676.

[3] H. H. Dixon, *op. cit.*, p. 324.

bought for about half the price of Shorthorns; the monster dairy in Glasgow kept by a Mr Harvey had, in 1865, just before the cattle plague, about 300 Shorthorn cows and about 700 Ayrshires, with a sprinkling of Dutch recently imported.[4] And the lower price of good Herefords or Devons or Aberdeen-Angus was an advantage to the commercial farmers in the areas where these breeds were native.

The Aberdeen-Angus was, in this period from 1850 to 1870, undergoing the same development as the Shorthorn had seen in the previous thirty years. It was, like the Shorthorn, bred for early maturity when fattened in stalls and yards on the crops of arable farms, aided by beans or cattlecake. Its progress to fame involved a competition against the better known breed which had been widely used as a cross on the local polled cattle in the north-east of Scotland in the previous decades. M'Combie of Tillyfour set himself to obtain from the native stock as good a beef carcase as the Shorthorns and at the same age; and to make his success widely known by constant exhibition of the best animals. At the International Exhibition at Battersea, in 1862, the two best females were judged to be Richard Booth's 'Queen of the Ocean', and M'Combie's 'Pride of Aberdeen', and it was noted how closely the two animals resembled each other in general conformation – a square frame set on short legs, deep-bodied and short in the back. M'Combie's prize-winning ox 'Black Prince' received a halo of fame when it was commanded to appear at Windsor in 1867 for inspection by Queen Victoria herself; Her Majesty afterwards visited M'Combie's farm and caused a herd of Aberdeen-Angus to be established on the Balmoral estate. Between 1850 and his dispersal sale in 1880, M'Combie is believed to have sold some 350 breeding animals for a total of some £14,000; his success in establishing the black polls as a hardy and profitable beef breed was to be demonstrated in the twenty years after his dispersal sale, when descendants of his animals were to be found in thousands in the United States.[5]

[4] H. H. Dixon, *op. cit.*, p. 324; *Field and Fern*, London, 1866, vol. ii, p. 2.
[5] J. Macdonald and A. Sinclair, *History of the Aberdeen-Angus Cattle*, London, 1910.

In these two decades, the Shorthorn and the Aberdeen-Angus became the two fashionable breeds for the production of beef on arable farms, the Shorthorn generally and the Aberdeen-Angus mainly confined to its own district in the north-east of Scotland. On hill and upland farms the foundation stocks of Highland, Galloway or Welsh black cows could undergo little improvement themselves without losing their native hardiness, but crossed with a Shorthorn bull they produced useful animals for fattening either upon arable crops or upon lowland grass: the dairy herds of un-pedigreed Shorthorns also produced a regular supply of steers for the graziers. In other parts of Britain, the Hereford, Devon and Sussex cattle were being slowly improved by judicious breeding that was little affected by showyard fashions; farmers in these districts aimed to produce animals that fattened readily on good grass, though not to such a high condition nor at such an early age as the stall-fed Shorthorn. Herefords and Devons were indeed frequent prize winners at the fatstock shows at London and Birmingham from the 1860s onwards; this publicity led to the development of an export trade to America at the end of the decade which later became an important factor in the profits of Hereford breeders. Vol. I of the *Hereford Herd Book*, published in 1846, contained only bulls, 551 of them with faces that might be white, grey, mottled or speckled; later volumes included cows as well, and concentrated entirely on the white-faced strain. As late as 1877, however, one highly pedigreed bull was found to be leaving calves 'having black, grey or dirty noses and nearly all showing the doubtful characteristics of some unknown breed'[6]; the white face had by then become a trade mark, the easily recog-nised sign of an animal that turned grass into profitable beef. But while the Hereford men bred only white faces, farmers in Norfolk and Lincolnshire, Devon and Sussex industriously bred white out of their local variants of the shorthorned race. And within the Devon breed, natural variations were encouraged by individual

[6] R. C. Gaut, *History of Worcestershire Agriculture and Rural Evolution*, Worcester, 1939, p. 347; R. Trow-Smith, *History of British Livestock Husbandry, 1700–1900*, London, 1959, p. 252.

breeders so that deep red cattle from north Devon and Somerset became known for their beefing qualities, while a more yellow variety in central and south Devon retained the dairy tradition and was valued for the trade in butter and cream.

Such information as exists for store cattle markets indicates that sellers obtained sharply rising prices from 1852 to 1857, with a further rise from 1868, after the epidemic of cattle plague, to a peak in 1872. In these twenty years, store cattle prices apparently rose faster than the wholesale prices of beef, so that rearers obtained some share at least in the higher returns brought about by improved demand and the lower costs of transporting livestock from farm to market.[7] The extent of the trade in store beasts can be detected from the age distribution of the cattle herds within individual counties. The ratios of the cattle aged 'two years and over' and 'under two years' to the number of cows and heifers in milk and calf, given in Table 5 for 1870, varied markedly between the different types of cattle enterprise dominant in the main agricultural regions.

The arable counties in Group 1 had, in June when the census was taken, about equal numbers in all three classes; if a count had been taken in December when the stalls and yards were occupied by fattening beasts, the ratio of the older cattle might have been much higher. Group 2 reflects the greater importance of younger cattle on the Scottish arable farms, while Group 3, the midland grazing counties, had the highest ratio of the older fattening cattle. These three groups were the main importers of the six-quarter-old stirks and two- to three-year-old cattle from other counties, from Ireland and from overseas. The five mainly arable counties in Group 4, all round London, kept some dairy cows or fattening beasts on their riverside meadows and clay pastures. Counties in Group 5 sold many of their cattle at two to three years old for fattening elsewhere, and this trend was taken further in Group 6 which includes Wales, five English and fourteen Scottish hill counties. The sixteen dairy counties in England and Scotland dis-

[7] E. H. Whetham, 'Livestock Prices in Britain, 1851–1893'. *Agric. Hist. Rev.*, vol. ix, 1963, p. 30.

tinguished themselves by their low ratios of 'other cattle'. Of those recorded, some would be dry cows fattening for the butcher and some would be bulls of which all sizeable dairy farms required one or two. According to local markets, the supply of dairymaids

Table 5. *Cattle Enterprises in Britain in 1870*

	Per 100 *cows and heifers*	
	Cattle 2 yrs and over	*Cattle under 2 yrs*
1. Fattening on arable and leys; 10 English counties	98	104
2. Fattening, some rearing; 13 Scottish counties	107	157
3. Fattening on grass; 5 English counties	171	136
4. Mixed with dairying; 5 English counties near London	61	77
5. Lowland rearing, some fattening; 7 English counties	69	95
6. Hill rearing; Wales and 5 English counties	57	92
14 Scottish counties	60	108
7. Dairying; 10 English counties	27	51
6 Scottish counties	34	59

1. Bedford, Cambs., Essex, Hunts., Norfolk, Notts., Suffolk, Sussex, Warwick, Yorkshire (East Riding).
2. Aberdeen, Berwick, Clackm., Fife, Forfar, Haddington, Kinc., Kinross, Kirkcudb., Linlithgow, Perth, Roxborough, Stirling.
3. Leics., Lincs., Northampton, Northumberland, Rutland.
4. Berkshire, Bucks., Hertford, Kent, Oxford.
5. Cornwall, Devon, Glos., Hereford, Monmouth, Salop, Worcs.
6. Cumberland, Durham, Westmorland, Yorkshire (North and West Ridings); Argyll, Banff, Bute, Caithness, Dumfries, Elgin, Inverness, Nairn, Orkney, Peebles, Ross and Cromarty, Selkirk, Shetland, Sutherland.
7. Cheshire, Derby, Dorset, Hampshire, Lancs., London and Middlesex, Somerset, Staffs., Surrey, Wilts.; Ayr, Dumbarton, Edinburgh, Lanark, Renfrew, Wigtown.

and the personal preferences of the occupiers, dairy farms might buy their milking stock, or rear replacements, or rear heifers and steers for later sale; the advantages of the Shorthorn breed were that the cows fattened quickly when dry and that the steers made useful beef. Middlesex and Dorset carried the lowest ratio of young stock, less than thirty to every hundred cows and heifers, and less than twenty of the older cattle; Somerset and the northern dairy counties reared a higher proportion of their calves.

The conflict of interest between the cattle rearers and the fatteners, between the sellers and buyers in the store markets, became public and conspicuous in the debates over the import of live animals from 1865 onwards. With the general use of railways and steamships, imports of live animals increased considerably after 1860; and with the animals came rinderpest (cattle-plague), pleuro-pneumonia and foot-and-mouth disease. The first two raged together in 1865 and 1866; it was not until the spring of the second year that the Government was pushed by the agricultural societies and the veterinary profession into using their powers to slaughter or quarantine animals at the ports, and also to give power to local authorities to slaughter both infected animals and their contacts. The control of livestock movements within infected areas, save for immediate slaughter (by the Contagious Diseases (Animals) Act, 1869), was a further step which was eventually found necessary, though it was highly unpopular with a number of dealers and farmers. The legislation devised to deal with these disastrous epidemics was gradually extended to include other diseases and its administration made more effective and more uniform by the Diseases of Animals Act, 1894. The 'germ theory' of disease advanced by Pasteur and others from the 1860s onwards received striking confirmation from the disappearance of pleuro-pneumonia and foot-and-mouth disease during the controls imposed in the last epidemic of cattle plague in 1877; by that time, farming opinion was more resigned to the inconveniences of control as the lesser of two evils, though there was strong resentment that the cost of compensating farmers for the compulsory slaughter of their animals was still a charge on local rates and therefore paid mainly by farmers themselves.[8]

[8] Sir Francis Floud, *The Ministry of Agriculture and Fisheries*, London, 1927, Ch. V; A. H. H. Matthews, *History of the Central Chamber of Agriculture*, London, 1915, pp. 39, 109; see also Ch. 7, pp. 200–2.

THE NEW SHEEP FARMING

As the Shorthorn bull brought profitable beef cattle from herds of upland cows, so the Leicester ram was the medium for getting profitable hoggs for the hill farms to sell for fattening in the lowlands. The Leicester cross on Blackface or Cheviot ewes produced respectively 'mules' and 'half-breds', both of which fattened easily on lowland grass or on arable crops. Writing in 1867 of the half-bred, the Leicester-Cheviot cross, G. Murray thought that the 'increased value of the lamb at weaning time has of late been about 15*s* per head over the pure bred Cheviot', while in south-west Scotland there were 'many farms from which a few years ago the Black-faced lambs averaged 10*s* per head that are now selling the produce of the same ewe by a Leicester ram at 24*s*'.[9] Five years earlier, James Sanderson commented on the changes which he had seen in the previous twenty years in the stock sold at the lamb fairs of St Boswells and Melrose. 'Formerly, at the first-named fair, Cheviots were exhibited in great numbers; now not a Cheviot lamb is shown. Formerly, at Melrose Fair, some lots of Blackface were shown, and the number of Cheviots far exceeded that of half-breds. Now, no Blackface lambs are exhibited and the show of half-breds far exceeds that of Cheviots.' The same trend had developed on the upland farms in Perthshire, many of which in the 1860s were selling Blackface-Leicester lambs, and buying pure Blackface ewes from the mountains to replenish their breeding stock.[10]

By this trade, profits flowed back to the hill and mountain farms which could maintain only the hardy breeds of Blackface or Cheviot sheep, but which now found a ready market for cast ewes and surplus ewe lambs. And on the other side, a number of upland farms with good feeding pastures came to specialise in pure Leicester flocks for the production of the rams required in such

[9] G. Murray, 'On the Improved Value of Scotch Sheep', *J.R.A.S.E.*, vol. 3.ii, 1867, p. 571.

[10] J. Sanderson, 'Agriculture of Berwick and Roxburgh', *Tr. H.A.S.* Oct. 1862, p. 354; H. H. Dixon, Report on Farms, *J.R.A.S.E.*, vol. 5.ii, 1869, pp. 394–5; J. Dickson, 'Agriculture of Perthshire', *Tr. H.A.S.*, 1868–9, p. 167.

numbers. By the time James Sanderson was writing in 1862, Kelso had become an important centre for the trade in Leicester tups, with an annual sale of some 2,000, bred locally and sold to the farmers from the north of England, the Borders and up into central Scotland. These 'Border Leicesters', for which pure descent from Bakewell's Dishley flock was claimed, were nevertheless larger and longer in the leg than the English variety and carried a heavier fleece; all through the 1860s there was ill feeling over the judging of the Leicester classes at the shows, until it was agreed that two breeds had developed where only one had been known, and from 1869 the Highland and Agricultural Society allowed separate classes for 'Leicesters' and for 'Border Leicesters'.[11]

The greater production of the Leicester half-breds was technically possible because of the many improvements undertaken in preceding decades on the lower fields and slopes of upland farms. Drainage, lime and wire fencing all led to improved grazing on which farmers could rear heavier lambs than the pure Blackface or Cheviot. 'All upland improvements tend to make the Cheviot breed supplant the Blackface', wrote Sanderson, 'and again the half-Leicesters supplant the Cheviot and the full-bred Leicester goes on extending its range'.[12] And the process was economically possible because the lowland farmers were willing to pay higher prices for the half- or three-quarter-bred lambs, knowing that they fattened easily to produce the large joints favoured by the butchers; their fleeces were also heavier and more highly priced than those of the hill breeds. Prices of Cheviot sheep at Inverness Fair confirm the general impression obtained from those given by the Teviotdale Farmers' Club that there was a marked upward trend from the early 1850s until 1865–6 which, after a short check, was resumed at the end of the decade.[13]

[11] J. Wilson, 'The Long-Woolled Sheep of Tweedside', *Tr. H.A.S.*, Oct. 1862, p. 320.
[12] J. Sanderson, *op. cit.*, p. 354.
[13] The prices struck by the Teviotdale Farmers' Club were printed in the *Report of the Royal Commission on Agriculture*, 1895, Wilson Fox, *Report on Cumberland*, vol. iv of *Reports on Counties*. See also E. H. Whetham, 'Livestock Prices in Britain, 1850–1893', *Agric. Hist. Rev.*, vol. xi, 1963.

The changing distribution of sheep breeds in Scotland and northern England was not recorded by official statistics, which were concerned only with 'sheep', irrespective of breed. But the rising profitability of all stages of sheep production can be further confirmed from the rising numbers recorded in Scotland between 1856–7 and the early official counts from 1867 (Tables I and II); the increase of about 22 per cent in numbers was fairly uniform over all districts, and it is reasonable to assume that a similar expansion occurred on the southern side of the Border. Dixon noted the increasing use of the Leicester cross in those districts of northern England where the basic stock was of the Blackface type, the areas of the Herdwick, the Lonk and the Swaledale; all these breeds were found to yield useful lambs when put to Leicester rams.[14]

It is curious that the third mountain breed, the white-faced Welsh sheep, was apparently little crossed with the Leicester. The flavoursome Welsh mutton preferred by connoisseurs was still obtained from the four or five-year-old wethers kept on the hills until they were sent to the autumn fairs at Welshpool or Newtown, together with the dark-faced sheep from the upland farms. The wethers might be sold fat off the autumn grass on lowland farms or finished on turnips to catch the high prices at the end of winter, while the cast ewes might be put to a Leicester ram, but Shropshires or Southdowns were more commonly used. For south of Yorkshire and east of Severn, the Southdown remained the principal source of rams for the production of mutton from the various breeds on lowland farms. At the Canterbury Show in 1860, Jonas Webb's first prize Southdown ram was sold for the enormous sum of 250 guineas; this was a fitting close to twenty years of exhibition at the shows of the Royal Agricultural Society, for Webb's famous flock of Southdowns was dispersed in 1861 and 1862 and Webb himself died in November of the latter year. The statue placed in the Cambridge Corn Exchange, erected by subscriptions from the farming community of his day, and the popularity of Southdowns in many countries of the world, both commemorate the success of this great livestock breeder.

[14] H. H. Dixon, 'Mountain Breeds of Sheep', *J.R.A.S.E.*, vol. 2.ii, 1866, p. 365.

In previous decades, many local sheep had been judiciously improved with a dash of Southdown blood, to give earlier maturity and a more compact frame; careful selection and in-breeding among the results led to the fixing of certain character-istics until the existence of distinct breeds could be claimed. The Royal Agricultural Society allowed separate classes for Shrop-shires from 1859, for Hampshire Downs from 1861 and for Oxford Downs from 1862; at the Oxford Show held in 1870, the classes were Leicester, Cotswold, Lincoln, Ryelands and other Long-wools, Oxford Downs, Southdowns, Shropshires, Hampshire Downs and other short wools, and Dorset Downs, while the Kent or Romney was also accorded a separate class when the Society frequented the south-eastern counties.

A symposium on the relative profitability of different classes of stock, published in the *Journal of the Royal Agricultural Society* in 1876, revealed the general opinion that sheep had been by far the most remunerative enterprise in recent times. Sheep provided mutton and wool, and there had been an almost continuous rise in the prices of both products from 1852 until the middle of the 1860s. Then, indeed, wool prices began to fall away under the pressure of rising imports; a short-lived recovery from 1871-5 was succeeded by a further fall which brought wool prices in general to a level barely 60 per cent of that obtained on the average of 1865-74. That fall in wool prices struck especially at the profits of the mountain farms keeping wether flocks and selling chiefly wool, wethers and draft ewes; but it also reduced the profits on many lowland farms which fattened sheep to be sold after shearing at fifteen or eighteen months old. Still, mutton prices rose sharply after a short fall from 1865 to 1868 and continued to rise until 1883; though the prices of store sheep fluctuated with the state of the turnip crop and the severity of the winters (which affected the supply of lambs from the upland farms), they generally followed the main trend in mutton prices, so that the rearing farms obtained some share in the prosperity of the sheep industry. It will be noted that price records for this period always refer to mutton. Lamb was a luxury product produced only for a limited and wealthy market which could afford to pay a high price per pound for a light weight animal. The ordinary market was supplied with mutton from animals seldom less than fifteen months old, while the hill and mountain wethers might be three or four years old before they came down on to lowland farms for the final process; the urban market liked its meat to have both flavour and a good proportion of fat laid on with the lean.

HORSE BREEDING

The same symposium also showed a consensus of opinion that the breeding and rearing of horses had been the least remunerative of all livestock enterprises, in spite of the high prices obtained for cobs, hunters, hacks and heavy dray horses. There was a lack of good stallions, and of good grooms to train young horses; breeding mares that could not be heavily worked in the spring were unprofitable stock, and they and their progeny required dry pastures, well watered and fenced; and finally, there was too much risk of accident and disease before young horses became old enough to have a saleable value. Yet horses were bred on lowland farms, and the horse classes at the local shows were well patronised in most counties, perhaps especially so in those districts with a large area of permanent grass and rough pasture. A large number of farmers reared a foal or two, gradually breaking them into harness in their third year by putting them with a steady horse for the lighter work; others obtained a regular profit by selling made horses at five or six years old to the urban trade, thus offsetting the cost of carrying on their farms a large number of mares and young horses. Other farmers again enjoyed their hunting in the course of training and selling horses to other members of the field; and in the spring, there was much travelling of stallions, whether dray or thoroughbred, and much talk on their relative merits whenever ploughmen took their dinner together in the shelter of a hedge, or drank their evening pint at the local inn.

DAIRYING

It is interesting to note that this symposium did not mention dairying. The bailiffs of the landowners and the men with large arable farms who contributed to the discussion were not normally concerned with dairying for the market. Dairying was the business of the family farmers, of a different social class from the arable farmers; the judging of Channel Island cows, of butter and of cheese at agricultural shows had little of the glamour and publicity that attended the prize winners among the beef cattle and the fat lambs. The Prince Consort did indeed cause to be erected at Windsor a model dairy where cheese and butter were made for the use of the Royal Household, among marble shelves and specially designed tiles,[15] but ordinary commercial dairying seems to have attracted little attention in these years from the agricultural experimenters and journalists. It is also significant that Sauerbeck's price index for butter in the London market was based on quotations for Friesland butter; even the market reports given in the *Journal of the Royal Agricultural Society* dealt only with imported butter, including Irish and did not mention the home product. The wholesale butter markets in London and the other large towns seem to have been increasingly dominated by imported produce, which arrived by ship loads conveniently packed in containers suitable for mass distribution; as more people crowded into larger towns, the wholesalers increasingly favoured the more standardised sources. The very large number of butter- and cheese-making farms in Britain supplied a varying quantity of a varying quality ranging from the very good, finding its market among the wealthy and the discriminating, to the almost bad, sold locally to the poorer consumers; the aggregation of quantity performed by the butter and cheese factors in rural districts could not overcome the variety in quality, in the units of sale and in the containers used. The manager of one of the largest hotels in the Midlands was quoted in 1878 as buying all his fresh butter through agents

[15] J. C. Morton, quoted in J. Macdonald, 'Queen and Farmer', *Tr. H.A.S.*, vol. 9.v, 1897, pp.6–7.

from Normandy, because he could not obtain 200 lb weekly of a standard quality from his local market.[16] Within twenty years from 1850, the imports of butter and cheese had trebled, leaving out of account the imports of butter from Ireland into Britain. Holland and France were the main foreign suppliers of butter and they sent steadily increasing quantities. In the 1850s Holland sent three-quarters of the cheese imports, but by 1865 American factories were the largest source of British supplies; a decade later, they were putting one million cwt of cheese a year on to the British market, and were setting the level both of prices and of quality for the trade in the home produced commodity.

This rising tide of imports stimulated the home trade into defensive action. Cheddar-type cheese, bearing the name though made in many other places besides Cheddar, dominated the urban markets largely because its manufacture was simpler than that of other types, and the result was less variable. A deputation from the Ayrshire Agricultural Association visited Somerset in 1854 and inspected the dairy of Joseph Harding of Marksbridge (1805–1876) whose cheeses won first prizes at local and national shows. On their return, they propagated the Cheddar method in their home district, aided by the Highland and Agricultural Society, which offered prizes for the new product. McAdam, writing in the Transactions of the Highland and Agricultural Society for 1862, noted that the Scottish Cheddar obtained at least 3s per stone (of 24 lb) more than the native Dunlop in wholesale markets, and that a greater weight of Cheddar was obtained from the same quantity of milk.

Harding himself introduced new equipment into the process of cheese making, including a revolving breaker for curd cutting, which saved much manual effort, and double-sided tin vats which enabled the milk to be warmed or cooled by a jacket of water, and thus more easily brought to the right temperature before the rennet was added. Since the formation of the curd depended on attaining a particular combination of temperature and acidity, this latter invention brought one variable under control, while

[16] G. Murray, 'Report on Dairy Implements', *J.R.A.S.E.*, vol. 15.ii, 1879, p. 142.

the greater use first of thermometers and then of acetometers eliminated an area of judgment in favour of scientific fact; the introduction of dried and standardised rennet from 1874 onwards was another help towards the uniformity of product which might be deplored by some but which was becoming essential in the large urban markets.

But farm-house cheese-making remained a tedious burden on the energies of farm families, or on the services of hired dairymaids, whose number, skill and devotion to duty (over twelve or fourteen hours a day on a seven day week) appeared to decline as their wages rose. The popularity of American cheese stimulated efforts in this country to convert the processing into a factory trade; the advantages of machinery, economy of labour, uniformity of product and cheaper marketing should outweigh the extra costs of carting milk to the factory. Some farmers indeed argued that factories could only increase costs, for 'the cheese being made either by the farmer's wife or one or more of his daughters, he considers that the labour costs him nothing; that the work is a duty in the former case and a wholesome discipline in the latter; ... if the cheese were not made at home, an extra man would be required to take the milk to the factory', and he of course would require wages in cash rather than in discipline.[17] And farmers blessed with dutiful wives and daughters judged that their make of cheese would continue to secure higher than average prices, and therefore had no use for a communal factory. But the obvious advantages of large-scale manufacture induced a group of land owners and farmers to set up two factories in Derbyshire in 1869–70; two managers had to be imported from the United States where nearly twenty years of factory cheese making had produced a race of professional dairymen.

The first few years showed that a successful manager could indeed make cheese for his suppliers at lower costs, and secure higher prices for the product, than they had achieved by individual efforts. It was reckoned that one of the Derbyshire fac-

[17] H. M. Jenkins, 'Report on the American Cheese Factory System', *J.R.A.S.E.*, vol. 6.ii, 1870, p. 202.

tories employed five men and some casual help to convert into cheese the produce of 750 cows on thirty farms, each of which would formerly have employed a cheese-maker; and that the product sold for some 5s a cwt more than the average price of farm-made cheese. The farm families were relieved of much tedious work, and the farmers had an accurate record of their daily milk output. In the season of 1872, the sales of the farms supplying the Derby factory ranged from 624 gallons per cow for a dairy of three cows to 343 gallons per cow in a dairy of thirty-eight;[18] these, one presumes, were farms of above average management, since their occupiers were sufficiently venturous to support a new enterprise. By 1875, there were operating, or in process of construction, nineteen cheese factories in five counties, some co-operatively owned by farmers, others financed by land-owners or merchants. Large-scale butter-making seems to have been less popular; before the invention of the centrifugal separator, the transport of whole milk by cart to a central point disintegrated the fat globules and made the churning less easy and the product less good. But a dairy company was established at Aylesbury which made both butter and cheese, and whose staff collaborated with the officials of the Royal Agricultural Society to exhibit a model dairy worked by steam power at the shows held from 1878 on-wards. It was in this dairy at the Kilburn show in 1879 that Laval's cream separator was first exhibited in Britain, the inven-tion which in the next decade was to turn butter-making from a farm craft into a factory trade.

British agriculture thus established cheese-making on a factory scale, only to find the new development swept aside by the growth of the trade in liquid milk. Between 1851 and 1871, the population of Britain increased from 20·9 millions to 26·1 millions and a sub-stantial part of this expanding population enjoyed rising incomes. It bought more meat, dairy products and vegetables and also more liquid milk. The revelations of the medical journal *The*

[18] J. Coleman, 'English Cheese Factories', *Country Gentleman's Magazine*, vol. vi 1871, p. 228; J. C. Morton, 'Cheese Making', *J.R.A.S.E.*, vol. 11.ii, 1875, p. 284; V. Cheke, *Cheese Making*, London, 1959.

Lancet between 1852 and 1854 on the adulteration and decay in many foodstuffs might indeed have deterred many townspeople from buying milk; the Adulteration of Food and Drink Act, 1860 made adulteration a legal offence, but few local authorities exercised their powers, until compelled to do so by the Adulteration of Food, Drink and Drugs Act, 1872. From this period, public analysts and medical officers of health brought about a steady diminution in the grosser forms of adulteration practised on milk, and demand expanded in every urban area, drawing into this new trade many farms within reach of a railway station which had hitherto sold butter and cheese.

This trend had been stimulated by the epidemic of cattle plague in 1865–6, which swept out of existence many of the urban dairies and forced the urban wholesalers to seek supplies from rural areas. There was a rapid improvement in transport facilities in this crisis, including the introduction of special milk trains timed to reach central stations at hours appropriate to the custom of delivering the milk for breakfast. Equipment was also improved; wooden tubs of varying capacity were replaced first by tin churns more easily handled and cleaned, and then by tin-plated steel churns, with double lids to prevent spilling and stealing. Farms with an adequate water supply also learnt to cool their milk before dispatch by standing their churns in water; in the 1870s a device known in the brewery trade was adapted to perform the rapid cooling of milk – the circulation of milk over a zigzag of metal tubes set in a frame through which water continuously circulated. In his 'Report on Cheese-Making in Derbyshire' in 1881, G. Gibbons noted that only one-half to two-thirds as much cheese was made in the immediate area of Derby as twenty years earlier, as all farms within reach of stations sent liquid milk to market, either in London or in the nearer industrial towns; some of the cheese factories had also turned over to this trade, using their premises to cool the milk before dispatching it on the retail rounds. Gibbons reckoned that the current wholesale price in urban markets of 1*s* per gallon (from which farmers paid rail costs and the cost of carriage to the stations) gave a return approximately equal to the 8*d* per gallon commonly received by the manufacturer of butter and cheese of average quality.[19] The farm families were saved the drudgery of churning or cheese-making and the returns accrued regularly throughout the year, without the customary delay of several months while the cheese was slowly ripening, and losing weight in the process. J. C. Morton considered that in the 1870s, one-fifth of the output of milk was sold as butter, and two-fifths each for the liquid trade and as cheese.[20]

This new and expanding trade in liquid milk considerably changed farming practices in the areas concerned. Butter- and cheese-making were essentially seasonal trades, occupying seven or eight months, after which the cows were kept cheaply over the winter on hay and grazing in the west, and on hay, straw and roots in the north. The sale of milk to the towns required a level output, which in turn involved a regular succession of calvings throughout the year, and the regular feeding of cows and in-calf heifers throughout the winter. Turnips were little used for this purpose; given in bulk they did not support a good flow of milk and they were notoriously apt to taint it. Increasingly therefore, dairy farmers used purchased feeds to supplement their hay or grass – brewers' grains if a maltster happened to be within carting distance; or maize, cheaply imported through Liverpool, Hull or Bristol; or the new cotton-seed cake which was found to be as good as linseed and considerably cheaper. Further, these supplements came to be used not only in winter but also in those weeks when the grass did not provide adequate nutrients – during a dry spell in summer, or a wet spell in autumn. This cake-feeding on grass overcame the objection of many landowners to dairying – that it robbed the land of fertility; and the maintenance of the daily milk yield, with its immediate cash return, encouraged many farmers to dress their pastures regularly with farm-yard manure, with nitrates or superphosphates.

[19] G. Gibbons, 'Report on Cheese-Making in Derbyshire', *J.R.A.S.E.*, vol. 17.ii, 1881, p. 533–41.

[20] J. C. Morton, 'Dairy Farming', in 'Memoir on the Agriculture of England and Wales', *J.R.A.S.E.*, vol. 14.ii, 1878, p. 647.

This new type of dairying, selling milk all the year round, also involved landowners, since it required consequential changes in the farm buildings. When milking was a summer occupation only, cows might be milked in the nearest field or in the open yard; the basic necessity was adequate space for churning or cheese storage. But milking cows in winter as well as in summer required stalls in which they could be fed and milked, as well as a constant supply of pure water, both for the cows and for cooling the milk before it started on its journey to the station, or on the round of the urban streets, while the cheese store, often an attic over the dairy, was of little use for storing and mixing the large bulk of purchased foods. An occupying owner might find the finance for such alterations in his own equipment, some tenant farmers might deal with a sympathetic agent and an accommodating owner, but many farms were handicapped in this new trade by lack of buildings and bad layout. The judge of the dairy implements at the Bristol Show in 1878 commented that 'the principal obstacle which at present impedes the progress of improved dairy husbandry is the want of adequate buildings'.[21]

In this respect, as in so many others, the success of new forms of farming depended on the willingness and ability of landowners to provide their tenants with the essential equipment. Tradition dictated that landlords must find the money for new buildings, since the farmers had, over most of Britain, neither security of tenure nor any guarantee of compensation for the cost of such permanent improvements as they might wish to make on another man's property.

[21] G. Murray, 'Report on the Trial of Dairy Implements and Machinery at Bristol', *J.R.A.S.E.*, vol. 15.ii, 1879, p. 136.

6

Landlord and Tenant

The Personal Tie between Landlord and Tenant – Customary Tenant Right – Land Improvement – Agricultural Leases – Estate Management – Scottish Leases – Conditions in Wales – The Agricultural Holdings Act, 1875 – The Privileged Creditor – The Game Laws – Lack of Security of Tenure

DURING the struggle for Repeal, one of the tactics of the Anti-Corn-Law League had been to try to drive a wedge between landlords and farmers, by arguing that protection was no help to the tenant, for it served only to keep rents artificially high. In the early part of the campaign, paid lecturers were sent into the rural districts to put forward this argument, but their reception was not happy. A Welsh-speaking lecturer received considerable support in Wales, but English farmers as a class felt that their interests were bound up with those of their landlords and were not prepared to listen to attacks upon them.[1] But Cobden, the great leader of the Anti-Corn-Law League, put his finger on some of the weaknesses of the landlord-and-tenant system as then practised when he said: 'Though I have not promised reduction of rent, I have, however, always maintained that with the Free Trade in corn, and with moderate prices, if the present rents are to be maintained, it must be by means of a different system of managing property from that which you now pursue. You must have men of capital on your land; you must let your land on mercantile principles; you must not be afraid of an independent and energetic man who will vote as he pleases; you must give up inordinate game-preserving.'[2]

[1] Norman McCord, *The Anti-Corn-Law League*, London, 1958, pp. 73, 74.
[2] J. Morley, *Life of Richard Cobden*, London, 1881, p. 320.

THE PERSONAL TIE BETWEEN LANDLORD AND TENANT

In England the personal tie between landlords and farmers was strong. On many estates tenancies were almost hereditary, son succeeding father in the same farm for generations. The greater part of the land of Britain was farmed under the landlord and tenant system. The contract between the two was regulated either by a lease, in which the length and terms of the tenancy were clearly stated, or by letting from year to year, under conditions which might or might not be embodied in a written tenancy agreement, and which could be terminated by either party at any time by a six months' notice. But the relationship was more than a mere legal contract. One landlord's point of view is well expressed by Trollope in *The Vicar of Bullhampton*:

The Marquis's people were all expected to vote for his candidates, and would soon have ceased to be the Marquis's people had they failed to do so. They were constrained, also, in many respects, by the terms of their very short leases. They could not kill a head of game on their farms. They could not sell their own hay off the land, nor, indeed, any produce other than their corn and cattle. They were compelled to crop their land in certain rotation: and could take no other lands than those held under the Marquis without his leave. In return for all this, they became the Marquis's people. Each tenant shook hands with the Marquis perhaps once in three years; and twice a year was allowed to get drunk at the Marquis's expense – if such was his taste – provided that he paid his rent. If the duties were heavy, the privileges were great. So the Marquis himself felt; and he knew that a mantle of security, of a certain thickness, was spread upon the shoulders of each of his people by reason of the tenure which bound them together.

On the larger estates of the aristocracy there was probably not much personal intercourse, but the tenants felt a certain pride in being 'under a nobleman', especially if their families had been on the estate for generations. They enjoyed the feasting and junketing when the heir came of age and when he married; they were prepared to watch critically the experiments on the Home Farm, and to copy them if they proved successful; and though they grumbled frequently, on well-managed estates there was undoubtedly confidence and a sense of belonging.

Inclosure Acts and the agricultural depression after the Napoleonic Wars had combined greatly to reduce the number of small freehold farmers, and the buyers of their land were usually the bigger landlords of the neighbourhood. Thus the great estates of the landed aristocracy came to be built up and rounded off. After the inclosure of the open fields came the inclosure of commons, wastes and woodlands, and here the lord of the manor was generally the largest allottee. The allotments of the smaller men were far from being the economic equivalent of the old rights of common which they were compelled to surrender. The exclusive possession of a few acres of land, perhaps in a remote part of the parish, could not compare with the right to run some stock on a grass common or waste. The cost of fencing alone was generally more than they could meet, they were only too ready to part with their allotments for cash, and in many cases the buyers were the larger landlords.

CUSTOMARY TENANT RIGHT

It must be remembered that until the last quarter of the nineteenth century, there was no *statutory* control of the relations between landlord and tenant. Their dealings were governed entirely by *custom* and by personal agreements. Custom was something 'to which the memory of man ran not to the contrary', and this was the basis of proof required to establish it; at the same time, it could be extended or it could become obsolete. With the passage of time, a body of customary law developed from the old legal maxim '*Quidquid solo plantatur, solo cedit*', which may be interpreted as 'whatever improvements a tenant may make to his holding pass to the landlord'. The hardship of this to the farmer came to be mitigated, with the slow development of farming technique and production for the market, by the customs of 'pre-entry' and 'holdover'. The landlord, or his incoming tenant as the case might be, enjoyed a customary right of pre-entry upon the farm – including house-room for himself and stabling for his horses – so that he might do the work needed for the production of his first crop; at the same time, an outgoing tenant had the right of holdover, which enabled him to retain possession of such buildings and yards as were necessary for the harvesting and realisation of the produce of the last year of his tenancy. There were obvious drawbacks to this arrangement, and the double occupation of parts of the holding must have been a nuisance in many ways. Hence these customs were beginning to be superseded by others under which money payments were made to the out-goer in substitution for his rights of holdover, and to re-imburse him for cultivations, etc. performed by him in substitution for the incomer's right of pre-entry. These came to be known as the 'Custom of the Country'.

Customs varied widely in different parts of England. To begin with, the date of giving up the farm might be Candlemas (2 February), Lady Day, May Day or Michaelmas. Lady Day or Candlemas entry was usual in Cheshire, Derbyshire, Lincoln-shire, Nottinghamshire, Shropshire, Somerset and Yorkshire, but both were to be found elsewhere, particularly in parts of the eastern counties. In Durham and parts of Northumberland the date of entry was May Day, and much the same customs pre-vailed.

Where the time of entry was Michaelmas, the custom was for the outgoer to prepare the fallows and plant the turnips. He might be paid by the landlord, or by the incomer, for the straw, for the work he had done on the fallows, for the seeds he had sown and for manure left in the yards. Caird in his survey had some hard things to say about the farmers and valuers of Surrey and Sussex in particular, where this custom of payment prevailed. There was no way of telling how much manure had been applied to the land, nor how thoroughly the cultivations had been carried out, except the word of the outgoer, and the system opened the door to all sorts of trickery and deceit. Some farmers did so well with their outgoing payments that a man would stay on the next farm for only a few years, work it out, and then move to another, making his profit on the outgoing inventory, sometimes in collusion with the valuer.[3] Such a system, if abused in this way, crippled the ingoing farmer, if he had to find a large sum when he needed all his resources for stocking his new farm.

Michaelmas entry customs were to be found chiefly in Bedfordshire, Berkshire, Essex, Hertfordshire, Hampshire, Kent, Norfolk, Suffolk, Surrey, Sussex and Oxfordshire, but were not uncommon in other counties, with many variations in detail. Roughly, it may be said that the spring time of entry was more convenient on mainly arable farms, and the Michaelmas time on grassland farms.[4]

In Wales, many different customs were found with entry at Candlemas, Lady Day, Michaelmas and, in Anglesey and part of Carnarvonshire, 12 November. Arrangements were made between outgoing and incoming tenants more or less on the same lines as in England, but with appropriate local variations.

An interesting form of custom had grown up in the Vale of Evesham, which was working satisfactorily. It originated among a small group of landowners whose tenants, early in the century, were beginning to develop commercial horticulture. By this a tenant who wished to give up his holding would find another man who would be willing to pay him for the whole of his improvements, including the fruit trees he had planted, the bush fruit and other growing crops. If the landlord approved him, he became the new tenant, but the whole transaction was carried out between the outgoer and the incomer. The custom spread through the whole district and worked well, because it protected the industrious market gardener from loss and made for stability, and it saved the landlord from demands for compensation, whilst enhancing the value of his land. The 'Evesham Custom' as it was called, was undoubtedly a stimulus to commercial fruit growing and market gardening.[5]

[3] J. Caird (1), pp. 119, 120, 130–2.
[4] Clement Cadle, 'Farming Customs and Covenants of England', *J.R.A.S.E.*, vol. 4.ii, 1868, p. 146.
[5] R. C. Gaut, *op. cit.*, pp. 418, 419.

LAND IMPROVEMENT

By the middle of the nineteenth century, much equipment of new farms and homesteads had been completed or was going on all over the country. When each man's farm was scattered in strips among those of his neighbours, in fields extending over many hundreds of acres, houses and homesteads were grouped in the village and everybody shared a rough equality of inconvenience in getting to and about his land. After inclosure, some men got their new farms blocked out close to the village; others found that they would have to walk a mile or two to reach holdings allotted to them on the outskirts of the parish. Convenience of working required, then, that these remote farms should be equipped with new houses and buildings, access roads and so forth; and the same provision was needed for the first equipment of holdings laid out upon the inclosure of the larger commons and wastes not previously cultivated nor used for anything more than rough grazings.

There was no general custom, still less statutory procedure, regulating the responsibility of the two parties, landlord and tenant, for the work of equipping the new farms. Land was brought under cultivation and given houses, cottages and buildings, it was fenced, drained and so forth, under contracts between the two parties which varied not only from district to district but also from estate to estate. On farms of bare land, bargains seem commonly to have been made with the prospective tenants that the landlord should spend an agreed sum, dependent upon the size of the holding and the type of farming, on house and homestead. He would lay out accommodation roads, erect boundary fences and make certain inclosures within them. Thereupon the tenant could enter and get to work at once, for the task of reclaiming land and waste worthy of cultivation and improvement devolved upon him, and was undertaken with the protection of specific covenants creating a 'tenant right' in the value of his improvements effected in the landlord's freehold. Caird commended the progressive landowners in Lincolnshire, whose estate management had made the phrase 'the Lincolnshire Custom' a household word amongst farmers all over the country by the middle of the nineteenth century. He quotes, particularly, the improvement of the Lincolnshire Wolds in the north-east, and of Lincoln Heath between Lincoln and Sleaford, on each of which great areas of waste were being brought into productive use in Arthur Young's time, under the enlightened administration of the leading landlords. In the parish of Limber, for example, some 4,000 acres on the Brocklesby estate, let at half-a-crown an acre at the beginning of the century, was yielding some £4,000 a year to Lord Yarborough when Caird saw the land fifty years later. At Blankney, at the same time, Mr Chaplin was getting 20*s* an acre from several thousand acres which had been producing no more than a few shillings as rabbit warrens.

It was very fortunate that the leading landlords were liberal and enlightened men. Amongst these may be named the late Earl of Yarborough, and Mr Chaplin of Blankney. They saw the advantage of encouraging tenants to embark their capital freely; and as leases were not the fashion of the county, they gave them that security for their invested capital which is termed 'tenant right' or compensation for unexhausted improvements.

Though this tenant right may not be a strictly legal claim, it is universally admitted in Lincolnshire, the landlord paying it when a farm falls into his own hands, and refusing to accept a tenant who declines to comply with the custom.[6]

The Lincolnshire Custom varied considerably in different parts of the county, and it evolved as the technique of agriculture developed. In North Lincolnshire the usual allowances which might be due to an outgoing tenant in 1850 included draining, marling, chalking, claying and liming the land; the application of bones, guano and rape dust to the soil; and oil-cake fed to sheep and cattle. The amount of compensation payable to the outgoer for his improvements was based upon their initial cost, the estimated life of the work when well and properly done, and the number of years which had passed since it was done. Thus the whole cost of chalking and marling was allowed, if performed during the last year of tenancy; if done in the previous year,

[6] J. Caird (1), pp. 193–4.

seven-eighths of the cost, and so on, diminishing the amount by one-eighth for each year, on the assumption that the benefits of these improvements would be exhausted at the end of eight years. Other scales were adopted for other improvements, the cost of manures, such as guano or rape dust, and oilcake fed to cattle and sheep, being regarded as returned to the farmer more quickly in the better crops than the expenses of more permanent improvements.

AGRICULTURAL LEASES

The alternative, of course, to reliance upon an acknowledged customary tenant-right was to farm under an agricultural lease. The two practices could go on side by side; in the adjacent county of Norfolk, the great landowner Thomas Coke, of Holkham, for example, built up his magnificent estate entirely upon a system of leaseholds. His twenty-year leases, carefully devised and full of directives to his tenants, became models to other progressive landowners of the eastern and midland counties. While Coke was an upholder of the Norfolk four-course rotation, it is of interest to note that his leases gave virtual freedom of cropping to his tenants, always provided that unless arrangements were entered into by the parties at the end of the sixteenth year for a new lease for a further twenty years, the tenant must cultivate the last four on the four-course rotation. Freedom of cropping with a return to a prescribed course of cropping if a tenancy were being surrendered did not become a statutory right of tenant farmers until the Agricultural Holdings Act, 1908, was passed, nearly a hundred years after Coke had adopted it.

At the same time, while Coke's leases allowed this measure of freedom to his tenants, covenants controlling their practice were often included in leasehold tenancies for their educative value to less progressive farmers, at a time of rapid technical development, when landowners and their professional advisers were leaders of the agricultural partnership. Caird, for example, writing of Norfolk farmers in 1850, said that the general opinion amongst the best of them was that leases and covenants were necessary to bind bad farmers, not good ones.

In the adjoining county of Suffolk, Lord Tollemache of Helmingham had adopted on his estates a modification of the yearly tenancy as an alternative. This was a 'Lease-note', which bound the landlord to allow undisturbed possession without any increase of rent for twenty-one years, upon the condition that the tenant should keep the land clean and in good heart, and execute certain specified improvements, such as draining or boning a certain number of acres yearly. Thus, while the tenant remained free to give up his farm, the landlord resigned the power of giving him notice to quit except upon a breach of the conditions.[7]

In another part of the country, Somerset, the system of improving leases was being introduced with great effect during the middle years of the century. When John Knight bought 15,000 acres of the Forest of Exmoor in 1818, his original idea was to reclaim and farm it himself, but it became clear after a time that the expense of the undertaking was too great, and that to bring the land into a state of cultivation it must be divided up into separate farms and let to tenants. In 1848 Robert Smith, a notable farmer and breeder from Rutland, was appointed agent to the Knight family, and he proceeded to advertise, in Midland papers, farms to be 'let upon liberal terms to enterprising tenants'. Twenty-year leases were offered, which could be broken every four years, on a scale of rents very low to begin with and rising at the end of the fourth, eighth, twelfth and sixteenth years of the lease, as the farms increased in value. A schedule of allowances for works of improvement, upon the lines of the Lincolnshire Custom, was attached to each lease. In Smith's own words: 'In the carrying out of these subsequent agreements there need not be the least difficulty, provided that both parties meet on the footing of having their mutual interest in the progress of improvement as fast as their respective capitals can be laid out with a prospect of reasonable returns; and that the consideration of these

[7] G. C. Brodrick, *English Land and English Landlords*, London, 1881, p. 373, fn.

two distinct interests is regulated by mutual confidence and goodwill'.[8]

These are examples of improving leases, where a real partnership between landlord and tenant, under conditions carefully laid down, were a definite encouragement to investment of capital and better farming. But there were plenty of landlords in England who were not interested in improvements, who went on granting leases which merely laid down the length of the period, the rent to be paid, the course of cropping, etc., without any provision for the changes which modern farming methods might necessitate. Moreover, the tendency on such estates, as leases ran out, was to convert them into yearly tenancies and to raise the rent.

On estates owned by ecclesiastical and corporate bodies such as the Oxford and Cambridge Colleges, a usual form of tenure had been the beneficial lease, which dated from the sixteenth century. By this a tenant was given a twenty-year lease, paying a substantial 'fine' or premium on entry and a low yearly rent. After seven years another fine was paid and the lease was automatically renewed for another twenty years. The annual value of the land was represented by the low annual rent plus the recurring fine, and to all intents and purposes it became a lease for life, the tenant safe from being turned out and the corporate body secure of its revenue. But as the nineteenth century went on and the value of land rose, it became obvious that the bodies were not getting the full value from their estates, and that they would do better to turn them into yearly tenancies. In 1851, St John's College, Cambridge, passed a resolution that no further renewals of beneficial leases should be granted, and by the 1860s the remaining leases had all run out and more realistic rents were charged.[9] The University Commission of 1852 recommended the discontinuance of beneficial leases, and gradually other Colleges and Corporations let them run out, so that by the end of the century this form of tenure had disappeared everywhere. It had been

[8] C. S. Orwin, *The Reclamation of Exmoor Forest*, Oxford, 1929, pp. 54–65.

[9] H. F. Howard, *Finances of the College of St John the Evangelist in the University of Cambridge, 1511–1926*, Cambridge, 1935, p. 179.

a useful system for a corporate body having properties scattered in different parts of the country, which before the days of railways would have been difficult to manage directly. Often the farms were let to a middleman who found the tenants, and all the College had to do was to collect the fines and rents from him. But these middlemen exploited the properties, and when the estates were taken into direct management, the Colleges found that the farms and buildings were in a bad state of repair, and they were faced with heavy expenditure to put them in order.[10]

The farms on the Crown estates, on the other hand, were managed very efficiently on a system of twenty-one-year leases, with full freedom to tenants to cultivate according to the best mode of husbandry in the district, and with some direction of cropping during the last three years of the tenancy. Payments were made to outgoing tenants for purchases of cotton cake, etc., for the same period, and the Crown executed all permanent improvements, buildings, roads, under-drainage and so on.

ESTATE MANAGEMENT

In England the great technical advances in farming were still far from being recognised or put into practice throughout the country when Caird started on his tour in 1850. His comments on the estate management he found are very illuminating. He was no respecter of persons and was outspoken in his criticisms of bad landlords and commendations of good ones, however eminent the parties concerned. His admiration for the estates of the Duke of Bedford and the Duke of Wellington was unqualified, and likewise for the improving landlords of Lincolnshire, Lord Yarborough, Chaplin and others. But he did not hesitate to say of the Duke of Marlborough's estate in Oxfordshire: 'The country exhibits a poverty-stricken and neglected look, and there is no confidence of a friendly or even of a feudal character between landlord and tenant.' Rents had been raised by a third about

[10] Geoffrey Faber, *Notes on the History of the All Souls Bursarships and the College Agency.* (Privately printed, 1950.)

ten years before, many farmers had left the estate, and much land was in hand. One of the Oxfordshire farmers said: 'We know that we are not farming: we are only taking out of the land what we can get from it at the least cost, as we don't know how long we may remain in possession and have no security for what we might be disposed to invest in improved cultivation'.[11]

In fairness to the Blenheim estate, it must be noted that when the Royal Agricultural Society held its Show at Oxford in 1870 and started its Farm Prize Competition, the winners of the first and second prizes were both tenants of the Duke, one farming under a twenty-one-year lease and the other under a yearly tenancy.

But if a hard landlord did not make for a prosperous estate, Caird was equally critical of an easy-going one. The Duke of Cleveland's estate in Durham had been valued about fifty years before his visit, and the rents then fixed had not been changed. Tenancy was practically hereditary, and though the Duke himself had carried out many improvements, in draining and building, he exacted no corresponding energy from his tenants, who continued to farm as their forefathers did.

> The certainty they felt that no additional rent would be exacted, and that the son would, as a matter of course, succeed to his father on the same terms, led to an indolent feeling of security. Lower prices have found them even less prepared than their more highly-rented neighbours; and the Duke, in declining to make abatements, is not more exempt from complaint than other landlords who have not the same excuse.

As he went through the Dukeries, he said of the Duke of Portland: 'While he is one of the largest, he is also one of the best landlords in the kingdom.' To meet the changes caused by free trade, the whole estate was being revalued and one-hàlf of the rents commuted to a corn rent, taking 56s a quarter of wheat as a basis. The tenants were well satisfied and continued to farm with confidence. The Duke had also carried out vast improvements on the estate, particularly in tile drainage. But 'few of the

[11] J. Caird (1), pp. 24–6.

other great proprietors of Nottinghamshire have the same means at their disposal, or the same taste for agricultural improvement'. Speaking of West Cumberland, he said:

The principal estate in the district, that of the Earl of Lonsdale, is chiefly let by verbal contracts from year to year, without any stipulation whatever as to the mode of farming. Notwithstanding the absence of leases, the farmers on this estate are a very enterprising class; and as the most perfect confidence subsists between landlord and tenant, the latter most liberally invests his capital in the cultivation and permanent improvement of his farm. When a farm, from any cause, falls into his Lordship's hands, a good young tenant is carefully sought out; and as this has long been the practice of the estate, the farmers are mostly selected men, vying with each other in the management of their farms. They have no tenant right or repayment for unexhausted improvements, but they know they are dealing with a family which has always felt its own interest identified with the prosperity of the tenantry.

Owners of very large estates had, of course, to employ an agent or steward and, in the mid-nineteenth century, land agency had not yet acquired a professional status. Caird says of the landlords of Northamptonshire:

Some men employ men of low standing with a small salary, and in a dependent position, butlers, gardeners, and sometimes gamekeepers, performing the functions of land-agent.[12] Lawyers are employed by some; but they merely receive the rents. The duties of a competent agent, embracing an inspection of the farms, a general intelligent supervision of the property, with that confidential communication with the landlord as to the measures best adapted to promote the interests of both landlord and tenant, and the suggestion of such improvements as may be made at the least cost for the benefit of both, cannot of course by such agency be contemplated.

There were then few educated men available with the necessary qualifications, and landlords were not prepared to pay salaries to attract them. The Royal Agricultural College at Cirencester had been founded in 1845, and was intended for the sons of farmers; but Caird notes that in 1850 most of the students were the sons of professional men, and he hoped that in time the College would provide a body of educated and competent land agents.

Caird's survey brings out the amazing diversity in the efficiency

[12] Mr Jorrocks employed his huntsman, Pigg.

of farming and estate management all over the country, and he discusses thus the landlords' responsibility for improvements:

What then is the actual state of England in regard to these important improvements? Drainage in the counties where it is needed has made considerable progress, the removal of useless hedgerows is slowly extending, but farm-buildings everywhere are generally defective. The inconvenient, ill-arranged hovels, the rickety wood and thatch barns and sheds, devoid of every known improvement for economising labour, food and manure, which are to be met with in every county in England, and from which anything else is exceptional in the southern counties, are a reproach to the landlords in the eyes of all skilful agriculturalists who see them. One can hardly believe that such a state of matters is permitted to exist in an old and wealthy country. Buildings of such a character that every gale of wind brings something down which the farmer must repair, and of so combustible a nature that among ill-disposed people he lives in continual dread of midnight conflagration. With accommodation adapted to the requirements of a past century, the farmer is urged to do his best to meet the necessities of the present. The economies of arrangement and power which are absolutely necessary to ensure profit amid the active competition of manufacturers are totally lost sight of here. And even the waste of raw material, which would be ruinous in a cotton-mill, is continued as a necessary evil, by the farmer, whose landlord provides him neither sufficient lodging for his stock, nor in that lodging, such as it is, the power of economising food by warmth and shelter . . .

A work so necessary could not have been so long neglected if the great body of English landlords had been practically acquainted with the management of land. . . . Let him learn his profession – that of a landowner. He will soon discover the benefits of improvement and therefore its necessity, the advantage of drainage, the evils of numerous hedgerows, the destructiveness of game preserves, and economy to the farmer, and, by consequence to himself, of good roads and well-arranged buildings. He will appreciate the difference between an improving tenant and a sluggard, and will encourage the one and get rid of the other. He will see the advantage of promoting the investment of capital in cultivation, and the necessity therefore of giving his tenant the security of a lease. He will perceive the hardship of stringent covenants to a good tenant, and their inefficiency in preventing deterioration by a bad one.[13]

SCOTTISH LEASES

In Scotland, the advantages of a long lease as an encouragement to agricultural improvement were more widely recognised than in

[13] J. Caird (1), pp. 360–1, 416–17, 490–2.

England. It is noteworthy that leases became popular in the Scottish lowlands, and tenant right became established in Lincolnshire, two areas which were largely reclaimed and inclosed in the half-century after 1780 by the combined enterprise of landlords and tenants. Professor David Low, who held the chair of Agriculture in the University of Edinburgh from 1831 to 1854, laid down that the essential conditions for happy relations between landlord and tenant were security of tenure; equitable rents; suitable conditions with respect to methods of culture and general management; and adequate provision by the landlord for the fixed capital invested in buildings, enclosures and other necessary appendages of the farm. These principles applied not only to new and recently reclaimed farms, but also to old ones, and to ensure them, he thought, a lease was the necessary instrument.[14]

Scottish leases might be of different lengths. Nineteen years, representing the metonic cycle, during which every kind of good and bad season might be experienced, was a common one, or twenty, twenty-one, sometimes 'three-nineteens', or a period of three lives. Whatever the length, during it the tenant had absolute security of tenure, and could safely adventure his own capital knowing that he would have time to reap the benefit of it. A good lease was one which stated clearly all the essential points of the contract but which was not overloaded with petty detail. After giving the time of entry, the duration, the rent and the time of payment, it might lay down the principles of farming to be followed, the course of rotation of crops, the prohibition of two consecutive corn crops, the proportion of the land to be kept under grass, the consumption of hay and straw on the farm, the return of manure to the land and so forth. It was here that the danger arose. If too many details were included, the good farmer felt hampered and frustrated, was not able to experiment and employ new methods or to take advantage of new markets. On the other hand, if he were left to 'practise the rules of good husbandry and not to mislabour the farm' as the phrase ran, the landlord would find it difficult to prove if, during the closing years of the lease, a

[14] David Low, *Landed Property and the Economy of Estates*, London, 1844, p. 8.

bad farmer 'ran the land' by selling his hay, straw and farmyard manure, neglecting his fallows and generally taking out as much as he could before moving elsewhere. Much litigation was caused by leases in which the terms of the contract were not precisely stated; moreover the same leases were copied over and over again in the estate office for succeeding tenants, regardless of their applicability to changed circumstances. Even in the twentieth century, farms in England were to be found upon which the cultivation of woad was prohibited in the lease, and the summer fallows were to be ploughed five times.

But valuable as was the long lease, giving security of tenure and encouragement to the enterprising farmer to adventure his own capital, it was a double-edged tool. In a time of rising prices, it was particularly advantageous to the farmer, as his rent was fixed and could not be raised to meet new conditions. But in a time of falling prices, it was a millstone round his neck. The rent was fixed, but the improvements he was making would not bring in so much as he had hoped. The farmer on a yearly agreement could get an abatement of rent from the landlord, or get out before he lost his capital, but the man with a lease was tied. Memories of the great depression after the Napoleonic wars and fears that prices might fall after the removal of protection may partly account for the unpopularity of leases in many parts of England. From the landlords' point of view, the high war-time prices gave them their opportunity to raise rents, and when leases fell in they did not renew them, but let the farms to the highest bidders under yearly tenancies. Moreover, under the Chandos clause of the Reform Act, 1832, a tenant paying a yearly rent of £50 and over became a county voter, and to those landlords to whom politics was more important than estate improvement, a docile tenant who would vote the right way, or who could be turned out if he did not, was more desirable than a secure tenant who might be recalcitrant on polling day. Sporting landlords, too, preferred the yearly tenancy, under which they could more easily get rid of tenants who interfered with the game or objected to excessive hedgerows and covers on the farms.

Caird was a strong advocate of long leases, though he admitted that they were popular in England neither with landlords nor tenants. But he was convinced that if agriculture was to be developed and production to increase, long leases were necessary. Except in Lincolnshire, he was not impressed by what he saw of farming under tenant-right, feeling that at best it might become too rigid and tend to stereotype farming methods, and that at the worst it opened the door to trickery and robbery on the part of the outgoing tenant.

Under many Scottish leases the rent was not fixed in money, but varied with the price of corn, with a maximum and minimum limitation. This protected the farmer from violent fluctuations in prices and made for stability, and certain English landlords adopted the same system after Repeal.

The Scottish banking system was one of the factors contributing to the success of the Scottish farmers. Lavergne was immensely impressed with this, which he regarded as a manifestation of national character. In England he found a spirit of speculation and extravagance, but 'in Scotland, on the other hand, the character of the people is so cool, calculating and correct, that the widest system of credit has not only been unattended with any disadvantages, but productive of the most magnificent results'. There were branches of the larger joint-stock banks all over the country which were freely used; runs on the banks, frequent in England, were uncommon in Scotland. Deposits of £10 and upwards were accepted and allowed interest of $2\frac{1}{2}$ or 3 per cent, so cash was not hoarded but paid in, and transactions were paid for by cheque. Credit was given at 4 or 5 per cent interest to anyone of good character with two sureties, so in the country districts where everyone knew everyone else, any enterprising farmer could get credit for his improvements without any difficulty.[15]

---

[15] Leonce de Lavergne, *op. cit.*, pp. 292–5. See also Henry Hamilton, *The Industrial Revolution in Scotland*, Oxford, 1932, Ch. xii.

CONDITIONS IN WALES

In Wales leases for lives or long leases for twenty-one years had been the practice in the eighteenth century, but by the 1840s nearly all these had fallen in and the rents had been raised. Most farmers were now tenants-at-will, few with any written agreement, and this was one of the causes making for social unrest and bad feeling between landlord and tenant. The population was rising fast, many holdings were small and there was fierce competition for them. Moreover, the strong family feeling of the Welsh made a man desire passionately to keep the holding which his father and grandfather had farmed. But if he did not apply for it almost before his father's funeral, he might find it let to someone else, for alien landlords or agents did not understand this strong feeling and were more interested in getting the best rent they could for any vacant holding. Some of the farms were really too small for economic working, but the Welsh were roused to intense fury if two were thrown together and let to one man. During the Rebecca Riots some such farms had their ricks and buildings burnt, for the fury was directed more against the man who took two farms than against the landlord who let them to him.[16] The land hunger and competition kept rents high, and with no written agreement and no customary tenant right, there was little incentive to Welsh farmers to improve their farming methods. They feared that any improvements they might make would only result in a raising of their rents, and they did not have the advantage of easy bank credit as the Scottish farmers had. There had been a number of private bank failures in Wales earlier in the century, which had shaken confidence and ruined many people, and Welsh farmers, with long memories, would have been chary of borrowing even if they had been credit-worthy. Their poverty was such that they could do little except go on farming in the traditional way.

Conditions in Wales were at their worst in the 1840s and gradually improved as the century advanced. Emigration, both to the growing industries at home and also overseas, drew off

[16] D. Williams, *op. cit.*, p. 104.

some of the surplus population, and better education and more
prosperous farming brought some mitigation of the grinding
poverty of earlier years. But relations between landlord and
tenant were slow to improve. The two passions of the Welsh
people, their religion and their national pride, grew stronger with
their increasing literacy, but religious and cultural differences
only emphasised the barriers between classes. In the Report of
the Welsh Land Commission this point is hammered home:

> The immense majority of the tenant farmers in the country districts are
> Nonconformists, and a state of things in regard to religion is disclosed that
> finds no parallel in any part of England of equal area. . . . On most typical
> estates in Wales, the landlord and his family belong to the Established Church,
> while the bulk of his tenants belong to one or other of the Nonconformist
> organisations. . . . There can be little doubt that this remarkable fact has had
> a powerful influence in creating a marked divergence between the opinions of
> the landowning class and the mass of the people, in enlarging the social
> differences between class and class, which to some extent would have existed
> in any case, and in emphasising the opposing interests of landlord and
> tenant.[17]

As the differences between the political parties crystallised
during the 1850s, Nonconformity came to be identified with
Liberalism, whereas most of the landlords of Wales adhered to
the Conservative Party, and this did not make for happier relations. Tenants who voted Liberal alleged threats of eviction; in
the General Election of 1859, after a contest in Merioneth, tenants
who voted Liberal were actually evicted, while others had their
rents raised on several estates. These actions roused a storm of
indignation all over the country, but in the General Election of
1868, just after the extension of the franchise, there were again a
number of evictions, particularly in Cardiganshire and Carmarthenshire, and a debate on the subject was held in the House of
Commons in July 1869. In Aberystwyth a relief fund was raised
to help those evicted. Even when there was no eviction, notices to
quit were sent out and rents raised. Sometimes the notices to quit
were withdrawn, one landlord telling his tenant 'not to make a

[17] R. C. 1894 (Wales), *Final Report, 1896* (C–8221), pp. 86–98, etc.; see also K. O.
Morgan, *Wales in British Politics, 1868–1922*, Cardiff, 1963, pp. 20–7.

fuss about the matter, as the notice was only given just to show who the master was'. All this strengthened the demand both for the ballot in elections and for a law of tenant right which would give compensation for disturbance and the greater security of tenure so badly needed. Even after the Ballot Act of 1872 became law, political pressure did not stop. There may not have been actual evictions for political reasons, but many tenants were afraid to take any active part in politics, and there were numerous ways of making a recalcitrant tenant's position uncomfortable and driving him to give notice himself if he wished to express his political convictions openly.

THE AGRICULTURAL HOLDINGS ACT, 1875

The first serious attempt to give tenant right the force of law was made by Philip Pusey in 1847, when he moved the Agricultural Tenant Right Bill, but he withdrew it when promised a Select Committee, because 'he felt convinced that the principle of the Bill must become law within a very few years; he was satisfied that the justice of the cause would work its way; but he was most anxious that it should not be carried in any way calculated to do violence to the feelings of the landlords, who he was sure would soon come to find their interests to be bound up with the just rights of their tenants . . .'[18]

The Committee on Agricultural Customs, under Pusey's chairmanship, described the customary systems of compensation then prevailing and commended them as beneficial to agriculture, leading to an increase in productivity and extended employment of the rural population. They recommended that limited owners who could not bind their successors should have their leasing powers extended, but were strongly opposed to making tenant right compulsory.[19]

Even when tenant right was recognised by the landlord, it was always inadequate to meet the needs of a developing and progressive industry, since a practice must have been established for

[18] *Hansard*, 12 May 1847.
[19] S.C. 1848 (Customs), *Report*, p. iv.

many years before being enshrined as a 'custom'. In spite of all that had been done both through covenants of farm leases and tenancy agreements and by the growth of custom to soften the asperity of the position at Common Law, the situation called for reform. The tenant's rights needed statutory recognition, they required classification and they called for some agency by which they could be recognised more speedily than by the passage of time.

But nearly a generation was to pass before another attempt was made to give tenants legal security for their improvements. In 1875 the Agricultural Holdings (England) Bill was introduced into the House of Lords by the Duke of Richmond. It was based upon prevailing customs, but it took account, also, of new practices in farming which still awaited the recognition accruing to antiquity. A schedule in the Bill comprised a list of improvements for whose unexhausted value compensation might be claimed by a leaving tenant, classified in three types. First, there were certain improvements for which an outgoing tenant could claim compensation only if his landlord had consented to their execution. Things in this category were mainly works of construction and the more permanent farming improvements, such as the erection of buildings or the planting of orchards – activities relatively costly in themselves which it was felt ought not to become a charge upon the landlord without his previous knowledge and consent. Secondly, there were certain other improvements for which an outgoing tenant could claim compensation only if he had given previous notice to his landlord that he intended to carry them out. This type included works temporary in their effect but of fairly long duration, such as draining land, liming, boning, chalking, etc.; the landlord having the opportunity of inspecting the work and seeing that it was properly done. Thirdly, there were certain acts for which a tenant could be compensated without previous notice to the landlord. These were temporary improvements such as acts of cultivation and manuring covered by custom, and things such as consumption of purchased feeding-stuffs on the farm and the application of purchased manures. It may be noted that these principles of compensation were an advance on those advocated by the Pusey Committee, reflecting the work of agricultural scientists during the period which appeared to make possible some measurement of the value to the incomer of the improvements applied to the soil.

The measure of the compensation payable, in whatever class, was to be its estimated value to an incoming tenant, though the landlord could put in a counter-claim for any breach of covenant or dilapidation. Provision was made for the removal of certain fixtures by the tenant, such as engines and machinery he had installed, if he gave one month's notice to the landlord, during which time the latter had the option of purchasing them. One year's notice to quit was made compulsory instead of the more usual six months, and the Bill was passsed in the same session.

The fatal defect of the new Act was, of course, the power it gave landlords to contract out of its provisions. As Knatchbull-Hugesson said in the House of Commons: 'The Bill allowed everybody to do exactly what he could do at present without it, and compelled no one to do anything which he had not hitherto done and did not wish to do.' [20] Even so late as 1875, landowners were very tenacious of their rights and suspicious of anything which looked like intervention by the State in their relations with their tenants, and all over the country they took advantage of the clause. But a good many of them saw the red light, and though contracting out of the Act, proceeded to make new agreements with their tenants embodying some of its provisions. Farmers welcomed the Act, for which the more articulate of them had been pressing for a long time. Even if their landlords did contract out, it gave them a lever to get a better agreement. Welsh farmers would have liked it if they had understood it, but the Act was never translated into Welsh, and few of them realised its possibilities, while nearly all the landowners in Wales contracted out.

But the Act led sometimes to unreasonable demands for compensation, which landlords countered with equally unreasonable claims for infringements of covenants, so that the arbitrating judge

[20] *Hansard*, 24 June 1875.

usually split the difference and neither achieved very much.[21] It was difficult to guard against claims based on fraudulent invoices for feeding-stuffs and fertilisers alleged to have been used. Valuers were often ill-informed on commercial prices, as is shown by the valuations awarded on hill sheep farms in Scotland for flocks that were 'bound' to the land.[22] Finally, compensation for un-exhausted improvements only benefited farmers when they left their farms – men who improved the land and stayed on were still liable to have their rent raised or to be given notice. The farmers' old saw

> Let alone and you sit,
> Improve and you flit !

was still true on many estates where the first object was to get the largest possible rental, and competition for farms was still strong in the 1870s. What the farmers wanted was better security of tenure.

THE PRIVILEGED CREDITOR

Political pressure and lack of compensation for improvements were not the only grievances felt by tenants during the Golden Age of farming. In Common Law, the landlord was a privileged creditor, and if a tenant went bankrupt he had the first claim on his assets for any rent owing. Moreover he had the power to dis-train for rent arrears – i.e. to enter on the property and to carry off goods and chattels up to the value of what he was owed; before 1883 this might be up to six years' rent. On well-managed estates this power can rarely have been used, and there is no reason to think that it was considered unfair in England and Wales.

In Scotland however, this privilege of the landlord was con-siderably more onerous and was a real grievance to farmers. Under Scots law the right of hypothec was a survival of the days when the landlord provided stock and seed-corn for a tenant. The tenant did not have to pay any rent during the first twenty-three months after his entry, but he was not allowed to dispose of his

[21] W. E. Bear, 'Tenant Right' in *Land, its Attraction and Riches, by Fifty-seven Authors.* London, 1892 pp. 580–9.

[22] *Report of the Committee on Hill Sheep Farming in Scotland*, 1944, Cmd. 6494, pp. 34–7

crops until the rent was paid. If the farmer failed, the landlord took the value of his rent in full and the other creditors divided what was left. Thus there was nothing to prevent a landlord from accepting a tenant with inadequate capital, provided he had enough to start farming. He might offer a higher rent than the farm was worth and the landlord knew that he could not lose even if the man went bankrupt after two years. It was alleged that this sort of thing frequently happened, and that it kept rents artificially high, besides being hard on other creditors of the bankrupt tenant.

The agitation for the reform of the law of hypothec came to a head in 1864 with the famous Ayrshire Oatmeal case of Barns *v.* Allen. Allen had bought some oats from a farm where the rent had not been paid in the year in which the oats were grown. The farmer then went bankrupt, the landlord claimed the oat crop, and Allen was found to be liable to pay over again to the landlord the price of the oats he had bought. This roused a considerable storm, and in 1865 a Royal Commission reported that the following of crops in the hands of *bona fide* purchasers ought not to be permitted, and also that landlords should not be allowed to seize household furniture and necessary farm implements. A Bill based on this report was introduced, but was not passed, and the law of hypothec as applied to agricultural holdings was not finally abolished until 1894.[23]

THE GAME LAWS

Game Laws were another source of friction between landlord and tenant. Here again the law was weighted heavily in favour of the landlord, for he could make what conditions he pleased about game in the lease or tenancy agreement, and the tenant had to comply.

Arable farmers in both England and Scotland complained of

[23] George Hope, 'Hindrances to Agriculture', in *Recess Studies*, ed. by Sir Alexander Grant, Edinburgh, 1870, pp. 386–400; R.C. on ... Landlord's Right of Hypothec regarding Agricultural Subjects, 1865; S.C. (H.L.) on Law of Hypothec, 1868–9; Hypothec Complete Abolition (Scotland) Act, 1893/4.

the damage caused by the depredations of pheasants. On the Welsh hills and the moorlands of North England and South Scotland, sheep farmers similarly complained of grouse and mountain hares. In the Highlands of Scotland, deer-stalking was becoming popular and fashionable as the century advanced, and in that mountain country it was difficult to know the exact boundaries between sheep farms and deer forests. Certainly the sheep and deer did not know them and would trespass freely. Keepers would impound straying sheep, but when the deer came down at night to graze on the sheep farms and to damage root and grain crops, the farmers could do nothing.

In 1872 a Select Committee recommended that occupiers of game preserves should be liable for damage to crops, and that rabbits should not be classed as game.[24] But it was not until 1883 that tenants were legally allowed to shoot hares and rabbits on their own farms, and until that date these animals continued to take their toll of farmers' crops, to the detriment of good farming and harmonious relations. But as in everything else in the relations of landlord and tenant, in game preservation the personal factor was everything, and whether there were friction or not depended upon the character of the landlord. Many allowed compensation for game damage, though tenants seldom felt themselves indemnified for it; some sent them substantial presents of game during the season. But improving landlords like Pusey were emphatic that game preservation was incompatible with high farming.

LACK OF SECURITY OF TENURE

Though the period 1846–75 showed many fine technical advances, though English agriculture seemed to have settled down under Free Trade and to be producing more than ever before, though land was still a good investment and the social prestige of the landed gentry still supreme, there were tensions between landlord and tenant all over the United Kingdom which needed legislation

[24] Select Committee on the Game Laws, 1872.

for their relief. That they were not universal, that on so many estates they were not even apparent, was due to those landlords who were more progressive and far-seeing than their fellows, who were prepared to lead, who had the means and the will to improve their estates and to redress grievances before they became acute. But the weakness of the landlord and tenant system at that time was that although the rights of property were enforceable by law, the duties were not; they were left to a man's conscience and the force of public opinion. Though it might be thought that enlightened self-interest would lead landlords to good estate management, there was no security that it would work that way. If men were shortsighted, greedy or indifferent, as many of them were, their tenants suffered accordingly. Moreover, there was still the problem of the settled and encumbered estate which prevented some well-disposed landowners from doing as much as they wished.

In the Highlands of Scotland and in Wales, tenants were more at the mercy of their landlords because of their passionate attachment to the particular piece of land which their forebears had farmed, so that they would put up with anything rather than move. English farmers were on the whole more mobile and less sentimental. If they quarrelled with their landlords or thought they could do better elsewhere, they left. Though the time was coming when the Scots and the Welsh would move to English farms, it was not so in the 1850s and 1860s. If forced to go, they went overseas.

Lack of compensation for improvements, game damage, political pressure, hypothec, arbitrary raising of rent, all these might be suffered in greater or less degree in various parts of the country, but the overriding danger for the tenant farmer was the same everywhere – lack of security of tenure. The tenants of the Lowlands were the safest, with their long leases, but even here there was no certainty that they would be renewed at the end of the period, nor that the rent would not be raised. Even so notable and successful a farmer as George Hope, who had farmed Fenton Barns all his life, and his father and grandfather before him, found in 1873 that his lease was not renewed, because eight years before he had stood as a Liberal candidate against Lord Elcho, who was a friend of his landlord.[25] We have seen the effect of the power of eviction in Wales, and on some estates in England with tenants on yearly agreements it was still exercised quite arbitrarily.

Lack of security did not make for good farming, nor did it encourage a farmer to adventure his own capital in improvements. All the serious agricultural writers of the century are in agreement upon this. G. C. Brodrick, writing in 1880, says:

The best agriculture is found on farms whose tenants are protected by leases; the next best, on farms whose tenants are protected by the Lincolnshire or other customs; the worst of all, on farms whose tenants are not protected at all, but rely on the honour of their landlords. And the reason is self-evident. The farmer who holds without a lease or legal security knows that a model landlord may at any moment be succeeded by a heartless spendthrift, or a liberal agent by one whose pride consists in rack-renting every farm on the estate. He is, therefore, deterred by a traditional instinct from incurring expenditure which may lead to a re-valuation, with an advance of rent, if not to an appropriation of his invested capital.[26]

[25] J. A. Scott Watson and M. E. Hobbs, *Great Farmers*, London, 1937, p. 111.
[26] G. C. Brodrick, *op. cit.*, p. 378.

7

The State and the Land

State Action – James Caird – Tithe Commission – Copyhold Commission – Inclosure Commission – Commons Act, 1876 – Exchanges of Land – Drainage and Improvement of Land – The Cattle Plague – Board of Agriculture

STATE ACTION

THE great constitutional lawyer, Professor Dicey, divided nineteenth-century legislation into three periods: 1800–30, the period of Tory repression and paternalism; 1830–60, the period of Benthamism and *laissez faire*; and 1860 onwards, when legislation became increasingly socialistic, as one aspect of national life after another became the subject of State interference.[1] This rough classification may be borne in mind in considering the legislative and administrative action applying to land and agriculture during the period under review. The repeal of the Corn Laws was the triumph of *laissez faire*, and the theory that the greatest good of the greatest number would best be obtained by leaving men to pursue their own interest, with State action limited to the enforcing of contracts and the protection of life and property, was on the whole accepted both inside Parliament and out, by the upper and middle classes.

Thus in the twenty years after repeal it is not surprising that we do not find any great legislative measures specifically designed for the improvement of agriculture, but instead a number of measures dealing with special subjects, some of them designed to free the land from various legal disabilities. Caird, in summing up the results of his 1850 survey of English farming, stressed that

[1] A. V. Dicey, *Lectures on the Relation between Law and Opinion in England during the Nineteenth Century*, London, 1905.

education and knowledge were the things most needed by both landlords and tenants if agriculture were to progress and flourish. He was a strong believer in individual enterprise, but he thought that as a special protection had been taken away, the agricultural interest 'had a right to demand that all trammels on their enterprise and industry should now be withdrawn'.[2] He listed five measures by which he thought the State could help the industry: (1) the cheapening and facilitating the transfer of land, (2) the sale of over-burdened estates, (3) the encouragement of leases with liberal covenants, (4) an alteration to the law of settlement, (5) the collection of agricultural statistics. All these points were, in one way or another, the subject of legislation in the second half of the century, though its effects were not always what he anticipated.

JAMES CAIRD

Just as Philip Pusey, by his life and writings, left his mark on English agriculture in the early part of this period, so James Caird, from a very different background, was for some forty years an authority on the agricultural problems of his day, and in both legislation and administration made an outstanding contribution to its well-being. This has not, perhaps, been sufficiently recognised, and a brief picture of his career is not out of place in a chapter dealing with state action towards the industry.

Caird was a Scotsman and essentially a practical man. Born in 1816, he was educated at Edinburgh High School and University. He went to Northumberland to learn farming, and then joined his uncle who was farming in Ayrshire, at the same time working in the uncle's law and banking business. In the 1840s he took the lease of a farm at Baldoon, near Wigtown, from the Earl of Galloway, where he remained until 1860. He began to take an interest in public affairs while the Corn Law controversy was raging, and produced a pamphlet called *High Farming as the best substitute for Protection*, based on his own farming experience, to show that good farmers need have no fear of free trade.

[2] J. Caird (1), p. 526.

In 1850, when it seemed that another agricultural depression might be imminent, he made his famous tour of England on behalf of *The Times*, to look at farming practice and conditions. He was well placed to do this. As a practical farmer he knew what he was looking at, but as a Scot who had lived and worked under very different conditions he accepted nothing in English practice as necessarily right because sanctioned by custom. Moreover, as a man of complete independence and detachment, he spoke his mind very forcibly when confronted by evidence of stupidity, inefficiency and indifference among farmers and landowners alike. At a time when the power and prestige of aristocratic landlords were unchallenged, his comments on the estate management of some of the highest in the land were devastating in their frankness. His book, *English Agriculture in 1850–51*, is still the best picture we have of English farming in the mid-century. It is uneven, some counties are treated in scant detail and certain interesting developments missed, but when the speed with which his tour was accomplished in those days of difficult travelling is remembered, it remains indeed a *tour de force* in every sense.

In 1857 Caird entered Parliament as member for Dartmouth. In that period of coalitions and uncertain party lines he was a supporter of Lord Palmerston and spoke mainly on his own subject, the land, in all its aspects. In 1859 he was returned as member for Stirling Boroughs, which seat he held until 1865. He was a member of various Commissions and Boards, but the great contribution of his Parliamentary career was his fight for the collection of agricultural statistics.

The question was first mooted in 1835, when a Committee on Agricultural Distress was sitting. Then in 1845 Milner Gibson, M.P. for Manchester, raised it again, and the debate which followed showed that while members were not unfavourable to the idea, the difficulty and expense of collecting statistics seemed almost insuperable. Various methods of collection were suggested, that the Poor Law Commissioners, or the Tithe Commissioners, or the schoolmaster or some other responsible person in each parish should undertake it. The last idea drew from Colonel Sibthorp the remark: 'Let me catch a schoolmaster on my land, that is all. We live in extraordinary times, when these dictatorial attempts are made to invade the sacredness of private property.' The question was dropped for the time being, though it was revived in 1854 when a vote of £13,000 was agreed, to facilitate the collection of statistics in eleven counties as an experiment. Agricultural statistics were collected in Scotland from 1853 to 1857 by the Highland and Agricultural Society, but ended abruptly, owing to a dispute with the Treasury over a small grant made towards the cost.

For the next few years Caird continued his campaign by means of draft Bills, resolutions, questions to Ministers, and an attempt to get agricultural statistics included in the 1861 Census. He proposed that the County Police might do the job, and when that failed, the Ordnance Survey. By the 1860s opinion was beginning to change, and in the debate on 7 June 1864, there was little opposition to the idea, only disagreement about the method and expense of collecting agricultural statistics. But in July 1865 the outbreak of Cattle Plague, its rapid spread through the country, and the policy of slaughter and compensation by which it was eventually met, emphasised the importance of knowing the actual numbers of cattle on the farms, and it was agreed that the collection of statistics throughout Great Britain should be undertaken by the Officers of the Inland Revenue and published by the Statistical Department of the Board of Trade. The first volume appeared in 1867.

Caird did not stand for Parliament again after 1865, but devoted the rest of his life to the service of agriculture in administration. He continued his close association with the land by farming an estate in Kirkcudbrightshire which he had bought in 1860, and in 1865 he became an Inclosure Commissioner.

In 1846 there were very few Government Departments, and those there were had small staffs appointed by the patronage and influence of Ministers and Members of Parliament. The growth of an efficient and impartial Civil Service was one of the glories of the nineteenth century, but it was not until 1870 that appointment by patronage was finally superseded by competitive examination. Of course the patronage system was open to the most shocking abuse and jobbery, but in addition to all the Tite Barnacles of the Circumlocution Office, it did produce some brilliant administrators like Edwin Chadwick as well as many able and conscientious men like James Caird.

When an Act of Parliament was passed requiring administrative action which was not appropriate to any of the existing Departments, it was usual to set up a special Board or Commission to deal with it. Thus in the middle of the century, there were three Commissions dealing with land – the Tithe Commission, set up under the Tithe Act of 1836, the Copyhold Commission, under the Copyhold Act of 1841, and the Inclosure Commission under the General Inclosure Act of 1845. In 1851 these bodies were merged into one Commission, which in 1882 became the Land Commission, and in 1889 became the Land Department of the newly-formed Board of Agriculture. Caird was concerned with all these bodies, remaining in land administration for the rest of his life and finishing as Director of the Land Department.

However, this was by no means his only activity. He was a prominent member of the Royal Agricultural Society of England and of the Statistical Society, becoming President of the latter society in 1880. He wrote many articles on agricultural subjects in the journals of these societies, as well as pamphlets on food, American farming, the Irish land question and India (to which he went as a member of the Famine Commission). His only other book besides his *Tour* was *The Landed Interest and the Supply of Food*, a general picture of British agriculture written for the International Agricultural Congress of Paris in 1878.

Caird was made a Fellow of the Royal Society and received a knighthood; he died in 1892, a year after his retirement from the Board of Agriculture. One of his last publications was an article in the *Journal of the Royal Agricultural Society* called 'Fifty Years' Progress in British Farming', which he was well qualified to write having been in close touch with every aspect of it all through the period. His approach was never an academic one, for he was always a practical farmer himself. After he gave up his Scottish estate, he took a farm in the Home Counties which was managed by his son, and he was never so happy as when he went out for a day's farming. He was always optimistic about British farming, even in the darkest days of the depression, as his evidence before the Richmond Commission showed. He saw that the prosperity of farming was bound up with the commercial prosperity of the country, and he had faith in the capacity of the British farmers to adapt themselves to the needs of the market, by turning from cereals to livestock products, a faith which was abundantly justified. Of landlords he was more critical, especially English landlords, for their slowness to take advantage of schemes for land improvement and to grant long leases, as he saw high rents and lack of security of tenure as the greatest of the farmers' handicaps. Though most of his life was passed in England, Caird was essentially a Scotsman, with a Scottish farmer's attitude towards the land. To him farming was a business, and land, being limited in supply, must in the national interest be put to the best possible use for the production of food. Agricultural statistics made it possible to get an overall picture of the state of production, and the Commissions of which he was a member were all directed in one way or another to the promotion of more efficient land use.[3]

TITHE COMMISSION

Tithe was a form of property going back to the very early days of Christianity in England, when the Church was financed by the receipt of one-tenth of the annual produce of the land, both crops and stock, at first a moral and later a legal obligation. For centuries it was collected in kind – every tenth sheaf of corn, every tenth sheep in a flock, and so on. (The smallest pig in a litter is still sometimes known as 'the parson's pig'.) In some places, tithe did not go to the parson of the parish, but was appropriated to a monastery or other religious house. Thus, at the dissolution of the monasteries in the sixteenth century, the tithes in

[3] E. Clarke, 'Sir James Caird', *J.R.A.S.E.*, vol. 3.iii, 1892, pp. 179–82.

their possession passed to the Crown, and were later granted to laymen who became known as lay impropriators. These new tithe owners did not necessarily have any connection with the place from which the tithe was collected. To them tithe was just income-yielding property which could be bought and sold, and the farmers from whose land such tithe was collected disliked it very much. The parson's tithe they could understand, for they realised that the man must live, even though they avoided paying it as much as they could; but payment to a distant tithe-owner who sent his collector down to exact the uttermost farthing was often deeply resented. When the Tithe Commutation Act was passed in 1836, the annual value of all tithe was estimated at about £4 million and nearly one-quarter of this was in the hands of lay impropriators.

With changes in social conditions and agricultural techniques, collection of tithe in kind had become very complicated and full of anomalies, and by the nineteenth century much of it had been commuted to a money payment. 'The rector of a parish has much to do;' said Mr Collins in *Pride and Prejudice*, 'in the first place, he must make such an agreement for tythes as may be beneficial to himself and not offensive to his patron. . . .' The Tithe Commissioners were charged, first, with the duty of confirming these voluntary agreements between tithe-owners, whether clerical or lay, on the one hand, and occupiers of tithable land on the other, provided they were satisfied that the agreement was reasonable and equitable. Secondly, in parishes where there was no voluntary agreement, they were to assess the value of the tithe and apportion it between the various occupiers. The payment of commuted tithe, known as the tithe rent-charge, was usually based upon a seven-year running average of the prices of wheat, barley and oats. The apportionment was intricate and complicated, but it was carried through with great care by the Commissioners. When all objections had been heard and agreement reached, the apportionment was engrossed on parchment with a map attached showing the exact size, ownership and value of every bit of land in the parish. These maps are an invaluable source of information to historians

and others. The originals are in the custody of the Tithe Commission, but two copies were made and deposited, one with the
Incumbent and Churchwardens of the parish in question, and
the other with the Registrar of the Diocese to which it belonged.

In Wales, at the time of the passing of the 1836 Act, tithe was
an acute grievance with farmers. There had not been much commutation, farmers preferring to pay in kind, when they had some
opportunity of bargaining with the collector, and in any case
their economy was such that they used little money. The great
tithes were mostly in lay and absentee hands, and the vicarial
tithes were particularly resented when the majority of farmers
were nonconformists and saw no reason why they should support
an alien church. Where there had been voluntary agreements
there were complaints that the surveyors appointed to make the
apportionment were inefficient and venial, and farmers sometimes found their tithes increased and did not easily understand
the seven-year average upon which their payment was based.
Also the period immediately after the passing of the Act coincided
with that time of great unrest in South Wales which culminated
in the Rebecca Riots, of which the tithe grievance was one of the
contributory causes. The Commission of Inquiry for South Wales,
appointed after the rioting, reported an increase of 7 per cent in
tithe over South Wales, and recommended that landlords should
grant their tenants some redress for this. The Tithe Commission
encountered more difficulty and protest in getting agreements to
tithe awards here than they did in England, and in many parishes
compulsory awards had to be made, the parties on the spot failing
to agree. But tithe continued to be a grievance in Wales all through
the century, some farmers refusing to pay it until distrained
upon.

The Scots, on the other hand, with their unfailing common
sense in cutting difficult knots and giving a simple legal basis to
changes in custom, had settled their tithe question as long ago as
the seventeenth century. By an Act of Charles I, all lands and
revenues formerly belonging to the Church were made over to
the Crown, and heritors were allowed to buy their teinds or tithes

at nine years purchase of the tithing, fixed at one-fifth of the annual rental.[4]

After tithe had been commuted to a tithe rent-charge, the next stage was for it to be redeemed altogether. This was done by capitalising it at twenty-five years purchase, and in certain cases, such as the purchase of land for any public building or purpose, redemption was compulsory. By the time that the Tithe Commission was merged with the Board of Agriculture, practically all tithe had been commuted and much of it redeemed, though it was still to be the cause of disputes. The Tithe Act, 1891, made a few changes, the chief being that tithe rent-charge unpaid might be recoverable through the County Courts, and that liability to pay was transferred from the occupier to the owner of the land. This last measure was of some help to farmers during the agricultural depression, though it diminished the income from landowning. At a time when many landlords were reducing rents, and in some cases remitting them altogether in order to keep their tenants, tithe rent-charge remained a tax on diminishing profits; further, as it was based on the seven-year average of prices, the value of the annual payments was slow to follow the falling prices of corn, a further grievance for the payers of tithe rent-charge.

COPYHOLD COMMISSION

The Copyhold Commissioners were charged with the duty of assisting the enfranchisement of copyhold tenures. Copyhold tenure, which went back to feudal times, ended after 1925, but in 1841 it was still fairly common. As Caird pointed out: '... wherever there is a manor there are many copyhold properties; and much yet remains to be accomplished before this injurious and obstructive kind of tenure shall altogether cease to exist.'[5]

A copyhold tenant held his land by copy of the court roll of the manor, paying some nominal rent and being liable to feudal customs such as heriots, fines, reliefs, limited rights to timber and so on.

[4] J. A. Symon, *Scottish Farming Past and Present*, Edinburgh, 1959, p. 82.
[5] J. Caird (2), p. 128.

He could leave it to his heirs and for most practical purposes the land was his own, but there were various restrictions which were tiresome. The joint rights of timber, by which the copyhold tenant could not cut trees without leave of the lord, nor the lord enter the land to cut without leave of the tenant, were sometimes irksome and might lead to a complete deadlock, and so was the payment of a heriot (originally the best beast or best chattel) on the death of the tenant or the lord; so it was generally to the interest of both parties that the copyhold should be converted into a simple freehold. This could be done by voluntary agreement, but until the Act of 1841, limited owners could not enfranchise copyholds. It was the duty of the Copyhold Commissioners to arrange what compensation the tenant should pay to the landlord to free his copyhold and to extinguish the manorial dues to which he had been liable. Further Acts passed in 1852 and 1887 made enfranchisement compulsory at the application of either the lord or the tenant; gave the Commissioners power to appoint valuers to assess the amount which a tenant should pay, and ordered to be published a scale of compensation of the various manorial fines and reliefs to which copyhold tenants were liable. From 1841 until the end of the century 19,650 copyholds were enfranchised.[6]

INCLOSURE COMMISSION

The work of the third body, the Inclosure Commissioners, is the most interesting from the point of view of agriculture. The Act of 1845 which set up the Commission was one of a series designed to make inclosure of commons and wastes easier and less expensive. Another point stressed in the Act was the desirability of finding work for the labouring poor, because unemployment, or underemployment, of agricultural workers was a chronic problem, at any rate in the south of England. So the preamble to the Act sets out its objects as being 'to facilitate the inclosure and improvement of commons and other lands . . . subject to the rights of

[6] Board of Agriculture, *Annual Report of Proceedings under the Inclosure Acts, Copyhold Acts, etc., for the year 1892* (1893, C-6891); for the year 1900 (1901, Cd. 502) p. 19.

property which obstruct cultivation and the productive employment of labour'. Thus in theory it was another measure for freeing
the land from restrictions and giving men opportunities for improving their property and finances, the State appearing in the
role of benevolent umpire. James Caird, who was himself an
Inclosure Commissioner from 1865 to 1882, defined in 1878 the
status of the Inclosure Commission: '. . . the only department of
the State which has a direct connection with the land is the Inclosure Office, which combines several objects, more or less apper-
taining to landed property, but with no power to interfere except
when applied to for the means of facilitating improvements. The
costs of all proceedings effected through this department are provided by those who make use of it.'[7]

Under the Act of 1845, persons interested in inclosing any land,
whether common field, commons or wastes, instead of going
through the old procedure of a private Act of Parliament, applied
direct to the Inclosure Commissioners. When the Commissioners
had satisfied themselves that in addition to being to the advantage
of the owners of the land, inclosure was desirable 'having regard
as well to the health, comfort and convenience of the inhabitants
of any cities, towns, villages, or populous places in or near any
parish' where inclosure was proposed, they would make a provisional order. This would set forth the terms and conditions under
which it should be done, 'and especially the quantity and situation
of the allotments (if any) which, under the provisions of this Act,
should be appropriated for the purposes of exercise and recreation
and for the labouring poor'. This provisional order was deposited
in the parish, and if persons entitled to two-thirds in value of the
interests in the land consented, the Commissioners certified in
their next Annual Report that inclosure would be expedient. An
annual Act of Parliament authorised any inclosures they had certified, and a valuer was appointed to divide and set out the land as
agreed, and generally to settle all incidental details. After this had
been done and a report and map prepared, another meeting was
held in the parish by the Commissioners, to hear objections and

[7] J. Caird (2), p. 112.

to make amendments if necessary. When all was finally agreed, an award was prepared and confirmed by the Commission and the work proceeded.

The actual business of inclosure would take several years, from first to last, varying of course according to the size and nature of the area to be inclosed and the number of people concerned in it. In addition to the re-allotment of land, new roads had to be laid out or old tracks made up, and the lands allotted as places of exercise or recreation had to be fenced, and sometimes drained and levelled and so on. Though the Act of 1845 set out the procedure for inclosure in considerable detail, further powers were given to the Commissioners by subsequent Inclosure Acts in 1846, 1848, 1849, 1852, 1857 and 1859. These were concerned with questions of determining boundaries, exchange of land, roads, fencing, alteration of parish boundaries, drainage, sales of land, allotments, minerals and other problems which had arisen in the course of the Commission's work; so it would appear that every effort was made to ensure that the whole business of carrying through inclosure was fair and equitable and that the public interest was safeguarded.

The provision for allotments in the Act of 1845 reflects the growing consciousness that earlier inclosures had often dealt hardly with the poorer villagers, as Arthur Young had stated so emphatically; that it was wise and desirable to give labourers some direct interest of their own in the land; and that self-interest often failed to meet the demand for allotments in southern England. Very careful directions were given to the Commissioners that allotments were to be placed under the management of allotment wardens consisting of the incumbent of the parish, a churchwarden and two other persons, who were to let them on yearly tenancies, not exceeding a quarter of an acre, free of tithe, rates and taxes, at rents corresponding to the letting value of the same land for farming purposes; any surplus of rents, after paying rates, tithe rent-charge, expenses etc., was to be handed to the overseers of the poor in aid of the poor rates. No buildings of any kind were to be put up on these allotments.

How far the Inclosure Commissioners were successful in attempts to extend allotments is very difficult to estimate. Hasbach, himself a keen advocate of peasant farming, thought that they deliberately neglected this part of their work, quoting the statistics of enclosure made in 1869 which show that of 614,800 acres inclosed since 1845, only 2,223 had been assigned to allotments: 'Thus once again, as so often in England, great parliamentary exertions ended in insignificant results, and administrators did their best to obstruct the intentions of the legislature.'[8]

Shaw-Lefevre says that the allotments for recreation grounds and gardens were miserably meagre and that in the Annual Inclosure Bill for 1869, when schemes embracing 8,900 acres were proposed, only three acres were reserved for recreation grounds and six for allotment gardens and that the Bill was objected to in the Commons on these grounds and stopped.[9] But the reports of the Commissioners show that they did make careful enquiries into the needs of each parish, and in many cases they noted that the labourers already had good gardens adjoining their cottages, and that there was no demand for allotments.

By the Commons Act of 1876, certain changes were made in the regulations regarding allotments, or field gardens as they were more generally called. Any surplus arising from their rents, instead of being handed over for poor relief, was to be devoted to improving or maintaining the gardens, by drainage or fencing, or to buying additional land for them. Moreover, if any gardens were unlet and there was no demand among the poor inhabitants, wardens might let them to anyone at the best rent obtainable, and in quantities of up to one acre. This looks as though the demand for field gardens was not so strong as it appeared to be in 1845, and that they were no longer regarded as a means of poor relief. The state of the farm worker was beginning to improve.

The Commons Act of 1876 made other important additions to the work of the Inclosure Commissioners, the nature of which

[8] W. Hasbach, *A History of the English Agricultural Labourer*, London, 1908, pp. 116, 241.

[9] G. Shaw-Lefevre, *Agrarian Tenures*, London, 1893, p. 62.

was changing as the century proceeded. In their report for the year 1876, the Commissioners gave a summary of their first thirty years' work. Since 1845 they had made orders for over 900 inclosures of commons, wastes and commonable lands, covering 600,000 acres, which had been divided among 26,000 separate owners. More than 2,000 miles of public roads had been constructed, and the estimated value of inclosures amounted to £6,140,000. Nearly one-eighth of this value had been devoted to what the Commissioners called 'objects of public utility and convenience', by which they meant roads, recreation grounds, field-gardens, public quarries, fuel, schools and churches, burial grounds and so on. The cost of all this had been met by sales of part of the newly enclosed lands, and some 35,450 acres had been sold in this way, to 3,500 purchasers. The Commissioners took pride in the fact that their work had made an appreciable addition to the number of small landowners in England. The idea was abroad in the 1870s that too much land was owned by too few people and that ownership ought to be more diffused,[10] and this part of their Report is probably a recognition of this growing concern. The Commissioners summed up their work as follows:

> Thus, in the course of one generation, an extent of land equal to that of a county had been redeemed from common and waste, and has been divided among a far larger and more varied body of landowners than that of any county in England. Valuable public roads of great extent have been constructed, opening up for business and pleasure many otherwise inaccessible localities and at no cost to the public. The area of production and employment has been increased, and in the same proportion that of public and local taxation has been extended. A great number of small landed properties have been created, and labourers' field gardens in the rural districts have been afforded in larger proportion to the extent of the land than appear by the agricultural returns to exist elsewhere in England.
>
> Upwards of 2,000,000 acres of common land are believed yet to remain uninclosed. Though the best of the land was probably first dealt with, there can be little doubt that much of this may be advantageously brought under the operation of the new law, which, in the altered state of the circumstances since 1845, provided more fully for the public interests of the neighbourhood and of large populations, and at the same time may still be found in less populous

[10] See p. 304 seq.

quarters, the useful instrument of adding some considerable extent of available land to the solid resources of the country.

This Report was undoubtedly written by Caird himself, then Chief Commissioner, for he incorporated much of it *verbatim* in his book *The Landed Interest*, written in the same year. It is in line with his general outlook on land matters, that with knowledge and enterprise farming could prosper and that if more land could be made productive, so much the better for the country. The urban population must of course be considered, but to him the real business of the Inclosure Commissioners was to facilitate land improvement for farming.

This was the work as it appeared to the administrators. What it meant in terms of human endeavour on the spot is another matter. Farming a rearranged open field or part of a well-grazed common pasture was one thing, but breaking in a piece of real unreclaimed waste was quite another. Tennyson's 'Northern Farmer', as he is dying, looks back on his life and feels that his greatest achievement was having 'stubb'd Thurnaby waäste':

> Dubbut looökat the waäste: theer warn't not feeäd for a cow;
> Nowt at all but bracken an' fuzz, an' looök at it now –
> Warn't worth nowt a haäcre, an' now theer's lots of feeäd,
> Fourscoor yows upon it an' some on it down i' seeäd.

> Nobbut a bit on it's left, an I meän'd to 'a stubb'd it at fall,
> Done it ta-year I meän'd, and runn'd plow thruff it an 'all,
> If godamoighty an' parson 'ud nobbut let ma aloän,
> Meä, wi' haäte hoonderd haäcre o' Squoire's, an' länd o my oän.

Thus speaks the prosperous independent Lincolnshire farmer, conscious of having won a stiff battle against nature and proud of having created good farming land, food and wealth by his own efforts – as man has been doing from time immemorial.

COMMONS ACT, 1876

The Commons Act of 1876 was the outcome of two developments of public opinion and social conscience which had been growing in the previous decade or so. One was the concern for the health and happiness of the people of London and other large towns, who were in danger of being cut off from the fresh air and open spaces they badly needed as more and more commons were inclosed and fenced off into farming or building land. In 1865 the Commons Preservation Society was founded, largely by the efforts of Shaw-Lefevre, and in 1866 the Metropolitan Commons Act forbade the Inclosure Commissioners to consider any application for inclosure of commons within the Metropolitan Police area. Instead they were to prepare schemes for the improvement and regulation of such commons, and to appoint conservators to make necessary by-laws to safeguard both the right of the public to free access and the grazing, fuel and other rights of those commoners who still used the common for those purposes. The initiative for preparing a scheme for a common could come from the Lord of the Manor, or the commoners themselves, or the local authority of the district, or any twelve ratepayers, and the scheme, when finally agreed, had to be confirmed by Act of Parliament. In this way, from 1866 to 1898, twenty-three commons in Kent, Middlesex and Surrey, covering nearly 4,000 acres, were the subject of schemes confirmed by Parliament, with incalculable benefit to the people of London.[11]

But this was not enough. Other large towns needed commons and open spaces for recreation, and the value of land for building purposes near them was increasing. Moreover, the railway companies often offended by taking parts of commons which cost them less in compensation than established farm land. So if public interests were to be safeguarded, further legislation was needed.

The other development of public opinion was concern for the condition of agricultural workers and the realisation that the field gardens were really no substitute for the loss of grazing rights, which had often in the past helped a man to get a start on the agricultural ladder. The Second Report of the Royal Commission on the Employment of Women and Children in Agriculture in 1868 emphasised that the agricultural population had lost

[11] *Annual Report and Proceedings of the Board of Agriculture*, 1900 (Cd. 502). See also L. Dudley Stamp and W. G. Hoskins, *Common Lands of England and Wales*, London, 1963, Ch. vi.

opportunities for bettering their condition through the inclosure of waste lands and the absorption of small farms into larger ones.

The Commons Act of 1876 was thus the outcome of both these concerns and from henceforth the Commissioners, on any application for an enclosure, were not to grant it unless it were certain to be in the public interest. They were given powers to make regulation schemes, on the same lines as for the Metropolitan Commons, safeguarding existing rights and if necessary making arrangements for planting for ornament or shelter, for draining and for adding to the amenity of the common. From that time onwards, in spite of Caird's optimism, there were far fewer applications for inclosure; up to the end of the century only 28,000 more acres were inclosed, but 31,000 acres of common were regulated under this Act.

EXCHANGES OF LAND

Another duty which the Inclosure Commissioners were given under the 1845 Inclosure Act was to facilitate exchanges of land between two landowners without going through the cumbersome procedure of buying and selling and investigation of title and all that that involved. Cases were often found of irregular and awkward boundaries between adjoining estates, of lands intermingled and so on, where it was obviously in the interest of good estate management that they should be rectified. If the Commissioners were satisfied, after local enquiry, that the proposed exchange was beneficial, and the lands to be exchanged were of roughly equal value, they could make an order to come into force in three months transferring ownerships; some thousands of small exchanges were effected in this way, at a trifling cost.

DRAINAGE AND IMPROVEMENT OF LAND

In his opening speech in the great debate on the Corn Laws in 1846, Sir Robert Peel declared his intention that British agriculture should receive compensation for the loss of protection, by means of Government loans to landowners who wished to improve their property by drainage. These loans would be a first charge on their estates, having precedence over all existing mortgages; they would be available even to owners of settled estates, who were otherwise only able to impose such a charge by the complicated process of the Court of Chancery. The administration of the scheme was handed over to the Inclosure Commissioners, who were to examine all applications, satisfy themselves that the work was desirable and reasonable, and likely to enable the borrowers to pay the stipulated interest of $3\frac{1}{2}$ per cent and to repay the principal over twenty-two years.

The scheme was an instant success. The original £2 million allotted was quickly exhausted and a further £2 million was provided by the Treasury in 1850; of this total, nearly half was spent in Scotland. Such was the demand that several public companies were formed to borrow money from the public through sale of stock, and to lend it again to landowners not only for drainage but also for inclosure, fencing and buildings. There was the West of England Company; the General Land Drainage and Improvement Company set up in 1849; the Lands Improvement Company, which dates from 1853; the Land Loan and Enfranchisement Company, the Scottish Drainage and Improvement Company and others, some of which amalgamated later. The Lands Improvement Company began with a capital of £100,000, and over the next hundred years it lent, with its amalgamated companies, over £17 million for improvements to estates and farms. The safeguard for the lenders to these Companies was that the schemes proposed by the borrowers had to be approved by the Inclosure Commissioners, and the loans repaid within a set term of years.

By 1864, it was estimated that some £8 million from the Treasury and public companies had been spent on land improvement, by 1878, £12 million and by 1912 over £18 million, and these sums take no account of the amounts spent by landowners out of their own resources.[12]

[12] J. Bailey Denton, 'Land Drainage, etc. by Loans', *J.R.A.S.E.*, vol. 4.ii, 1868; J. Caird (2), p. 82.

The following table shows the amounts spent by landowners on improvements under the various Acts passed during the century[13]:

Expenditure charged on estates in Great Britain for Improvement under the Drainage and Improvement of Land Acts, 1846–1912

(in thousands of pounds)

	1847–72	1873–82	1883–92	1893–1902	1903–12	TOTAL
Drainage	7,381	1,030	531	63	26	9,031
Farm Buildings	1,875	1,673	1,020	554	425	5,547
Cottages	342	510	180	157	190	1,378
Mansion Houses	17	189	309	267	161	944
Fencing and Em-banking	217	148	62	38	18	483
Roads	77	50	31	45	41	244
Clearing and Re-clamation	116	26	4	1	—	147
Planting	44	26	21	8	10	995
Subscriptions to Railways	22	43	52	10	4	131
Water Supply	—	—	—	47	98	145
Other	86	89	80	23	69	347
TOTAL	10,177	3,786	2,290	1,212	1,040	18,505

Some landowners carried out the work themselves with estate or contract labour, recouping themselves by raising rents when the improvements had been made, or charging their tenants interest to cover the 6¾ per cent annual charge for interest and repayment of the loan. According to Caird: 'We are sorry to say that more than one instance exists in Yorkshire, where the landlord charges his tenant 7½ per cent, thus putting into his pocket 1 per cent, besides securing a permanently higher value for his land by an outlay to which he does not contribute a single farthing. This grasping conduct, so utterly at variance with the intentions of the Legislature, is quite unworthy of the character and

[13] From an unpublished thesis by J. J. MacGregor on 'The Economic History of Landownership since 1870', 1938.

position of a respectable landlord.'[14] On other estates, the owners provided the tiles or pipes and left the tenants to carry out the work, a practice of which Caird was critical, since few farmers were skilled at laying out a drainage system for a large area.

In general, farming prosperity was such that borrowers had little difficulty in repaying these loans, though there were of course some defaulters. Mrs Gaskell's Squire Hamley of Hamley Hall, in *Wives and Daughters*, was one of these:

> He would not, if he could, have sold any part of the estate which he inherited from his father; and besides, it was strictly entailed. He had sometimes thought how wise a step it would have been could he have sold a portion of it, and with the purchase-money have drained and reclaimed the remainder; and at length, learning from some neighbour that Government would make certain advances for drainage, etc., at a very low rate of interest, on condition that the work was done, and the money repaid, within a given time, his wife had urged him to take advantage of the proffered loan. But now she was no longer there to encourage him and take an interest in the work, he grew indifferent to it himself, and cared no more to go out on his stout roan cob, and sit square on his seat, watching the labourers on the marshy land all overgrown with rushes; speaking to them from time to time in their own strong nervous country dialect; but the interest to Government had to be paid all the same, whether the men worked well or ill.

The Inclosure Commissioners were thus called upon to execute an enormous volume of work – inspecting plans, checking them on the ground with the intending borrowers, and approving costs and progress. Their functions were extended by the Emigration Advances Act, 1851, which authorised loans to landowners to pay part or all of the expenses of poor persons emigrating from their estates – a provision designed to relieve the acute distress of the Scottish crofting districts;[15] but in fact only some £5,000 was advanced for this purpose.

The Improvement of Land Act, 1864, considerably extended the improvements for which a limited owner could charge his estate (thus committing his successors) to include irrigation, reclamation from the sea, fencing, construction of roads, tramways,

[14] J. Caird (1), p. 328.
[15] See p. 21.

railways and canals, the building or improvement of farm houses, cottages and steadings, sluices, jetties, planting shelter belts, etc., 'provided that the Commissioners shall be satisfied that such works will add to the permanent value of the lands to be charged to an extent equal to the expense thereof'. In addition to all these schemes, the Inclosure Commissioners also supervised, under the Land Drainage Act, 1861, the setting up of thirteen Commissions of Sewers covering 31,000 acres and twenty-nine Drainage Districts covering 68,000 acres, with powers to improve and repair existing watercourses and outfalls. The costs incurred by these bodies were obtained by imposing a drainage rate on the land improved by their operations.

These loans from the Government and from public companies provided a real opportunity for limited owners, and also of course for unencumbered landlords who might not have much spare capital. The interest rates were low, compared with the market; the time for repayment was generous, and skilled advice was available from the office of the Commission. The need to prepare a scheme for improvement and to submit it to the Commission was distasteful to some landowners. A scheme of land drainage was a straightforward proposition and the return in increased value almost certain. But all these other improvements, highly desirable though they might be, meant having Assistant Commissioners going into estate finances, perhaps altering or turning down the scheme, visiting farms to see if the work was properly done, and all this was an interference with the sacred rights of property which those who had been absolute autocrats on their own domains for so long found hard to stomach. There were complaints that these men from London did not understand local conditions; Scottish landowners thought they demanded too high a standard for labourers' cottages; and it was a grievance that loans were confined to agricultural purposes and could not be given to improve the family mansion – though this was remedied by the Limited Owners Residence Acts of 1870 and 1871. There was the criticism, too, that when a loan was coming from one of the public companies, it was an anomaly to make such a transaction the subject of Government control. But it was the Government's view that the improvement of farming land was a matter of public interest, and that if the money so spent on it were to be a first charge on the estate, then a Commissioner's certificate was absolutely necessary and in the landlord's interest. Moreover, limited owners could not raise loans in any other way.

So the work went on, many landowners taking advantage of the loans, the Commissioners becoming more skilled in their assessments, and the face of the countryside changing as new farm buildings and labourers' cottages replaced the old ramshackle structures on many an estate. Drainage schemes continued to occupy the first place, as they were the most quickly remunerative work a landowner could undertake. It was not always so easy to show a quick return on new farm houses and buildings, and labourers' cottages could not possibly be built to let at economic rents; at the rate of wages then operating, the labourers could not have paid them. But the Commissioners took a wide view of their duties in this direction, realising that if farms were to be profitable they must be furnished with proper accommodation for both man and beast, and that in the long run the estates would benefit from such expenditure.

In 1873, a Select Committee of the House of Lords on the Improvement of Land was set up to review the work of the Commissioners under the 1864 Act and to consider whether any further legislation were necessary. The enquiry covered every side of the improvement work and a picture of great activity emerged from the evidence, with many interesting sidelights on agricultural society and practice.[16]

The Committee did not consider the interest charged by the Commissioners or the Companies was too high, nor the control exercised by them too rigorous, in view of their duty to safeguard the interests of future owners of the estates. While recognising that many owners found control distasteful, the Committee said of the Commissioners 'that they have performed their duties both with ability and courtesy is disputed by no one'. Their recommendations

[16] S.C. 1873 (H.L.) (Lands).

were directed towards making the position of the limited owner a little easier by allowing him to invest trust money upon estate improvement, and by extending the period of repayment of such investments up to forty years. These recommendations were embodied in the Settled Lands Acts of 1882 and 1890, which did not apply to Scotland.

Altogether the Report was a complete endorsement of the work of the Commissioners and the Improvement Companies. But the evidence of Caird and of Bailey Denton, the engineer, stressed that though much had been accomplished, a very great deal more remained to be done before the equipment of the land for farming could be considered really satisfactory and efficient. Caird estimated that only about one-fifth of what ought to be done had been accomplished, while Bailey Denton had calculated that out of twenty million acres of land in England and Wales requiring it, only three million acres had yet been drained.

THE CATTLE PLAGUE

In the 1860s the State was again obliged to intervene in agricultural matters and to act quickly in an emergency. In July 1865 a case of the dreaded rinderpest, generally known as the Cattle Plague, was reported in London and the disease spread quickly over the country. Under an Act of 1848, passed during an outbreak of sheep-pox (which the farmers unkindly called 'Peel's Pox', coming as it did just after the repeal of the Corn Laws) the Privy Council had powers to issue orders for the control and movement of animals. In July and August 1865 they delegated powers to Justices of the Peace to appoint inspectors to enter farms and to slaughter and bury infected animals, to prohibit movement of diseased stock and to close fairs and markets. But more and more animals contracted the disease, till the number reached 10,000, and on 29 September a Royal Commission was appointed to make recommendations to prevent its further spread.

The Commission, headed by Lord Spencer, found unanimously that orders so far issued had been a failure, the number of beasts known to be attacked having then risen to 14,000. Many of the Inspectors were quite unqualified, beasts were sent to the metropolitan market where the disease started and were brought back again, markets were not closed uniformly, for vested interests were too often involved, and there was much evasion of the orders.

But when it came to recommending what should be done, the Commissioners could not agree. The majority, headed by Robert Lowe, wanted to suspend all movement of cattle for a limited time, and to have all foreign cattle slaughtered at the point of landing. But the minority felt that total stoppage of movement was quite impracticable. It would be impossible to enforce all over the country and the price of meat would rise.

No action was taken on this Report [17] and the epidemic continued to spread; by the end of the year the number of animals attacked had reached 73,000, and by the end of January 1866, 120,000. The Royal Agricultural Society sent a deputation to Lord John Russell urging the Government to take strong action, which they set out in detail. [18] On 5 February the Royal Commission issued their Second Report recommending drastic measures. The Cattle Diseases Prevention Act, which became law on 20 February 1866, gave increased powers to magistrates and inspectors to control all movement of cattle and to enter farms and slaughter diseased animals; it also authorised the payment of compensation to farmers for stock slaughtered at the rate of £20 or half the value of the animal when well. This compensation was to come from the county rates, and local authorities were empowered to borrow for it. After the application of these measures, the epidemic abated very quickly and during June only 300 cases were reported.

In spite of heavy criticism in the House of Commons over the proposal to pay compensation to farmers for animals slaughtered

[17] *Report of R.C. to enquire into . . . the Cattle Plague,* 1865 (13530).

[18] J. A. Scott Watson, *History of the Royal Agricultural Society of England, 1839–1939,* London, n.d., pp. 108–12; Arvel B. Erikson, 'The Cattle Plague in England 1865–67', *Agricultural History,* vol 35, No. 2, April 1961, pp. 94–103.

in the public interest in order to control such a major epidemic, the principle was conceded and compensation had come to stay. The Department responsible for administering this Act was the Privy Council, and its Veterinary Department (so designated in 1870) also administered the series of Contagious Diseases (Animals) Acts passed later, and the Destructive Insects Act of 1877.

BOARD OF AGRICULTURE

In 1883, the Veterinary Department became the Agricultural Department of the Privy Council, and took over from the Board of Trade the collection of agricultural statistics; in 1889, in response to a public demand for a single department responsible for all agricultural matters, it became the Board of Agriculture. The new Board took over the powers and duties of both the Agricultural Department and the Land Commission, and was made responsible for the administration of other matters relating to agriculture and forestry which might arise in Great Britain.[19] To ensure it a good send-off with the agricultural interest, Sir Henry Chaplin, a popular land owner, was made the first President of the Board, and Sir James Caird became a member. Its most important new function was to help and encourage agricultural education, through a grant of £5,000 distributed among schools where instruction was given in agriculture or forestry.[20] This was the start of one of the most hopeful developments of the twentieth century, which is described in Chapter 13.

[19] In 1911 a separate Board of Agriculture for Scotland was established in Edinburgh.
[20] Sir Francis Floud, *The Ministry of Agriculture and Fisheries*, London, 1927, Ch. I.

8

The Farm Workers
1851-1875

The Slow Improvement – Child Labour – The Royal Commission of 1867 – Feeing Markets – Canon Girdlestone – The Beginning of Combination – Joseph Arch – The Lock-out of 1874.

THE SLOW IMPROVEMENT

WITH the passing of the 'Hungry Forties', conditions were never again quite so bad for the farm workers. The gradual relaxation and final repeal of the Acts of Settlement combined with the building of railways to make it easier to travel about Britain in search of work, and the chronic under-employment in many southern areas showed some diminution. Farming prices and profits improved after 1852; more land under cultivation, more fields drained, bigger crops and more livestock on farms, all added up to increased employment, though it seldom equalled the increase in the number of boys born in rural parishes, who naturally sought work first on the farms.

Just as the relations of landlord and tenant at this time were controlled by custom, not by statute, so were the relations of farmer and worker. It is true that there was the Law of Master and Servant, but this applied only to the contract of service; it was indeed weighted in favour of the master, and pressed more hardly upon Scottish farm servants with their yearly contracts than upon the less mobile English labourers. But since the introduction of the New Poor Law there was no machinery for regulating wages, hours or conditions of work in British agriculture. The nineteenth-century insistence upon freedom of contract and the free play of economic forces normally gave the farmers power to dictate their own terms which the labourers had to accept; they could not live without wages, and in rural areas there was seldom other work to be had. Generally there was a tacit understanding between farmers of one parish or district not to undercut each other nor to attract each other's men away by offering an extra shilling a week. Wages thus came to be regulated by what farmers thought they could afford to pay, and by what the men would put up with, supplemented only by what their wives and children could earn, by what they could get off their allotments (when they had them) and by private charity.

Thomas Hardy has a picture of a hiring fair in Dorset on a wet day, where an old shepherd was leaning on his crook on the pavement waiting to be hired, and he heard the following dialogue:

'There's work in en', says one farmer to another, as they look dubiously across. 'There's work left in en still; but not so much as I want for my acreage.' 'You'd get en cheap', says the other.[1]

Charles Kingsley, no sentimentalist, who had written in 1851 a savage indictment of the treatment of agricultural workers in his novel *Yeast*, wrote in 1859, referring to the workers in the southern counties:

I believe things are improved. Twelve years more of the New Poor Law have taught the labouring men greater self-help and independence; I hope these virtues may not be destroyed in them by the boundless and indiscriminate alms-giving which has become the fashion of the day, in most parishes where there are resident gentry. If half the money which is now given away in different forms to the agricultural poor could be spent in making their dwellings fit for honest men to live in, then life, morals and poor rates would be saved an immense amount. . . . Meanwhile cottage improvement, and sanitary reform, throughout the country districts, are going on at a fearfully slow rate. Here and there high-hearted landlords, like the Duke of Bedford, are doing their duty like men; but in general the apathy of the educated classes is most disgraceful. But the labourers, during the last ten years, are altogether better off. Free-trade has increased their food, without lessening their employment.[2]

This employment was provided at wages which varied widely. The weekly rates often differed by several shillings a week from

[1] Thomas Hardy, 'The Dorsetshire Labourer', in *Longmans Magazine*, July 1883. Excerpts printed in *The Countryman*, vol. 56, Nos. 2 and 3, 1959.

[2] Charles Kingsley, *Yeast*, Preface to 4th edn., London, 1859.

one county to another – from 15*s* a week in Lancashire to 6*s* in Wiltshire. In Scotland the shepherd was the aristocrat of farm workers; on some English farms the cowman or stockman received the highest wage; some wages were calculated on a yearly, and others on a weekly or daily, basis; in some areas men lived in the farm house and received all their food; in others they lived in a bothy and cooked their own meals; sometimes they paid no rent for their cottages, or a nominal one, while elsewhere there were no cottages near the farm, and workers had to find their own accommodation and might have to walk several miles to work. The perquisites received in kind also varied widely. Some farmers would give free milk, but elsewhere, on farms whose milk was made into butter and cheese, it was almost impossible for the workers to get any. Some farmers included in the wages a stone of pork or bacon and a hundredweight of potatoes, elsewhere men might have 'potato ground', land ploughed by the farmers on which they could grow their own potatoes. Some farmers let their labourers keep a pig, others would not. In parts of the lowlands of Scotland, it was the practice for the shepherd to run his own flock of sheep with his master's, and for the labourer to keep a cow with his master's herd. (George Hope of Fenton Barns encouraged all his married labourers to keep a cow, for the sake of their children, and advanced the money for them to buy it.) In many parts of England beer was given as part of the wage, and in the West Country, cider.

A further complication was the amount of work done on piece rates. Much of the field work, such as weeding and hoeing, was taken by the piece, as was the winning of the harvest in the eastern counties and elsewhere. Then again, local custom restricted the performance of certain tasks to certain classes of worker. In Wales all the milking and dairy work was done by women; elsewhere men often did the milking. In the Lothians, women were employed to fill the muck carts and to empty them on the fields, a job which elsewhere no woman would touch.

With all these variations in the methods of payment and in the manner of working, it is hardly possible to estimate what the 'average farm worker' earned at any date; indeed, farmers and labourers themselves were often hard put to it to ascertain such a fact. A contemporary writer, discussing whether a farmer really knew what his labour bill was, says: 'Wages are not represented by 13s or 14s in money, but by a mixed payment in coin and kind, not easily estimated; varying as rents, cottage accommodation and size of garden do vary even in the same parish and upon the same occupation; and misleading not only outside critics, but the very parties to the contract, who see only dimly where they stand.'[3]

What can be established is that farm wages were generally higher in the industrialised north and Midlands, where alternative work could be easily obtained, than in the south of England, where the decay of the old crafts had left a surplus of labour dependent upon agriculture. The returns of the Poor Law Commissioners also show that the percentage of paupers in the population was consistently higher in counties of low agricultural wages, ranging from 7.2 per cent in Wiltshire at the bottom of the wage scale to 2.4 per cent in Derbyshire near the top.[4] The scanty evidence also indicates that wages generally rose in the 1850s, with the improved profits of farming; though the rise was not everywhere maintained, wages seem never again to have fallen as low as they were in the 1840s, and the rise was resumed in the 1860s. In Chart III an index of average weekly earnings of farm workers summarises the main trends, so far as these can be ascertained from the fragmentary data.

CHILD LABOUR

The more glaring evils of child labour in industry had been brought under control by the Factory Acts of 1835 and 1847, inspired by the work of Lord Shaftesbury. The Poor Law Commission on the employment of women and children had commented unfavourably in 1843 upon the gangs in which many worked,

[3] F. Clifford, 'The Labour Bill in Farming', *J.R.A.S.E.*, vol. 11/ii, 1875, p. 117; G. Houston, 'Farm Wages in Central Scotland from 1814 to 1870', *J.R.S.S.*, vol. 118, 1955, pp. 224–8.
[4] F. G. Heath, *The English Peasantry*, London, 1874, Ch. 1.

particularly in the eastern counties of England, but no legislation had resulted. During the 1860s Medical Officers of Health drew attention to the high rate of infant mortality in some of these areas, which they attributed, together with many premature births and miscarriages, to the effects of the gang system on the health of women workers. These allegations were referred to the Children's Employment Commission, which published, in one of its annual reports, a survey of conditions in agricultural gangs.[5] There were public gangs, organised by gangmasters who contracted with farmers for certain kinds of work, and who moved their gangs from farm to farm as they were needed; and there were private gangs, which individual farmers collected for work only on their own farm. The work, payment, and conditions varied enormously, some gangs being well-conducted and reasonably paid, while others were highly undesirable. There were complaints that children were sent to the gangs too young, some from six years old; that they often had to walk several miles to work; that the hours were too long and the work too heavy; that they did not get any education; that some of the gangmasters and supervisors were brutal and knocked the children about; that mothers went to the gangs either leaving their babies unattended at home, or taking them into the fields and leaving them for hours under a hedge, sometimes drugged with opium to keep them quiet; that boys and girls were put to work together with disastrous effects on their behaviour and morals; that the girls became bold and slatternly, and as they grew up did not make good servants or mothers; that the women neglected their homes and that their language was often appalling.

The gangs varied greatly in size, anything from ten to a hundred persons, and the work they did varied also. Young children were employed in stone-picking and weeding, the older ones and the women in weeding, turnip singling, potato setting, hoeing, gathering root crops and so on.[6] Gangwork was deemed necessary in these eastern counties of large arable farms, and where newly

[5] *Sixth Report of the Children's Employment Commission,* (1862) 1867.
[6] See Chapter 4, p. 116.

reclaimed land required much hand work to get it clean. Many farms had an inadequate number of cottages, usually reserved for the 'confined' men, so labour had to be brought from a distance. The ill-paid day-labourers could not object to their wives and children earning a little, and many of the women and young people preferred field labour to work indoors. For the farmers it was cheap if inefficient labour, and often it was all they could get. But the work was clearly too heavy for little children, and the Gangs Act, passed in 1869, was aimed chiefly at their protection.

The Act laid down that no child under the age of eight was to work in a gang; gangmasters were to be licensed by two magistrates, who were also to control the distance which a gang might travel to work; mixed gangs of males and females were no longer allowed, and a licensed gangmistress was to accompany any gang of girls; publicans were not to be licensed as gangmasters; and for any breach of regulations the farmer on whose land the gang worked was liable as well as the gangmaster. The Act did not apply in Scotland, for few children were there employed in public gangs.

But there were many children working on the land who were not in such gangs. Boys began farm work very young, first on bird-scaring and then on all sorts of jobs, leading horses, herding, cleaning turnips and so on. George Edwards started work at six years old and was paid 1*s* a week.[7] Albert Pell, landowner and Tory M.P., who farmed in the Fens, has this to say upon child labour:

No statute restricted or regulated the hours of the child's work on the farm, and when in after life I drafted and carried the first Act of Parliament framed to spare the little limbs, I did it at the risk of my seat. I remember particularly the indignant remonstrances of a neighbouring squire, the father of a family of about ten children, on whom he doted, and whose happiness and health were his constant care. I asked him how he would tolerate his boys of eight to ten years of age driving plough on a heavy clay fallow. Did he know what it meant? I thought not. If we suppose that the conventional acre was ploughed between six and two o'clock, the child would have to walk in the blazing sun on a baked soil, or, in wet times, clogged with clay on his feet, from eleven to twelve

[7] See Chapter 3, p. 71.

miles a day (including, say, a mile's trudge from home and a mile back again) directing the movements and stimulating the actions of three, perhaps four, monstrous creatures who submitted to his presumptuous orders and infantile oaths with slavish docility and soft mild eyes. It was a marvellous sight to see these little dots get a collar on the necks of their plough-teams. First they reached it down from the bracket overhead with a hay-fork, then they hoisted it into the manger, then they scrambled after it themselves, then, drawing the huge animal's head towards them, with much exhortation 'to be quiet' and 'now then, what are you at?' they lifted the heavy harness over the head and ears on to the neck, and jumped down for the hames. All this was carried out with a very jaunty air of superiority to the other little chaps waiting at the yard gates for the ganger to take them to the monotonous toil of stone-picking, pulling charlock, or, worse than all, bird-scaring.[8]

Children of family farmers might work even harder than those of the labourers, and often the amount of schooling they got was negligible. In the 1860s little more than half the children in the country were receiving any education at all; but men were beginning to realise the need for more and better schools, and that the State must provide them. The extension of the franchise to town workers in 1867 provoked the phrase attributed to Robert Lowe, 'We must educate our masters.' Forster's Education Act of 1870 set up School Boards for new schools, but also provided grants to existing voluntary schools. The Agricultural Children's Act, 1873, directed that no child under eight might be employed in agriculture, but it was soon out of date, for in 1876 education was made compulsory for all children up to the age of fourteen or until passing the fourth standard. Country children between eight and ten were still allowed to work in harvest, and after ten they could get more release for farm work provided they put in a certain number of attendances at school.

Thus step by step child labour in agriculture was reduced and education provided, not without considerable opposition from some farmers, who wanted cheap boy labour, and from some labourers, who wanted the children's wages and grudged the pence they still had to pay, for education did not become free until 1891. But many welcomed it, realising that their children

[8] T. Mackay, *The Reminiscences of Albert Pell*, London, 1908, p. 141.

would have a better chance than they had had themselves, and some of them were first taught to read by their own offspring. It was now assured that the rising generation would at least be literate, though the peculiar provision of the Act resulted in the brightest children leaving school earlier than the others.

THE ROYAL COMMISSION, 1867

The report which led up to the Gangs Act disclosed other abuses, so in 1867 a new Royal Commission was appointed to enquire into the employment of children, young persons and women in agriculture throughout the United Kingdom, and to find out if further legislation was required to protect these classes. The Commission soon realised that if it were to do a thorough job it must also examine the conditions of men's work in agriculture, and the reports of its Assistant Commissioners give a comprehensive picture of the labour scene at this time.[9]

(a) *England*

The Commission confirmed the great variety of working customs still found over the country. In some areas, women worked on the land as a matter of course, doing most of the jobs men did, except work with horses. In others, they worked only at harvest time, or at special jobs like fruit-picking, hop-picking and so on. It seems to have been largely a matter of tradition. In some parts there were domestic industries where they could get alternative work, such as straw-plaiting, lace-making and glove-making, so here they did not work regularly on the land. Those who did so were paid at a lower rate than the men, varying from 7*d* to 1*s* 6*d* a day, and women working in gangs earned rather more than women working singly.

The picture that emerges of conditions in the northern counties is altogether much brighter than in the rest. In Northumberland men still boarded in the farmhouse, and were engaged and paid

[9] R.C. Employment, 1867; for a detailed analysis of these Reports, see W. Hasbach, *A History of the English Agricultural Labourer*, London, 1908, App. VI.

by the year. Married men still received much of their wage in kind, and their daughters worked in the fields, but the unpopular 'bondager' system was dying out, and children did not go regularly to work until they were fourteen. Fuel was cheap and the people well-fed and healthy. Much the same conditions prevailed in Cumberland, Westmorland, Lancashire, Yorkshire and Durham, men and women servants living in the farmhouses and the tendency was to save and marry late. There was therefore less demand for allotments in the north.

Over the rest of the country, wages were highest in the vicinity of manufacturing towns or industries, and allowances in kind were decreasing. There was no overtime pay, but men were sometimes given beer or food if they worked late. The lowest earnings were in Shropshire, Wiltshire, Devon and Dorset, though wages were low for day-labourers in the eastern counties. The reports frequently condemned bad housing and sanitary conditions, with commendation of some landowners who were trying to improve them.

The Commission interpreted its mandate widely, and discussed why children were working instead of being in school, and how the whole standard of life and morals of rural workers might be raised. There was approval for the 'cowgates' found in Rutland, Cheshire, Shropshire and Derbyshire, where some landowners commonly let two or three acres of grass to labourers to enable them to keep cows. This raised the whole character of the labouring population and encouraged them to be thrifty. A good cow would produce enough butter in summer to sell for 6s or 7s a week, besides milk for the family. The pioneer of this had been Lord Tollemache, an intelligent landowner who was deeply concerned for the well-being of his tenants and dependants.

Of course this system was only possible in grassland areas and then only for comparatively few of the labourers, and the Commission was inclined to think that the Scottish system of keeping the labourers' cows with the farm herd was a better one. But such workers as were able to have a little cowgate holding of this kind were often in a better position financially than many small farmers.

(b) *Wales*

In South Wales the Commission found a great change for the better in the condition of the labouring classes since the opening of the South Wales Railway. Many had migrated to work in the coal mines and iron works, and for those who were left cash wages had nearly doubled. They fed better, but cottages were generally very bad, particularly those built by squatters on the wastes, and those on the outskirts of large towns. Two small rooms and a loft above was the usual pattern, with no water or sanitation. Some of the big landowners had built new cottages with four rooms, but the poverty of so many of the smaller landowners, whose estates were heavily burdened, prevented much expenditure in this direction. The bad housing and overcrowding led to much immorality, but the Commissioners were told that public opinion generally held that marriage cancelled any previous immorality, and that there was little infidelity afterwards.

All over Wales the social division between farmer and labourer was much more blurred than in England. Most Welsh farms were so small that many of them employed no hired labour at all; others took boys to board in the farmhouse for part of the year, and labouring parents were glad of this, as the children were better fed than at home, and grew strong even if they were hardworked. Girls went as farm servants at about twelve years old, and as well as working in the house had to help on the farm, in the dairy, feeding stock, and so on.

Fewer older women than before worked on the land, but here again conditions varied. There were some larger farms, and on one of 400 acres the Commissioners found nineteen girls employed, in all kinds of work except that with horses; they were paid 8*d* a day and lived at home. In parts of North Wales children were employed for potato planting, and of course at harvest time.

The children's education suffered by their leaving school early or only attending for part of the year, and the Commission's comments on elementary education were not very favourable. Many teachers were untrained and very badly paid, 10s or 11s a week. The language difficulty slowed up progress, as many children arrived at school knowing no English. There were not enough schools, and they were badly distributed; often two small inefficient ones were to be found in a place where one would have been adequate, owing to the unfortunate rivalry between the Established Church and the Nonconformists, both of whom insisted on having their own schools. This, and the generally prevailing poverty of the country, combined to prevent much progress in education. As one farm labourer put it, 'Education is a good thing, but bread for a poor man is better.' But it was not only the farm workers who sent their children out to work when they ought to have been at school. According to Mr Culley, one of the Assistant Commissioners, 'The small farmer lives harder, employs his children earlier, and gives them less education than the ordinary agricultural labourer.'[10]

There was adverse criticism of the hiring fairs from some of the land agents and ministers who were interviewed. They maintained that they were rowdy and demoralising affairs, 'the curse of the country', which made the farm servants restless, staying only a year in one place so that they might come back to the Fair next year. As it was their one holiday when they could meet their fellows, when each pub had its fiddler and they could dance in the evening, it is not surprising that the fairs were popular with the young farm servants.

The general picture of farm labour in Wales is on the whole happier than that in England. There was no spectre of unemployment, and when everyone was poor together, with few resident gentry, there was a closer community spirit and more neighbourliness, while the chapel was generally the centre of social life. Labourers who did not migrate to industry might in time get a little land and become small farmers themselves, they were not a class apart as they were in England.

[10] R.C. Employment, 1867, *Third Report*, 1870 (C. 70), pp. 16, 130.

(c) *Scotland*

The evidence taken by the Commission disclosed conditions of infinite variety in Scotland. It was taken from ministers of religion, schoolmasters, doctors, landlords or their factors, farmers, farm servants, labourers, women and child workers, and from all this a composite and very human picture of the social scene emerges.

Everyone was agreed that there were no organised gangs of women and child workers in Scotland, except for a very few in Kirkcudbrightshire who came out from Gatehouse for turnip thinning and were well-conducted, and some in Lanarkshire for potato lifting. All were agreed, too, that though women and children did work on the farms, there was no oppression or ill-treatment, and no injury to health. Children were rarely employed before the age of nine or ten and then only in the summer months for herding, and even this was much reduced owing to the spread of wire fencing. They also helped in the harvest, tying bands and so on, and sometimes did weeding. Boys were seldom taken on full time before the age of fourteen. On the other hand, some schoolmasters complained bitterly of the summer break from May to October, as children who went out working then found it difficult to settle down in the autumn to their books and catch up with the others. But the parents needed their wages and the farmers their work. As one farmer put it: 'Require to be gay and mischievous to cowherd. Have to keep a boy for it. Came young but is getting over big for it. Get them at first for their meat and a pair of trousers. Giving now 30*s* the half year, but is doing other things now.' But another farmer said of boys, 'You will not get anything but mischief out of them.'

On the general subject of education the Commission said:

In the rural districts of England ... the farmers are too often opposed to education, the labourers, and sometimes the landowners themselves, are indifferent about it; and it happens not unfrequently that the clergyman is the only person in the parish who takes any interest in it, and struggles in vain ... against an unyielding mass of opposition or indifference. In Scotland the feelings of the people on this subject are totally different. There all classes, farmers and servants, ministers and laymen, are unanimous in their conviction of the importance of education, and are willing to co-operate for the purpose of securing it.[11]

Another important difference between the two countries was that Scottish children did homework, in which the parents encouraged and helped them. As the wife of a ploughman at Corstorphine said, 'We just keep our children at school till they are educated. It's all we've got to give them, poor things, and we do what we can to make them scholars.' Another mother in Berwick said of her three children, 'I want to make them good scholars. I don't want them to be hinds draggling on the land all their lives if they can better themselves.'

On the large sheep farms in hill country, far from schools, it was the practice of five or six shepherds to join together to keep a tutor for their children, who boarded week about with the families. He was generally 'a young lad or an old man who is good for nothing else', so possibly his teaching was not very skilled, but it was better than nothing, and the practice indicates what the Scots felt about education.

In Perthshire Lord Kinnaird had started weekly evening classes for ploughmen, which seemed to be very successful, from the evidence of the enthusiastic Mr Duncan, the schoolmaster who ran them. There was an average attendance of about 300 and the course wound up with a good supper and entertainment. The men showed a real love of learning and a desire to improve their position, and the courses had a favourable effect on their intelligence and manners. One would like to know the subsequent history of this early attempt at further education by this enlightened landowner.

Most people admitted that wages were higher and conditions better than they had been twenty years earlier. Farm workers still received part of their wages in kind, though one farmer in Dumfries-shire said he gave his ploughmen £32 a year and a cottage rent free, with no perquisites, and he did not allow them to keep a pig. (The cottage of the head ploughman, according to his wife,

[11] R.C. Employment, 1867, *Fourth Report*, 1870 (C. 221), p. 17.

was a one-roomed one in which they lived with eight children.) The married farm workers seemed to be content to have part of their wage in kind, which took various forms in different parts of the country. Mr Culley, who wrote on the south-east of Scotland in the Fourth Report of the Commission, has this to say of his area:

Not as a necessary, but as a very natural accompaniment of the farm cottage and yearly hiring comes the payment in kind, a custom which prevails generally throughout my district, with however some exceptions which I am afraid indicate its extinction or at least curtailment at no very distant date. Payment in kind reaches its widest development in the Border Counties, where a 'hind' or ploughman receives only £5 in money, the rest of his wage consisting of a cottage and garden, rent free, the keep of a cow, carriage of fuel, potato ground, and certain allowances of oats (or oatmeal), barley and peas; in Perthshire the grain payments are reduced to an allowance of oatmeal, and instead of the cow's keep a Scotch pint of new milk is given daily, the money wage being increased to £20. The change from what may be called the meal and milk system of Perthshire and Fife, to the cow and grain payments of the Border counties takes place gradually from about the line of the Forth. South of the Forth the daily allowance of milk ceases, but it is not until you enter Haddingtonshire that you find the cow's keep established as part (a very important part) of the hind's wage. Formerly hind's cows were common enough in both West and Mid Lothian, but there is now no such useful institution on any of the farms I visited in the former county, nor in the northern or more populous part of the latter. Elsewhere, too, where cows are still the rule, there are signs that the hind may soon lose this, to his family, the most important item in his list of payments in kind.

Mr Culley makes it clear that there was nothing static in the farm workers' conditions of life, and this is borne out by reports from other areas. Mr Boyle in the south-west found that near large towns farm wages were paid entirely in cash, but that as he went north more was paid in kind, and that in the Highlands very little money passed. The cash received by ploughmen ranged from £32 a year in Kirkcudbright to £8 in Caithness and £5 on the Border.

Conditions in the far north and west of the country, in the crofting counties, showed that many of the crofters had a lower standard of living than the farm servants. Gunn, the factor to the Duchess of Sutherland, said that those with crofts of under twelve acres could not support a family without doing other work. In Inverness, Ross and Cromarty, Caithness and Sutherland, nearly all the larger farms drew their labour from among the crofters and their families. In Caithness land reclamation was still going on and small farms were being carved out of the waste. But according to one doctor who gave evidence, though cottages here were improved, there were still some where the family and the cows used the same door. Extreme poverty and uncertainty were still the general lot of the crofter, as is shown by the evidence given to the Commission.

A crofter in Sutherland told them that he had 4 acres of arable land which he cultivated with a spade, and hill pasture for 4 cattle and 20 sheep, at a rent of £2 per annum. But 'I had about six sheep last summer, but four of them died during the winter and the remaining two are just about the house. . . . I have got a cow up the hill and a young beast here. . . . I never sell anything off my land.'

But in spite of all the hardships of the life, the crofters valued their independence and resisted any attempts at amalgamation of holdings. They would go off and work for wages, but all the time they felt that they were their own masters, with their own croft to come back to.

Side by side with the crofters were to be found the Scottish shepherds. In the north they worked on the great sheep farms carved out in the Highlands after the Clearances; while along the Border and in the south-west they worked on large mixed farms in the hill country. In all these areas the Commission found that shepherds were the best paid and most highly responsible of Scottish farm servants. It was calculated that their income was about £60 a year, almost entirely in perquisites. The practice of a shepherd having his own flock of sheep which he ran with his master's was beginning to die out, the man being paid a higher cash wage instead, but the old system was still common. Mr James Coulthead, a shepherd in Selkirk, described his conditions to the Commission. A shepherd had to look after 25 to 40 score sheep himself; if there were more he had a helper. He had his own flock of about fifty, which he reckoned were worth 8s to 10s a head. Then he had a free house and garden, a cow, 65 stones of oatmeal, 1000 yards of potatoes planted for him – he finding the seed – four tons of coal at pitmouth prices, or as many peats as he liked, led free. Others were allowed all the braxy sheep, then defined as sheep that died by disease or accident, or grazing for a few stirks, or hide to make shoes. It was an isolated life, so shepherds had to be provided with everything they needed in the way of food and fuel, living as they did far from other sources of supply. We have seen how they tried to provide for their children's education by hiring their own tutor. The general opinion was that they were a fine body of men, often well-educated and great readers themselves, but from the nature of their work taking little part in community life.

All over Scotland women worked on the farms, at any rate in the summer, and sometimes all the year round. Their wages ranged from 1s 4d a day in the south to 8d in the north. The bondager system was dying out, as in the north of England, though it was still to be found in Berwick and Roxburgh. In districts where there were few cottages near the farm, farmers got the female labour they needed by having girls on the bothy system.

The subject of bothies, both male and female, was carefully examined by the Commission. They were mostly to be found in the north-east, but sometimes in the south and west. Whether bothies were well-conducted or not depended entirely upon the character of the farmer. One Assistant Commissioner visited fifteen bothies in Caithness, and found that all except three of them were poor, cheerless places, with the barest minimum of rough furniture, where the farmers showed no sense of responsibility for the comfort and well-being of the young men. The practice of having the men to feed in the farm kitchen was passing, and most of them got their own meals, consisting almost entirely of oatmeal, milk and potatoes, in the bothy. Where both girls and men were housed on a farm conditions were often very undesirable, their sleeping quarters too near together and so on, with disastrous effects on their morals. On the other hand, where the gudeman and his wife exercised a proper supervision, and relations between them and their servants were happy, the Commission saw no objection to the system, and indeed, in the prevailing shortage of cottages, there was no other way of getting the farm work done. As the young people rarely stayed for more than a year on any farm, they got plenty of variety, both in work and in living conditions. Also, living in bothies, they rarely spent any money, and the Commission commented on the thriftiness of Scottish workers compared with their English counterparts. It was not uncommon for a man to have saved £40 or £50 before his marriage and the girls likewise generally had a nest-egg put by. This made a good start to married life, but the problem then was to find a farm on which there was a cottage available.

The shortage of cottages and the inadequacy of most of them was a complaint throughout the whole country. One farmer in Dumfries said: 'There are no cottages on my farm and very few in the parish, and most of those are very bad. The landlords have pulled many down, and have not built others. I am of the opinion that much of this want of cottage accommodation arises from a desire to protect game.'

Conditions in the south were slightly better than those in the north, and a few of the great landlords had built new and better houses. The Duke of Buccleugh claimed to have spent £50,000 on them, and the Duke of Argyll, the Earl of Selkirk, the Earl of Stair and Lord Lothian had done much on their estates; but the prevailing type was still the one-roomed house, with built-in box beds, though some had two rooms.

In parts of Aberdeenshire there were no cottages on the farms and a married worker had to live in a bothy himself and house his family in the nearest town, coming home to see them only at intervals, while they lived in great poverty without him. The doctors and ministers who gave evidence strongly condemned the bad housing for its effect both on health and morals. Pulmonary consumption, bronchitis and rheumatism were frequent, while the ministers were concerned at the high rate of illegitimacy; though what one of them called 'pre-nuptial fornication' was all too common, after marriage the couples rarely strayed. This was was to be found in Wales, and is probably the pattern of behaviour of peasant communities the world over.

Clearly public opinion was concerned at the state of housing, and farmers testified that they got better workers, who settled down and stayed with them, on farms where there were good cottages. One or two agents were inclined to say that farm servants preferred one-roomed cottages, that they could not afford to furnish anything larger and would not know what to do with it if they had more space; but this opinion was not borne out by the workers themselves.

FEEING MARKETS

All through the century it was the practice of Scottish farm workers to move frequently from one employer to another, and this practice was encouraged by the annual or biennial hiring markets where they were engaged for the coming year or half-year. As the time of the next hiring fair approached, both master and man waited to see whether the other would come and ask if the engagement should continue for another year. This 'speaking time' was a piece of ritual requiring very nice timing. Neither party wanted to appear too anxious, but if the farmer knew he had a good man, he must not wait too long or another farmer might engage him before the day of the hiring market. The man might be quite contented with his place, but did not want to miss the pleasures of the hiring fair or to let his master think he was satisfied with all the conditions of service; some weeks of manœuvring might take place before the matter was settled one way or another. Married men tended to stay in the same place longer than single ones, especially if they had a good cottage, but even they would move after two or three years to try their luck elsewhere.

The day of the hiring market was the farm worker's only holiday, and naturally he made the most of it; and as the only amusements offered by the town in which it was held were drink and women, the day was dreaded by the godly and respectable of the neighbourhood. In 1859, the Highland and Agricultural Society set up a Committee to enquire into and report on the various methods of engaging farm workers, male and female, and to find out whether it would be possible to dispense altogether with hiring markets.[12] The Committee sent out a number of schedules to 'influential individuals and leading agriculturists'. From their replies it appeared that the 'highest class of servants' were engaged privately, by local enquiries, and that these were often taken on on a monthly basis, but tended to stay in their places longer than those who were engaged by the half-year. They were given two holidays in the year, avoiding the days of the hiring markets, so that they could not easily go off and get another situation. Other farmers found they could get labour through advertisements in the local newspapers, and in some towns there were registry offices in which names could be entered. It appeared that hiring markets were the general practice except in one or two counties, such as Ross-shire and Wigtownshire, but great dissatisfaction was expressed at the way in which they were held. Masters were not able to make enquiries about the characters of the men and women they were engaging, drunkenness and immorality were rife for the rest of the day, and the existence of the market encouraged the desire of farm servants to change their situations so often. The Committee thought there should be more Registry Offices, and made various suggestions for improving the conduct of the markets. They did not extend their enquiries to the farm servants themselves. The markets meant a day out for them which they would not willingly forgo, when they could meet their fellows and enjoy themselves.

The Highland and Agricultural Society produced another report in 1872, which again urged the formation of Registry Offices, and added that if better cottage accommodation were provided on farms, men might not be so anxious to change their places every year.[13] But hiring fairs went on until well into the twentieth century as part of the normal pattern of Scottish life.

[12] *Tr. H.A.S.*, vol. 17.iii, 1859; vol. 18.iii, 1860, pp. 387–92.
[13] *Tr. H.A.S.*, vol. 5.iv, 1873, pp. 311–15.

CANON GIRDLESTONE

In the year 1862 the Rev. Edward Girdlestone, a Canon of Bristol, moved from a parish in Lancashire to become Vicar of Halberton, a small village in North Devon. The contrast between the conditions of life of the comparatively well paid labourers in the north and those he found in his new parish filled him with horror. Wages in Devon were 7*s* to 8*s* a week, with an allowance of poor quality cider. Carters and shepherds got a shilling a week more, or a free cottage. Sometimes there was an allowance of wheat at a fixed price all the year round, but as this was generally 'tailings', it was of little benefit. There were no other perquisites, and workers were forbidden to keep pigs, for fear they should steal pig food. Their diet consisted of 'tea-kettle broth', i.e. hot water poured on bread crusts, with a raw onion; bread and cheese, potatoes and cabbage, with occasionally a little meat on Sundays. Women earned 7*d* or 8*d* a day, and housing was very bad.[14] Remonstrances to the farmers had no effect except to make the Canon unpopular. Then, during the cattle plague of 1866, he preached on the text 'Behold the hand of the Lord is upon thy cattle', and roundly told the farmers that the plague was a judgment upon them for their treatment of their labourers. This provoked bitter fury, and farmers retaliated by 'withdrawing their hassocks' and leaving the Church for the nearest Nonconformist chapel.

Girdlestone realised that if some of the surplus labour of the Devon villages could be moved away, wages for those left might rise, according to the law of supply and demand. He wrote to *The Times*, describing the labourers' conditions and asking for offers of work elsewhere, to which he got a considerable response, as well as subscriptions. He then set himself to organise a regular system of migration from Devon to farms in the north of England. The labourers were at first apathetic and frightened at the thought of moving. Everything had to be done for them, their packing superintended, their tickets taken, they and their families and

---

[14] This description of conditions comes from a letter of Canon Girdlestone's quoted in F. G. Heath, *The English Peasant*, London, 1874, ch. v.

goods taken to the station and put on the train, etc. Between 1866 and 1872, when Girdlestone left Halberton, between 400 and 500 men, many with their families, had been moved from this and from neighbouring villages. Most of them went to farms in the north of England, but some into the police force in Yorkshire and Manchester. Once the movement had started and news came of the migrants settling down and doing well, Devon labourers became more willing to move, and the exodus went on even after the Canon had left. During these six years he himself was subjected to every kind of abuse, vilification and social ostracism, not only from farmers, but from local squires and clergy. Perhaps Girdlestone's greatest service to farm workers was the publicity he got for them. His letters to *The Times* attracted attention, and his contests with farmers, the unseemly brawls in which he was involved at vestry meetings and before the local Bench, were widely reported and even got into *Punch*. At the same time the Reports of the 1867 Royal Commission were being read, so that when farm workers began to help themselves, there was no lack of informed support from other sections of the community.

THE BEGINNING OF COMBINATION

At a time when workers in the towns were beginning to organise for the purpose of raising wages and improving conditions, farm workers, though out of touch with the rest of the country, were also inspired to make sporadic attempts in the same direction. Little is known about these, but occasional evidence crops up which indicates that they may have been fairly widespread, but limited to single farms or parishes, shortlived and with no sort of regular organisation. Two instances from England may be quoted. In 1848, Sir John Boileau, a Norfolk landowner and magistrate, was summoned by the police to deal with a strike of labourers from three parishes. He found 100 men assembled in the road, and their spokesman, 'a manly specimen of a British peasant' asked that the Board of Guardians should fix a higher wage for farm workers. Sir John explained to them that the Guardians and magistrates had no such powers, that wages were a matter of agreement between masters and men, but he added, 'It is my own feeling that wages ought to be raised to keep pace with the great rise in the price of provisions.' He had raised the wages of his own workmen two days before, and he went on, 'I firmly believe that the same right spirit will be found in the farmers and other employers if you go each to your own master and respectfully and properly show your case. But assembling together to obtain your object by intimidation or by stopping others from work cannot be allowed and you will get into trouble.'[15]

Another instance comes from Berkshire in 1866, in the form of a letter addressed by eighteen farm workers to Mrs Hannah Tull of Peasmore Farm, near Newbury, explaining why they had struck work and setting out their grievances as to hours, wages and perquisites. It is phrased most 'respectfully and properly', in almost biblical language. After comparing themselves to the Israelites in Joseph's time since the death of 'our dear *Mr Tull*', they go on 'Many of us with our *wifes* and 4 or 5 *Children* many times sit down to nothing but *Bread* and *Water* and a few *Potatoes* in addition on a *Sunday*, and scarcely any fire to have it by. *Truly* Madam we may say our garden of *roses* as was once the *Pride* of *Berkshire*, now become a *Garden of Bitter Herbs*. We have been asking for the advance of 1/– Per week for a long time but still the answer was *no*.'[16]

Unfortunately history does not relate the outcome of these attempts and others like them. Some may have succeeded, others not, but certainly the feeling among landowners and farmers was that they were at best an impertinence and at worst immoral and dangerous, and that any improvement in conditions must come by favour and not by coercion.

In Scotland the first record of a combination of farm workers goes back to 1805, when the convening of a meeting of ploughmen in the Carse of Gowrie to discuss wages and hours of work was quickly suppressed by the Sheriff with the threat that they would

[15] Owen Chadwick, *Victorian Miniature*, London, 1960, p. 73.
[16] 'A Strike of Farm Workers', *The Countryman*, vol. 56, No. 4. 1959, p. 622.

render themselves liable to imprisonment under the Combination Laws. But in 1834 the men of Perthshire tried again, and held a public meeting in Inchture which was attended by 600 people and which passed resolutions relating to hours of work and over-time pay, and elected a Committee 'to promote by every legal and constitutional means the object we have in view'. Farm servants were urged not to accept engagements from farmers in the forthcoming feeing market unless they complied with the resolutions, and similar bodies were formed in other parts of Perthshire. Comments in the local press condemned the movement, saying that it was inspired by the town unions and was a conse-quence of 'the late introduction of the demon of politics into the country districts', though there was some admission that the farm servants had grievances.[17] But it was not until the 1860s that the trade union movement became widespread among farm servants in the south-eastern part of Scotland. It began in Midlothian with a Farm Servants Protection Society in December 1865, and a num-ber of local societies were formed in other counties to press for improvements in hours and conditions, and in the Border counties for the abolition of the unpopular 'bondager' system. Mr Culley heard evidence from the secretary of the Border Farm Servants Protection Association, which had its headquarters at Jedburgh. It had been founded in 1866 to put down the bondager system and had been very successful at first, though in 1870 it had only sixty members. All farm servants in the borders of Scotland of good moral character were eligible for membership. Any member deprived of work because he took an active and judicious part in the Society's affairs was entitled to receive 6s weekly from the Society's funds, and allowances were made of £3 on the death of a member, £1 for a wife or child and £5 for the death of a cow. The Society intended to get up meetings to petition for household suffrage.[18]

Though these individual societies may not have lasted very long

[17] George Houston, 'Labour Relations in Scottish Agriculture before 1870', *Agric. Hist. Rev.*, vol. VI, Part 1, 1958, p. 38.
[18] R.C. Employment, 1867, *Fourth Report*, 1870, (C. 221), p. 193.

nor have directly achieved very much, they were certainly valuable as a means of ventilating grievances and getting publicity for them, and of educating the whole farming community, farmers and men alike, in the need for discussion and reconsideration of conditions of labour. Moreover, the clauses about mutual help in sickness or unemployment were showing the value of combination. There was no idea yet of a nation-wide union; the outlook of farm workers was still very parochial, for though they frequently changed their jobs from one farm to another, they did not go very far afield. The attitude of Scottish farmers towards combination may be seen in the evidence given by a Perthshire farmer before the same Commission:

Trades unions and strikes among the operatives a few years ago, had a bad effect on our agricultural population. In my own case it led me to part with my foreman or principal servant who had been with me 14 years. In this locality a combination of ploughmen was formed, having for its object to reduce or shorten the hours of labour, and to restrict the labour to a certain kind, at certain hours; that all extra labour beyond that done either at *seedtime* or *harvest even* must be paid for extra (at the rate of 6*d* an hour); that during harvest they must have dinner etc., extra, and that their pay should be quarterly, etc. etc. I and a few of the largest farmers over the county at once determined to oppose any such combination. We would have been willing to pay any wages, but could not submit to be under our servants' control, and we resisted successfully. . . .[19]

The feeing market itself acted in some measure as a trade union. The men attending it exchanged experiences on conditions and rates of wages on different farms, and a farmer who drove too hard a bargain would not easily find the ploughman he needed. Though there was no organisation, there would be a tacit agreement among the men to avoid him. It may be asked why, if the feeing market or hiring fair worked to the advantage of farm workers in Scotland and Wales in the middle decades of the nineteenth century, the same did not apply to Dorset, where annual hirings were still the practice. In Wales and Scotland the farmers were competing for the best workers, whilst in southern England

[19] R.C. Employment, 1867, *Fourth Report*, 1870, (C. 221), App. Part II, p. 96, Evidence of Thomas Ross of Methven, Perthshire.

the workers were competing for places. Dorset workers were far less mobile, there were few local industries where they could get alternative employment, and the spectre of being out of work was always with them, so they were apathetic and took what was offered them without undue bargaining.

The first workers' union worthy the name in England was the Agricultural Labourers' Protection Society, founded in Kent in 1866, and during the next five years similar unions were formed in several other counties, Buckinghamshire, Herefordshire, Hertfordshire and Lincolnshire. The Herefordshire Union, called the West of England Labourers' Improvement Association, was founded in 1870 with the help of the Rev. D. R. Murray, Rector of Brampton Bryan, who became its first President. Their watchword was 'Migration, Emigration and no Strikes', and they had considerable success, wages in Herefordshire rising by 2s a week from their former low level of 9s.

The trade union movement in the country generally was passing through a critical time in the '60s. The era of revolutionary strikes, violence and intimidation was over, and the leadership of the movement had passed into the hands of the London Trades Council and the five able men whom the Webbs call the Junta.[20] By 1875, the position of trade unions had been strengthened by three important Acts: the Law of Master and Servant had been replaced by the Employers and Workmen Act, 1875, which abolished discrimination against the worker, making instead two equal parties to a civil contract; the Trade Union Act, 1871, which gave unions legal recognition and the right to register as Friendly Societies, and thus protected their funds; the Conspiracy and Protection of Property Act, 1875, which allowed peaceful picketing during a strike, heretofore a criminal offence. Moreover the Reform Act of 1867 had given the franchise to town workers. Though there was still much bitterness and enmity towards trade unions in general, the more intelligent employers realised that they had come to stay, had given up refusing to employ union men and were beginning to see that settling disputes by negotiation and

[20] Sidney and Beatrice Webb, *History of Trade Unionism*, London, 1894, ch. v.

arbitration was less expensive than strikes and lockouts. Many thoughtful members of the middle classes, too, were favourable to the movement, and the sacred right of employers to make what bargain they pleased with workers was no longer taken for granted. Thus the stage was set for a big leap forward by the agricultural workers, and at the right moment the leader appeared.

JOSEPH ARCH

The meteoric rise of Joseph Arch, the founding and phenomenal success of the National Agricultural Labourers' Union, and its collapse in a few years, form an epic story which must never be forgotten in the English countryside. Arch, born in 1826, was the son of a farm worker in Barford, Warwickshire, and he went to work at the age of nine, after very little schooling. He was forty-six when the call to action came to him, and by that time he had three priceless assets which fitted him peculiarly for the leadership of his fellows. The first was that he owned his own cottage in Barford, which had been bought by his grandfather for £30. This meant that he was safe from the blackmail which silenced so many farm workers, the fear of losing their homes. Arch's second asset was that he was a fine workman, who early made a study of a new art of hedge cutting. He won prizes in shows for this, and became while still in his teens what he called 'the champion hedger of England'. He was also a fine and quick mower, and he did contract work at piece rates in both mowing and hedging. Thus he was never short of work, and in no danger of losing his job because of his opinions. The pay was good, he could choose his own times, and in the evenings he read and thought, while his knowledge and character were developing. Gradually he travelled further and further afield on his contract jobs, all over the Midland counties and into Wales, and what he saw appalled him. The poverty of his fellow labourers, their dreadful housing conditions, their general apathy and hopelessness made him long to help them to better their lot.

Arch's third great asset was his religion. He had early become disgusted with the Church of England as he saw it manifested in Barford, with its class-consciousness under a supine parson with a tyrannical wife. When the Wesleyans managed to build a chapel in the village, he joined them and here he found what he needed. He soon became a lay preacher and the practice in speaking was invaluable to him in his later work. He says he was 'a natural Nonconformist', and he began to feel himself to be a chosen vessel, a sort of Moses to lead his people out of the house of bondage. As he went about the country, preaching and working, he tried to stir them up with a word in season here and there. He had become convinced that collective action on a wide scale was the only way to improve conditions, though he was determined not to take the initiative in forming a union, but to wait until the workers sent for him. So here he was, independent, supremely confident, convinced of his mission and the justice of the cause, a practised and forceful orator, and when in February 1872 three men knocked on his door one evening and asked him to come over to a meeting at Wellesbourne, he knew that the moment was come. It was a hard winter, work was short, the new Education Act kept the children at school when they might have been earning, and the labourers were desperate. When Arch got to Wellesbourne he found on the village green nearly two thousand men who had come in from all the villages round to hear him. He spoke for an hour, under a chestnut tree by the light of lanterns slung on bean-poles, and the meeting passed a resolution to form a union. Men began to enrol at once, and in Arch's own words

> I knew now that a fire had been kindled which would catch on, and spread, and run abroad like sparks in stubble; and I felt certain that this night we had set light to a beacon, which would prove a rallying point for the agricultural labourers throughout the country.[21]

The response was indeed spectacular. In three weeks there was a membership of 5,000. Farmers round Wellesbourne were presented with a demand for a rise in wages to 16s a week, and when this was refused, the men (that is to say the day labourers, not the shepherds or stockmen) struck work. A few weeks later, a big

[21] Joseph Arch, *The Story of his Life, told by Himself*, London, 1898, p. 74.

demonstration meeting was held at Leamington, in which the Warwickshire Agricultural Labourers' Union was put on a proper footing, with rules and elected officers. Several M.P.s attended this meeting, Auberon Herbert took the chair, there were good press reports and cheques from supporters began to pour in. From the first Arch kept two aims steadily in view. There must be no violence or law-breaking, (in 1872 even peaceful picketing during a strike was a criminal offence); and the union must become a permanent and nation-wide organisation with funds to help wherever it was needed.

Arch was soon receiving requests to start branches in other counties; in May of the same year a Congress was held at Leamington, attended by representatives from twenty-six counties, and the National Agricultural Labourers' Union was fairly launched. This Congress displayed terrific enthusiasm and biblical fervour, with a deep sense of purpose, but the general objects of the National Union, as adopted that day, were practical enough. They were (1) to improve the general condition of agricultural labourers in the United Kingdom; (2) to encourage the formation of Branch and District Unions; (3) to promote co-operation and communication between the unions already in existence.[22]

The Warwickshire farmers, with the spring work crying out to be done, had to come to terms with their striking workers, most of whom got their 16s a week. Meanwhile more and more branches were formed, and by the end of the year union membership stood at 70,000. It was never, even at its peak, a nation-wide union. Some of the earlier unions, such as the Lincolnshire Labour League and the Kentish Association, held aloof, though many of the others were absorbed into the National. Nor did it catch on in the northern counties, where wages were already higher. But in the midland, eastern and southern counties its success was spectacular, while Arch toured the country, making speeches, encouraging the formation of branches, cheering the fainthearted with stories of success elsewhere, and always preaching moderation, patience and non-violence.

[22] Ernest Selley, *Village Trade Unions in Two Centuries*, London, 1919, Ch. iv.

Through 1873 the work continued, money came in from many sympathisers, and the other trade unions were not behindhand in subscribing. Arch was somewhat suspicious of the urban unions, though their advice was valuable and they provided him with many of his best officers, like Henry Taylor, the first general secretary of the National Union. The London Trades Council, too, was instrumental in getting an order prohibiting the sending of soldiers to farms to help get in the harvest when the men were on strike. They were anxious to help the unity of the farm workers' movement, and in 1873 called a meeting in London of representatives from all the unions, but as Arch would not have any union in the National except on his own terms, the Federal Union of Labourers was formed, with a membership of some 50,000.[23] Arch was not an easy man to work with, so certain was he of his divine mission that he would always have his own way, and it was not long before disputes and dissension within the National itself began to appear.

Another embarrassment was the band of Radical gentlemen who had helped in the formation of the union. They saw it as an engine for pressing forward other reforms they had at heart, reforms which would also help the labourer. Free education, extension of the franchise, reform of the Game Laws, land tenure reform, small holdings – each had his own particular political axe to grind and wanted to identify the Union with it. But Arch saw this danger and was determined that to begin with the Union must concentrate on raising wages and must not dissipate its energies. It was becoming clear that Canon Girdlestone was right and that the only hope of keeping wages up was to get some of the surplus labour in the south away. Late in 1873 Arch was sent by the union to Canada to find out what the prospects for labourers would be in the Dominion, and came back with full assurances from the Canadian Government that any men he sent would be looked after and settled on the land. Meanwhile at home membership continued to rise.

It was too good to last. Landowners and farmers at first were

[23] R. Groves, *Sharpen the Sickle! The History of the Farm Workers' Union*, London, 1949, p. 66.

staggered at the widespread movement. Many of them raised their labourers' wages, sometimes after a strike, sometimes for fear of a strike, by as much as 2s a week. But this is not to say that they were reconciled to the idea of labourers combining; far from it. Surprise, then anger, then vindictive reprisal were the stages through which they reacted, and soon the battle was joined. Many union members were sacked, but Arch and his officials were ready for this and helped them to migrate to jobs elsewhere. It is not easy for later generations to realise the rage aroused in most land-owners, farmers and country clergy by the very name of Joseph Arch. He was a rebel, a mischievous agitator, a blasphemer, he was trying to set class against class, to overturn society, and so on and so on. Anyone who associated with him in any way was immediately suspect and they might expect boycott and perse-cution from local society. An old lady living in Oxford in 1961 remembered how, as a small child, she sat on Joseph Arch's knee when he was entertained by her father, a smallholder in an Oxfordshire village. For this 'harbouring of a dangerous rebel', her father's tenancy was terminated and he had to move else-where. The present writer is proud to record that her grandfather, the headmaster of a grammar school in Gloucestershire, took the chair at one of Arch's meetings, a proceeding which roused some of the local farmers to such fury that they removed their boys from his school. These are only two small examples still remembered among the numerous acts of petty tyranny provoked by the move-ment.

The country clergy for the most part either stood aloof or openly opposed the union. The Methodism of its leader and many of his lieutenants was distasteful to them, and the idea of labourers listening to people outside the village instead of to their natural leaders within it seemed to them to cut at the roots of rural society. Moreover those who farmed their own glebes were employ-ers of labour themselves and so could hardly be impartial. Certainly Arch's remarks about them did not help matters, and when Bishop Ellicot of Gloucester hinted that he should be ducked in the horse-pond, in a speech at a farmers' dinner which received wide publicity, the labourers knew that the Church would not help them. The *Labourers Union Chronicle*, an independent weekly started in 1872, which circulated widely among farm workers at that time, had for its sub-title 'An Independent Advocate of the British Toilers Rights to Free Land, Freedom from Priestcraft, and from the Tyranny of Capital'. This paper reported many instances of bullying, eviction, withholding of parish charities from Union men and so on.[24]

But there were notable exceptions in the Church. The Hereford-shire Union had been started and encouraged by several of the local clergy. Men like Canon Girdlestone, James Lee Warner, James Fraser, later Bishop of Manchester, and others went out of their way to help and encourage the Unions, by contributions, by speeches and by writing to the Press. Another valuable ally was Cardinal Manning, to whom Arch paid a warm tribute in his *Autobiography*.

People whose prestige and pockets were not directly concerned by the movement were impressed by Arch when they came in contact with him. Thomas Hardy, writing some years later, said:

Nobody who saw and heard Mr Arch in his early tours through Dorsetshire will ever forget him and the influence his presence exercised over the crowds he drew. He hailed from Shakespeare's country, where the humours of the peasantry have a marked family relationship with those of Dorset men; and it was this touch of nature, as much as his logic, which afforded him such ready access to the hearts and minds of the labourers here. It was impossible to hear and observe the speaker for more than a few minutes without perceiving that he was a humorist – moreover, a man by no means carried away by an idea beyond the bounds of common sense. . . . On the single occasion, several years ago, on which the present writer numbered himself among those assembled to listen to that agitator, there was a remarkable moderation in his tone, and an exhortation to contentment with a reasonable amelioration which, to an impartial auditor, went a long way in the argument. The picture he drew of a comfortable cottage life as it should be was so cosy, so well within the grasp of his listeners' imagination, that an old labourer in the crowd held up a coin between his finger and thumb exclaiming 'Here's zixpence towards that, please God!' 'Towards what?' said a bystander. 'Faith, I don't know that I can spak the name o't, but I know 'tis a good thing,' he replied. . . .

[24] R. Groves, *op.cit.*, p. 58.

The result of the agitation, so far, upon the income of the labourers, had been testified by independent witnesses with a unanimity which leaves no reasonable doubt of its accuracy. It amounts to an average rise of three shillings a week in wages nearly all over the county. The absolute number of added shillings seems small; but the increase is considerable when we remember that it is three shillings on eight or nine.[25]

THE LOCK-OUT OF 1874

By 1873, farmers were beginning to be worried by the spread of the union movement. They hated to be confronted by the printed letter issued by the headquarters of the union to its branches, asking for a rise in wages or a meeting to discuss it,[26] and the feeling was growing that they must organise themselves. It was in the eastern counties that opposition to unionism was strongest. One after another, members of Associations of Agriculture, farmers' societies and discussion clubs pledged themselves not to alter wages and conditions without agreement among themselves, and to help each other during strikes; and many went on to say that they would not employ any union labour in the future. There was a lock-out in part of Essex in 1873, which was successful from the farmers' point of view, and in the following March farmers at Newmarket, faced with another wage demand, met and resolved 'that all union men be locked out after giving one week's notice', and this was taken up all over Suffolk.[27] Soon some 6,000 men were out of work, about two-thirds of them members of the National and the rest members of the Lincolnshire Labour League. Both unions were able to pay their locked-out members, the Lincoln League giving a slightly higher rate. The farmers were out to destroy the unions, and the lock-out quickly spread to the eastern counties, to the Midlands and to Dorset.

It was now a national problem, and supporters of both sides joined in. The urban unions were generous in their contributions, the Amalgamated Society of Engineers leading the way with

[25] Thomas Hardy, 'The Dorsetshire Labourer', *op. cit.*
[26] F. Clifford, *The Agricultural Lockout of 1874*, London, 1875, p. 12.
[27] R. Groves, *op. cit.*, p. 73.

£1,000 to the lock-out funds. The Press, both national and local, was on the whole against the labourers, except for the *Daily News*, but *The Times* sent a special correspondent to East Anglia, whose reports were very fair and balanced. The *Labourers' Union Chronicle* had a wide circulation among farm workers, and there was also the trade union paper, the *Beehive*. Much heat was engendered by a letter to *The Times* from Bishop Fraser of Manchester, beginning 'Are the farmers of England going mad? ... And what can they hope to gain by this ill-advised procedure? They may drive their best labourers either to the other side of the Atlantic or into some new employment; they may fill the workhouses with able-bodied men and women, stripped of their homes and all that has made life, amid their many hardships, still dear to them. But will they have settled the wage question, will they have improved their own condition or prospects?' ...[28]

Some members of the middle classes were alarmed at the spectre of a 'peasants' war', though actually there was no violence or destruction, even when blackleg labour from the towns was brought in to keep the farm work going. Some of those who realised that the farm workers had a case were distrustful of what they called 'professional agitators'. They were concerned at an attempt to raise wages above what they called 'the natural level', whatever that was, and appealed to economics to prove that the farmers could not afford to pay any more. Others again, realising the harm the lock-out was doing to both parties, sought to bring them together by arbitration, but with little success.

The case for the farmers was put in a pamphlet by 'A Farmer of the Wilford Hundred' (the district round Woodbridge), which was quoted by *The Times*' Correspondent.[29] Its main thesis was the old one that wages were a matter to be settled between farmer and labourer and that outsiders must not interfere; and it went on to attack the organisers of the Union for the inflammatory speeches they made in village alehouses and elsewhere. Clifford was sceptical about this, and also about the claim that farmers would

---

[28] *The Times*, 2 April 1874.
[29] F. Clifford, *op. cit.*, p. 90.

face ruin if they gave way to the men's demands. As the lockout proceeded, many farmers found that they were not losing, but were actually saving money. They and their families turned out to work themselves, some of the old men and young lads were kept on, unskilled labour from the towns was recruited for short periods; some land was laid down to grass, more machinery was installed and greater attention paid to labour management. Farmers had been prodigal of the cheap labour they could get, and the lock-out first taught them how to make a more economical use of it.

The great landowners of East Anglia, standing rather apart from the struggle, were mostly in favour of arbitration and agreement, and many of their tenants kept out of the lock-out. Sir Edward Kerrison, Lord Walsingham and the Duke of Rutland all made public pronouncements advocating moderation.

The Lincolnshire Labour League was the first Union to come to terms with the farmers. This union, an amalgamation of a number of small associations in that county and in Norfolk, had always stood aloof from the National. During 1873, after various small strikes and lock-outs, wages in Lincolnshire had risen to 18*s* a week, a high figure compared with the Midlands and South. The policy of its Secretary, William Banks, himself a farm worker, was to work closely with the trade union movement. Its membership reached 20,000, and for a time it ran its own weekly paper, the *Labour League Examiner*.

But when Lincolnshire labourers began to talk of 3*s* 6*d* a day and a nine-hour day, the Lincolnshire farmers followed the example of those in Suffolk and a lock-out began. The League was able to pay all its locked-out members, and before funds began to run low two Members of Parliament, Sam Morley and George Dixon, managed to bring the two sides together in a compromise. After a revision of the union's rules, the Lincolnshire Farmers' Association agreed to recognise the right to combine and to call off the lock-out. Work began at the end of May 1874.[30]

[30] R. C. Russell, *The Revolt of the Field in Lincolnshire*, Lincs. Co. Committee, Nat. Union Agric. Workers, 1956, pp. 50–69.

No compromise was yet forthcoming in other parts of the country. The lock-out dragged on through the summer months, the farmers demanding that the men give up their union cards before they would take them back. Many men left to seek work in other counties or to emigrate. Some of them came back again after a few weeks, finding that though they got higher wages, town life was expensive and lodgings difficult to get. In one village, out of nine men who went away eight returned, 'and the ninth would have been glad to do so, but had a warrant out against him at home'.[31] But many others settled down in their new jobs and never came back.

In Suffolk, as the harvest drew near, a drift back to work began. Though the union kept up its allowances to the locked-out men, it was a struggle to live and funds were running low. Seeds of suspicion were sown among the simple labourers; if the agent with the pay did not arrive on the right day, it was suggested that Union funds were being diverted from them and misused. Some of the wives with large families were feeling the pinch and urged the men to give in. Finally, on 27 July 1874, five months after the lock-out began, the executive of the National declared 'that in the face of the harsh and prolonged lock-out in the Eastern Counties, this Committee cannot feel justified in supporting the labourers in enforced idleness indefinitely; nor can they seek public support continually while the harvest is waiting to be gathered in. The Committee therefore resolve to place migration and emigration at the disposal of the labourers or the alternative of depending wholly on their own resources.'[32]

The Federal Union made a similar statement two days later. The lock-out was at an end.

The unions had put up a good fight but, inexperienced, torn by dissensions among themselves, faced with the problems of paying their scattered members, and with funds beginning to run low, they could not go on. Arch, with all his great qualities, had not the generalship needed to carry through such an operation. He

[31] F. Clifford, *op. cit.*, p. 73.
[32] R. Groves, *op. cit.*, p. 78.

had seen the need for a strong and centralised union, but he had entirely failed to persuade the other unions to join him, and had antagonised their leaders. There were bitter recriminations and accusations that an unfair proportion of the money subscribed by the public, the Engineering Union and other bodies had gone to the National, while the smaller unions had had to rely mostly on their own funds. Within the National, too, there was acrimony and accusation of misuse of funds, and altogether it was a sad close to a heroic story. But the movement was by no means dead and the rise in wages it had obtained was maintained – for the time being. In May 1875 the National still claimed a membership of 58,000 and many of the other unions were strong.

It might be argued that at the general level of prosperity at which farming was running in the early '70s, wages would in any case have risen without the pressure of the unions, and that the movement only generated political tension, bad feeling, and a widespread migration from the countryside of its best workers. But this is a surface view which overlooks the very real disabilities under which farm workers had laboured for so long, not only in wages, but in living conditions and status. The way in which the movement spread can only be explained in terms of a religious awakening, a 'wind of change' blowing through the countryside. The educative value to workers of an organisation of their own, spreading far beyond their own villages and making them feel that they were part of a great forward movement of the whole working class, was incalculable. The difficulties of organising a Union among such a scattered industry as farming are notorious, and of course many were untouched by it. The stockmen, and those living in tied cottages on remote farms, would be hard to get hold of. The figures of membership claimed by the unions are impossible to check, for men dropped out, came in again, branches leapt up under an active secretary and died away if he moved on, so that numbers varied almost from week to week. The amazing thing is that, considering the high rate of illiteracy in the country-side, the organisation ever functioned at all in remoter places. Nor is it easy to say how many men were actually locked out in the eastern counties, and the issue is still further obscured by the disputes between the unions themselves. But the fact remains that the National paid out at least £24,000 to its branches for lock-out pay between March and August 1874. The number of men out seems to have been about 6,000 at its peak, between the National, the Lincolnshire Labour League and the Federal Union. But the actual numbers do not really matter, for no one in the counties involved could be unaware of what was happening, and though the lock-out may have been a technical victory for the farmers, the principle of the right to combine was not destroyed. Though farm workers were not to get the vote for another decade, there was a new consciousness, a new feeling that they counted for something, and that their own efforts and those of their fellows would help them towards a better life. They wanted to be men and not objects of charity, and this attitude was never entirely lost, even in the dark days which followed.

9

The Great Depression
1875–1885

The Fall in Prices – The Wet Years – Costs and Rents in Arable Farming – Reducing Costs – Agricultural Employment and the Rural Population.

THE FALL IN PRICES

THE great depression that afflicted British agriculture for twenty years after 1875 stimulated both contemporary investigation and later controversy. Three Royal Commissions took evidence, collected opinions and reported on it, the Richmond Commission in 1881, the Royal Commission on Depression in Trade and Industry in 1886, and a second Commission on Agriculture in 1894–8[1]; its causes, course and results were frequently discussed in debates in both Houses of Parliament and in many books and pamphlets. It has been variously ascribed to a worldwide change in the general level of prices brought about mainly by changes in the supply of gold in relation to the monetary demand; to the adoption by the British Government in 1846 of free trade, whose ill-effects had been postponed for a generation, but not avoided; and to the culmination, in a vastly increased production, of all those technical changes in manufacture and transport called the industrial revolution.

The immediate impact of the great depression on British farmers in the years 1875 to 1883 was a severe and prolonged fall in the prices of wool and cereals in the home market, of which the immediate cause was undoubtedly the rising volume of imports. The effect of this fall in prices was accentuated by a run of

[1] Henceforth described as R.C. 1881, R.C. 1886 and R.C. 1894.

exceptionally bad seasons which reduced output and increased costs; arable farmers also suffered from the failure of many costs to follow at once the downward trend in the prices of the products they sold. These three strands in the great depression must be separately disentangled.

The course of wool prices has already been described (p. 142). They fell sharply after 1864, revived again during the Franco-Prussian war in 1871–2 and then fell with little interruption until stability was reached ten years later at some sixty per cent of the 1865–74 average, less than half the level of the highest years (Chart VIII). The demand for wool as an industrial product rose or fell with the general state of business expectations and its price was always liable to wide fluctuations; but the general fall in these twenty years was chiefly caused by the rising volume of wool entering international trade from the newly settled continents, which could only be absorbed by the lower prices. There could have been few farmers in Britain in the 1870s and 1880s whose production plans were not affected to some degree by the fall in wool prices, for the sheep enterprise was an essential part of both arable and grassland farming. The fall in cereal prices had a more complex effect, for though it brought heavy losses to arable farms which kept animals primarily to support their grain yields, it benefited the livestock farms using bought and home-grown grains to supplement their resources in grass, hay and fodder crops.

Before 1860 wheat prices fluctuated widely from year to year, largely because of the variable home yield, but these fluctuations gradually diminished in size in the course of the 1860s and 1870s as the rising tide of imports from other countries reduced this variability of total supplies (Chart IV). Because wheat prices after 1866 rose less in years of poor yields, the average gross return per acre of wheat probably had a diminishing margin over the average gross return from other grain crops in these years. As noted earlier (p. 119), the area under wheat in Scotland fell sharply between the unofficial census in 1854–7 and the start of the official census in 1866, while the area under both barley and oats increased;

wheat was little grown in Scotland after 1860, except in the Lothians. Wheat production may have fallen in the north and west of England and in Wales before 1866; yet the area under wheat in the counties of East Anglia increased until 1876, in spite of the shift in relative prices in preceding decades, which seems to indicate that the rise in wheat yields may have counterbalanced the effect on gross returns of a lower average price. The dozen counties that were taking wheat twice in their rotations did so partly because barley was apt to go down before harvesting and thus lose much of its grain, while the stiffer-strawed wheat gave a more satisfactory yield from fertile soils.

In the late 1870s it was the prices of oats and barley which fell most rapidly, while wheat prices remained fairly stable from 1875 until after 1882, with one abrupt peak in 1877. For these six or seven years therefore, price statistics alone favoured the production of wheat rather than that of the other grains, for farms where all three were possible choices. From 1882 and an average of 45*s* per quarter, the price of wheat fell precipitately to 30*s* per quarter in 1889 and then to 24*s* per quarter in 1894, actually below the average price of barley recorded in that year, and only 6*s* per quarter higher than the price of oats, instead of the usual differential of 20*s* or more. From 1882 onwards it was the fall in grain prices, and especially in wheat prices, which struck at the profits of arable farmers; in the seven years before 1882, it was the low prices of the other grains combined with the appalling weather which most affected their incomes and their capital.

THE WET YEARS

The wet autumn of 1875 was followed by the abnormally heavy rainfall in the winter of 1876–7, and the spring of 1878 began a period of $2\frac{1}{2}$ years of exceptional cold and wet. The heavy snow in March 1878 brought severe floods in many districts in April, while the winter of 1878–9 was most disastrous to livestock because of its severity and duration. For the rest of that notorious year 1879, the average temperature was below the thirty-eight-year average in all months, with severe frosts at the end of March; at most recording stations, the rainfall was well above the average for the first nine months, excepting only March. The excess of rainfall over local averages was greatest in the south and east, and progressively diminished to the west and north. While Cumberland and South Wales had rather less than the local average, Bury St Edmunds had fifty per cent more than its average rainfall, and Sir W. Bartelot, near Pulborough in Sussex, recorded thirteen distinct and separate floods in this year.[2] The sodden land in the Midlands, east and south then endured a second exceptionally long and severe winter; and this in turn was followed by a second wet summer in 1880, bringing floods in Lincolnshire. Heavy snow in January and February 1881 added more moisture to the soil, and it was not until July that a hot dry spell brought relief, but the summer of 1882 was nearly as cold, sunless and wet as that of 1879.

The effect of these wet years was perhaps most severe on the arable farms on clay soils, such as those to be found in Huntingdon, West Cambridgeshire and Essex which suffered the worst of the excess rainfall. It was these soils which required frequent bare fallows so that cultivation and desiccation could combine to kill the weeds. And it was these farms which found their fallows wet, leached of plant nutrients and unworkable in these years, and consequently covered with weeds; in the five East Anglian counties of Cambridge, Essex, Huntingdon, Norfolk and Suffolk, the area returned as bare fallow rose from 106,000 acres on the average of 1877–9 to 152,000 acres in 1881–3. To the extra costs of cultivating uncropped land was added the drastic fall in receipts from the low yields on the land under grain. Combining the Rothamsted data on yields with the average prices reveals that the average gross returns from an acre of wheat would have been in 1879 barely half that of 1876; for the three harvests of 1879–82 gross returns would have averaged about £6 per acre compared with about £8 10s in 1876–8, a fall of nearly 30 per cent and

---

[2] W. C. Little, *Report on Southern Counties*, R.C. 1881, p. 406.

one sufficient to remove the profit from many cereal-growing farms.[3]

The run of wet seasons from 1878 to 1882 also brought an epidemic of liver rot in sheep, on almost all arable and grassland farms in low-lying ground, such as the Somerset and north Dorset vales and the Lincolnshire marshes; a severe outbreak of foot-and-mouth disease also raged in 1881–3. In England, sheep numbers fell from 18·4 million in June 1878 to a low point of 14·9 million in 1882, and in some arable districts, such as East Anglia, the number recorded at the annual June census continued to decline throughout the depression. This seems to indicate that some farmers gave up their breeding flocks, which would be included in the annual census taken in June; we do not know whether these farmers possibly increased their autumn purchases of sheep to supply the butchers in the spring. It was unfortunate for lowland farmers that prices of store sheep showed a marked rise from 1879 to 1883, with especially high prices in the last two years. There had been heavy losses of hill sheep in the two severe winters of 1878–9 and 1879–80, so that supplies from this source were also depleted at a time when many lowland farmers were trying to restock after the epidemic of liver rot. The combination of a run of wet seasons, low grain yields and high sheep losses overwhelmed many of the heavy-land farmers whose financial distress was recorded in the evidence given to the Richmond Commission. W. C. Little, the Assistant Commissioner for the southern counties, had 'seen corn crops which would barely pay the cost of harvesting and marketing; hop gardens which the pickers have never entered; meadows from which the whole crop had been carried away by flood, and others from which the hay was being carted in the month of October, to be used as litter or manure; fallows upon which the labour and expenses of months had been absolutely thrown away; root crops upon which no expense had been spared, and yet the crop was worthless. These things I have

[3] J. B. Lawes, 'Home Produce ... of Wheat ...' *J.R.A.S.E.*, vol. 4.iii, 1893, Appendix Table; prices from Chart V.

seen not merely in single and isolated instances but frequently and in many different parts of the country; and, perhaps most serious loss of all, I learn from many quarters that whole flocks of sheep have been removed by the fatal disease, sheep-rot.'[4] S. B. L. Druce, who had toured the eastern counties for the Commission, commented on 'the foul state to which a succession of inclement seasons had reduced the land, and the increased farm labour thereby rendered necessary'.[5] R. Hunter Pringle noted that 'the strong soils, instead of being ameliorated by the repeated operations of tillage, instead of being cleaned, sweetened and pulverised, got into a hopeless state of weeds and confusion. . . . The consequences of 1879 were to severely cripple the old tenants, to ruin many of the new ones, and to inflict heavy losses upon landlords farming their own property.'[6]

At any time this run of bad seasons would have caused widespread loss, especially among those heavy land arable farmers who might for some reason be short of the capital and credit required to bring back into cultivation their weed-infested fallows and to restock their pastures after the epidemic of rot. Yet the better seasons which began with 1883 would in time have overcome the worst of these effects and given the majority of farmers the chance to restore their finances, but for its coincidence with the fall in grain prices. At the level of prices experienced by 1883 drastic transformations were required in some established patterns of arable farming; many farms which suffered from above average costs or from below average yields found that receipts from grain left an insufficient margin of profit to carry their overhead costs. But practical alternatives to existing systems often implied a radical change in the structure of farming, a change for which many farmers had neither the finance, nor the knowledge, nor, at first, the support of their landlords.

[4] W. C. Little, *Report on Southern Counties*, R.C. 1881, p. 394.

[5] S. B. L. Druce, *Report on the Eastern Counties*, R.C. 1881, p. 363.

[6] R. Hunter Pringle, *Report on . . . Essex*, R.C. 1894, p. 40; see his map of derelict land at end of this report. See also S. G. Kendall, *Farming Memoirs of a West Country Yeoman*, London, 1944, pp. 127–34.

COSTS AND RENTS IN ARABLE FARMING

The cold clay soils had, at this period, little alternative value save as grassland, for the costs and risks of arable cultivation by horse teams were too high for any ordinary cropping to be profitable at current prices. But to put this land down to useful grass required, firstly, fields free of weeds which would outgrow the young grasses; secondly, a long period of careful management with ample supplies of farmyard manure and of fertilisers before the grass was established; and thirdly, the capital to stock the new fields and, in many places, to provide water and fences. These requirements had not been met for those many derelict farms and fields reported to the two Commissions of 1881 and 1894. In Essex, Suffolk, Cambridge, Huntingdon and sporadically wherever there was an outcrop of heavy low-lying clay, farms and fields went derelict under a cover of self-sown weeds and the coarser, and unpalatable grasses, because capital had been lacking after 1879 to overcome the weeds.

In that arable belt which runs south from the Tees to Kent and westwards to Hampshire and the Cotswolds, livestock enterprises were traditionally subsidiary to the production of grain, whose yields were maintained by copious supplies of farmyard manure applied to the roots which fed the animals. From 1882 onwards many farmers found that the returns from wheat and barley no longer covered the expenses of the green crops, the overhead costs of rent and the maintenance of a family. Yet their system was so integrated in its use of by-products between crops and stock, so limited by the conventional rotations required to control weeds and pests, that changes were not easy; for if less grain was grown, there was less straw both for fodder and for litter, which implied fewer animals fattened over the winter, less manure and lower yields both of roots and of grain. The easy alternative of keeping the ley down for a year or two longer involved a drastic fall in output over the rotation, for the eastern and midland counties normally had high yields of grain but low yields from grassland, whether taken as hay or grazing. The effects of drought were here more frequent and more severe, while the grazing season was shorter at both ends than in the western counties with their milder winters and later autumn frosts; further, temporary leys under normal management were apt to give progressively less grazing after the first year and quickly deteriorated in feeding value. Elsewhere, in the north and west, land could economically be left longer in temporary leys, thus saving the costs of cultivation, or it could be put down to permanent grass with a quicker return in grazing and a smaller loss in total output.

Tenant right and landlords' opposition were further deterrents in the mainly arable counties against a radical shift between crops and grass in the 1880s. The 'custom of the country' gave outgoing tenants the right to claim from landowners or from incoming tenants the costs, at valuation, of certain acts of husbandry performed for crops that the newcomer would harvest or consume. (Older customs had allowed either early access to parts of the farm for the incomer or delayed access for the outgoer to reap and cart his crops.) These 'customs' varied greatly from district to district, but many legal cases had established them as binding on both parties on a change of tenancy, unless the leases concerned contained specific clauses to the contrary. In a symposium on the operation of the Agricultural Holdings Act, 1875, the value of such covenants in West Norfolk was estimated at £1–£2½ per acre according to the quality of the land and its fertility; tenant right in Lincoln was stated not to exceed 30s–40s per acre.[7] These sums were accredited to arable land; because pasture was relatively unimportant, local 'customs' seldom included any provision for claiming the costs of laying arable land to permanent grass. Until the Agricultural Holdings Act, 1883, came into force in 1885, the tenant of an arable farm who wanted more permanent pasture and less ploughing was therefore faced with the possible loss of the sums he had paid on entry on all fields taken out of the normal rotation, as well as losing the costs of establishing a pasture which might not become profitable until a newcomer was installed. Arable farmers in financial

[7] *J. Farmers' Club*, Feb. 1877, p. 45, and Mar. 1883, p. 23; see also pp. 198–9.

difficulties and contemplating an early termination to their leases would not be likely to undertake the conversion of arable land to permanent grass until the time had come when they could no longer afford so costly a change.

It is understandable that many landowners were at first unwilling to allow deviations from those crop rotations which had served to raise fertility, profits and rents in previous decades. Hardly any farmers kept accounts, so that few could provide factual evidence of losses, or give detailed estimates of the financial effect of proposed changes in cropping. Many obtained remissions of rent to meet the particular hardships of the wet years, or were allowed to accumulate arrears by informal agreements; such allowances seriously embarrassed many estates, especially those with family settlements charged against their income. Yet it became a common complaint in the arable districts that many owners refused permanent reductions in rent and deviations from prescribed rotations until their tenants were either bankrupt, or had given notice and gone. Then indeed estate owners found themselves unable to obtain tenants except at lower rents, with unrestricted freedom of cropping and sometimes only after investment in the buildings and fences required for a new type of farming. But the need for such changes in rents, rotations and equipment was not appreciated until many landowners were themselves severely embarrassed by the arrears of rents and by the losses incurred when they farmed their own property in default of tenants.

A further difficulty of arable farmers in these years was the general rise in the labour costs which had accompanied Joseph Arch's campaign and the formation of his National Union of Agricultural Workers. Though its effective life was brief, the publicity which attended this union in its early days had informed large numbers of farm workers of the prevailing wage rates in neighbouring areas, and it was reckoned that the general level of wages paid had risen by one or two shillings a week in the mid-years of the 1870s.[8] There was also the gradual withdrawal after

[8] C. Orwin and B. Felton, 'A Century of Wages and Earnings in Agriculture', *J.R.A.S.E.*, vol. 92, 1931, p. 233. See Chart III and p. 238.

1872 of the younger boys from field work into the new schools, which implied to many farmers that hoeing, singling and couch-picking must henceforth be done by men at men's wages. These higher labour costs affected farms in varying degrees, partly because of differences in wages, perquisites in kind and conditions of work to be found not merely between areas and types of farming but even between adjacent farms. The fall in wages which occurred in the 1880s was also varied and spasmodic, being most marked in the depressed arable areas of eastern and southern England, and hardly noticeable in the north of England and the Scottish industrial lowlands, where farm wages were maintained by the emigration of many farm workers and by competition from the expanding towns. In the north-east and central parts of Scotland, wages paid in farming had been rising sharply from about 1855, with a further spurt between 1871 and 1878; the subsequent recession was short and still left wages somewhat above the level of 1870, especially the wages paid to the diminishing number of women willing to work in the fields.[9]

REDUCING COSTS

The decade from 1875 to 1884 was thus a period of acute financial strain for arable farmers in Britain, especially for those whose income depended mainly on corn sales, those whose farms suffered from excessive rain or snow and those whose sheep died from liver rot or in storms. But a large number of farmers escaped these afflictions, and survived to benefit from the falling grain prices. There was little cause for anxiety among farmers in the western and northern counties who sold milk and dairy products from summer grass; among suburban farmers selling potatoes, vegetables or eggs, poultry and milk from inputs of purchased feeding-stuffs; among the upland farmers selling store stock at enhanced prices, though here, admittedly, wool brought in a steadily falling

[9] R. Molland and G. Evans, 'Scottish Farm Wages from 1870 to 1900', *J.R.S.S.*, vol. 113, 1950, pp. 220–8; G. Houston, 'Farm Wages in Central Scotland from 1814–1870', *J.R.S.S.*, vol. 118, 1955, pp. 224–8.

return and the output of many farms must have been reduced by the severe winters.[10] Throughout this decade, prices of milk, cheese, butter and meat showed only normal fluctuations round a trend which rose rather than fell, as far as the imperfect statistics indicate. This seems to have been the case for these products sold in Lancashire towns[11]; a record of butter and cheese prices taken from a Wiltshire farm for the twenty years after 1874 showed a steady level from 1878–9 to 1884 only a little lower than that secured in the boom years of 1874–7;[12] one record of Scottish cheese prices beginning in 1863 revealed a rise in 1873 and 1874, followed by a fairly stable market in the subsequent decade at prices only slightly lower.[13] With falling prices for bread, the urban wage earners could afford to buy more meat, vegetables and dairy products; with falling costs of feeding stuffs, the livestock farmers within reach of towns could economise in cultivation costs by putting their least profitable arable fields down to grass, making more hay and buying more imported maize and oilcake for their winter fodder. They had no need to give evidence to the Richmond Commission on agricultural depression, for they had little to complain about except, of course, the weather. Yet even in the grazing half of England, farmers grew in 1875 nearly two million acres of wheat and barley and in 1885 only 1·4 million acres; many were forced into a variety of expedients to check the decline in incomes as grain prices fell.

The statistical result of these expedients is shown in Tables 1 and 2, giving the agricultural returns for the years 1875, 1880 and 1885 for the grazing and arable divisions of England, and for Scotland and Wales. From 1875 to 1882, the greater part of this decade, the prices of barley and oats fell rather more than wheat prices, yet in both parts of England the area under wheat was reduced more sharply than the area under barley, while the pro-

[10] E. H. Whetham, 'Livestock Prices in Britain, 1851–1893', *Agric. Hist. Rev.*, vol. xi, 1963, p. 30.

[11] T. W. Fletcher, 'Lancashire Livestock Farming during the Great Depression', *Agric. Hist. Rev.*, vol. ix, 1961, p. 25.

[12] A. Spencer, *Report on the Counties of . . . Wilts.*, R.C. 1894, p. 34.

[13] J. Speir, *Report on the Counties of Ayr*, R.C. 1894, p. 23.

Table 1. *Crops and Livestock in Grazing and Arable Districts of England*, 1875, 1880, 1885

	Grazing Districts			Arable Districts		
	1875	1880	1885	1875	1880	1885
Thousand Acres						
Wheat	1,135	957	788	1,993	1,789	1,562
Barley	750	714	614	1,340	1,347	1,280
Oats	752	817	882	670	703	766
Pulse, etc.	233	159	159	655	508	518
TOTAL Corn	2,870	2,647	2,443	4,658	4,347	4,125
Potatoes	183	191	202	137	134	157
Root and Green Crops	1,003	913	926	1,526	1,421	1,276
Rotation Grass	1,440	1,401	1,474	1,167	1,245	1,453
Bare Fallow	244	309	194	272	451	325
TOTAL Arable	5,740	5,461	5,239	7,760	7,598	7,336
Permanent Grass	7,028	7,647	8,088	3,508	3,815	4,142
Flax and Hops	11	12	11	65	63	63
Orchards	117	134	164*	34	42	93*
Thousand Head						
Horses: for agric.	356	368	369	389	398	395
unbroken and mares	160	181	179	127	145	139
Cattle	2,751	2,707	3,076	1,468	1,451	1,637
Sheep	10,000	8,785	8,961	9,114	8,044	7,849
Pigs	903	807	1,004	973	891	1,033
Turkeys	—	—	177	—	—	180
Geese	—	—	427	—	—	188
Ducks	—	—	933	—	—	804
Fowls	—	—	5,260	—	—	4,297

* Including market gardens and nursery grounds.

Grazing districts: Chester, Cornwall, Cumberland, Derby, Devon, Dorset, Durham, Gloucester, Hereford, Lancaster, Leicester, Monmouth, Northumberland, Shropshire, Somerset, Stafford, Westmorland, Wiltshire, Worcester, Yorkshire (North and West Ridings).
Arable districts: Bedford, Berkshire, Buckingham, Cambridge, Essex, Hampshire, Hertford, Huntingdon, Kent, Lincoln, Middlesex, Norfolk, Northampton, Nottingham, Oxford, Rutland, Suffolk, Surrey, Sussex, Warwick, Yorkshire (East Riding).

duction of oats markedly increased, by 130,000 acres in the grazing counties and by nearly 100,000 acres in the arable counties. Some of the heavy land, which depended mainly on wheat for its profits, went down to permanent grass, the area of which increased by 100,000 acres in the grazing counties, and by nearly

Table 2. *Crops and Livestock in Scotland and Wales, 1875, 1880, 1885*

	Scotland			Wales		
Thousand Acres	1875	1880	1885	1875	1880	1885
Wheat	102	74	55	112	90	74
Barley	265	264	237	154	143	126
Oats	1,005	1,037	1,046	237	240	247
Pulse, etc.	39	28	32	9	6	6
TOTAL Corn	1,411	1,404	1,371	512	478	452
Potatoes	158	187	149	45	39	41
Root and Green Crops	427	510	511	86	81	83
Rotation Grass	1,385	1,456	1,572	361	332	332
Bare Fallow	17	22	23	26	31	18
TOTAL Arable	3,398	3,579	3,626	1,030	961	926
Permanent Grass	1,110	1,159	1,220	1,666	1,806	1,893
Orchards	—	—	8*	—	—	4*
Thousand Head						
Horses: for agric.	136	141	142	70	73	72
unbroken and mares	47	53	47	55	62	68
Cattle	1,143	1,099	1,176	651	655	709
Sheep	7,101	7,072	6,957	2,952	2,718	2,768
Pigs	151	121	151	203	182	216
Turkeys	—	—	61	—	—	57
Geese	—	—	35	—	—	234
Ducks	—	—	259	—	—	206
Fowls	—	—	1,971	—	—	875

* Including market gardens and nursery grounds.

600,000 acres in the arable counties. Other farmers omitted wheat from their rotation in favour of oats, normally a spring-sown crop, which yielded straw for the cattle yards and dairy stalls as well as grain for fodder or for sale. It may seem curious that more oats should be grown when the price had fallen so markedly in recent years, but presumably farmers calculated that the cash lost from wheat sales could be best recouped by economy in the purchase of feeds and by the sale either of more livestock, or of oats and oat straw as provender for the urban horses.

In Scotland and in Wales, the wheat acreage was almost halved. Scottish farmers continued to add to the area of arable by reclamation, and also grew more roots for winter fodder; in Wales, as in England, reclamation seems to have ceased and indeed, some of the arable land apparently slipped back into that vague class called permanent pasture. It is clear that many farmers in the arable districts of England did not rebuild their sheep flocks after the epidemics of liver rot and foot-and-mouth disease. Possibly they were deterred by the high prices of store sheep relatively to mutton prices; possibly much of the permanent grass added should more correctly have been classified as rough pasture, which might graze a few bullocks in the summer but which continued to be infested with liver flukes, and so remained dangerous for sheep. Possibly also, the daily moving of the hurdles over the turnip fields, and the cultivations required to grow fodder crops for the sheep, began to cost some farmers more than the combined produce in grain, wool and mutton. Certainly from 1879 onwards, sheep numbers fell in all the arable districts of England, while in lowland Scotland, where sheep were normally wintered on the leys with turnips carted to them from the clamps, numbers increased again after 1883, and by 1890 exceeded the earlier peak. In all counties of Britain, the yearly census taken in June showed an increase in cattle numbers. More were being bred on the hills and uplands; arable farmers may have fattened more in the winter, and the increased area of grassland may also have fattened more beef cattle as well as supporting the larger number of cows kept for the milk trade.

These changes in rotations and stocking were the recorded results of the actions of thousands of farmers trying to obtain profits from their individual farms, in the light of current techniques and the gloomy prospects of grain prices. What was not recorded, except indirectly, was the continuous search for economy in the costs of performing the customary rotations, which enabled many farmers to survive this decade without much change being shown in their June return. An adjustment in rent was the most obvious of such economies, accompanied or followed by a cut in wage rates, but help also came from the engineering trade. Perhaps the most important of the innovations of this decade was the self-binding reaper, which at last mechanised the laborious task of binding the sheaves of grain before they were stooked for drying. American sheaf binders using wire were exhibited at the Philadelphia Centennial Exhibition in 1877, and five years later McCormick's string binder was awarded the gold medal at the Royal Agricultural Society's show at Derby. By 1884, the judge at Shrewsbury could report that British-made binders 'can now cut and tie an average crop of grain in a manner superior to any other process of cutting and tying that I have yet witnessed'.[14] By 1886, the success of the sheaf-binder was beyond question, and the grain-growing farmers could cut, bind, stook and cart their corn crops with probably no addition to their regular staff but the boys on holiday from school, and only a slight addition to the strain on their horses.

By the 1880s, a pattern of harvesting was thus established which was to endure for half a century. From the early days of August, the overhead sails of innumerable binders clacked their way round the cornfields of Britain, powered by two or three horses and driven by one man; behind came other men, and possibly boys or women, who stood the sheaves in stooks according to a variety of local patterns, in order to dry in the sun and wind. Well-constructed stooks arranged with mathematical precision across the lines of yellow stubble marked the progress of the harvesting from south and east to north and west. When the stooks were carted to a stack either in the field or in the yards, the boys were invaluable, for while men pitched the sheaves on to the carts and thence on to the stacks, the boys could lead from stook to stook

[14] 'Report ... on String-Binders', *J.R.A.S.E.*, vol. 18.ii, 1882, pp. 264–301; 'Report ... of Sheaf-Binding Machinery', *J.R.A.S.E.*, vol. 21.ii, 1885, pp. 47–81.

(with cries of 'hold ye' to the men on the carts),[15] from field to corn rick, and back again, through gateways whose turnings the older horses knew better than the boys. Much skill was required in building from sheaves a stout stack, well 'hearted' up in the centre, vertical or slightly overhanging on all sides, and, again according to local tradition, round, square or an oblong with rectangular corners. Thatchers then made the stacks weatherproof, using the wheat straw saved from the previous harvest; so the stacks stood until, in the course of the winter months, the travelling threshers arrived. Many small improvements continued to be made to the steam thresher which gave cleaner grain and faster working with lower consumption of coal and water, but a day's threshing still required a baker's dozen of attendants, to pitch, untie and feed in the sheaves, to pitch and stack the threshed straw out of the way, to bag, tie and shift the grain and to feed the ponderous engine which supplied the power. For the smaller farms, threshing was a social occasion when neighbouring families helped each other out, and trays of food and drink were exchanged for the local gossip. Threshing was dirty work, thirsty work and expensive work, especially if heavy rain or snow kept the threshers and their attendants standing idle.

Another innovation taken up in this period was the double-furrow three-wheeled plough – Pirie's plough as it was commonly called after the most popular manufacturer – which had been on the market since 1868. The development of the metallurgical industries provided iron and steel of better and more uniform strength, and therefore implements which were stronger, lighter and more durable. The double-furrow plough might travel more slowly than the single plough, and it required more management, but one skilled man and two or three horses could plough in a day nearly as much as two men and four horses had previously done. The second man and his team could be eliminated, or he and his horse could be used in spring for the hoeing, now that hand hoers were becoming scarce and expensive, or in autumn for carting turnips and potatoes, thus again reducing the need for

[15] This reminiscence comes from Professor Sir Frank Engledow.

casual workers.[16] The tools that farmers still urgently needed, according to one speaker to the Farmers' Club in 1886, were really good machines for thinning turnips, and for topping, tailing and lifting them; a reliable potato planter; and an apparatus for spreading dung which could eliminate the laborious task of forking it by hand from middens into carts, from carts into heaps and from heaps over the fields or into the drills. A variety of hay and straw presses were available for those farmers who sold these products and sent them by rail, but all were crude and required improvement.

AGRICULTURAL EMPLOYMENT AND THE RURAL POPULATION

Economy in labour costs could thus be effected by reducing the standard of farming or by cutting wage rates, but it was more generally achieved by minor changes in management which made better use of the regular workers and markedly reduced the employment of casual workers in harvest and hoeing time. The most drastic loss of employment occurred in those areas of the heavy clay soils which fell almost derelict into self-sown pasture grazed by a few bullocks, for the villages had depended on the trade of the farm population and on the patronage of landowners, and both failed. Elsewhere, farmers did not fill all the vacancies which resulted from death, old age and dismissals, and looked more sharply after those who remained, so that the young and impetuous became still more inclined to move outside farming for a career. And the falling demand for casual workers had wide reactions, affecting many regions little touched by the direct consequences of falling grain prices. Many lowland small holdings and upland farms had provided subsistence and a winter home to families whose young men found seasonal employment as hay-makers, turnip-hoers, sheep-shearers, harvesters, hedgers, ditchers and threshing-machine attendants on the large arable farms. When the occupiers of these farms reduced their area under grain, bought a binder, another set of horse hoes, and one of the new

16 R.C. 1881, *Minutes of Evidence*, q. 52, 475 by H. Biddell; D. Pigeon, 'Evolution of Agricultural Implements', *J.R.A.S.E.*, vol. 3.iii, 1892, p. 55.

potato ploughs which lifted the crop and left it lying on the surface for easy picking, they reduced costs by reducing the incomes of farm families in many parishes. The decline in rural population, which had begun in some parishes in the 1860s, intensified in the succeeding decade and became general; the fall was not confined to the arable districts but was equally marked in many grassland areas. The counties of central Wales and also Anglesey showed a larger proportionate fall in population in the last three decades of the nineteenth century than the eastern arable counties where agricultural depression was the worst.[17] In Aberdeenshire, two-thirds of the total number of parishes attained their maximum population between 1861 and 1881, the migration thereafter exceeding the natural increase; most of these parishes lay inland and contained neither towns nor industries but were occupied by large numbers of small farms each providing a home and subsistence to a single family. Labour-saving devices and the relatively low wages to be earned on arable farms in lowland Scotland and northern England pushed many of the young people born in these parishes out of agricultural employment into the towns or on to the unpeopled lands of Canada, Australia and New Zealand. In almost all the purely agricultural areas of Britain, the same critical level of migration developed in the decade after 1871, that level which exceeded the balance of births over deaths. The parishes from which so many young people went were left with a declining population unduly concentrated on the middle-aged and deprived of many parents of the next generation. The progress of time meant therefore an accelerating fall in numbers in these rural areas, and in the numbers occupying the school benches. The families who remained in agricultural work came gradually to accept the inevitability of relatively low earnings and the relatively low social status which automatically followed, until many hamlets and villages sank into a dumb despondency which could barely be illuminated by the energy and determination of a Joseph Ashby.[18]

[17] J. Saville, *Rural Depopulation in England and Wales, 1851–1951*, London, 1957, p. 49; *Report on the Decline in Agricultural Population, 1881–1906*, C. 3273, 1906.

[18] M. K. Ashby, *Joseph Ashby of Tysoe*, Cambridge, 1961.

10

The Great Depression
1885-1895

The Fall in Prices – Marketing of Farm Produce – Changes in Farming Practice – New Methods and New Men – Practice with Science – Change and Continuity.

THE FALL IN PRICES

THE severe drought of 1883 mitigated the damage done to the clay soils by the run of wet seasons, but the continuing fall in grain prices intensified the damage already inflicted on the incomes of many arable farmers who had managed to survive the loss of profits and of capital after 1879. Between 1883 and 1895, the Gazette price for barley fell from an annual average of just over 30s per quarter to just under 25s; the price of wheat fell from just over 40s to the same level as barley, a previously unknown conjunction; oat prices fell from just over 20s to about 15s (Chart V). After 1885, the margin between these three prices was exceptionally small; local differences in yields, in market prices and in special costs thus became of more importance in determining the choice of grain to be grown. Many farmers who had sold wheat and bought feeding grain planted oats instead of wheat, and others turned to barley. By 1895 the English grazing counties had only 370,000 acres under wheat, compared with nearly 800,000 acres in 1885 and more than 1,100,000 acres in 1875; farmers in the arable counties grew a greater area in 1895 of both barley and oats than of wheat.

In addition to this continuing fall in grain prices, the second stage of the depression was marked by a fall also in the prices for meat, livestock and dairy produce, which appears to have begun late in 1883 and, after a brief check in 1888–90, continued for the next four or five years. Fatstock prices showed a fall between 1883 and 1895 of about 20 per cent for the best quality, and of 25–50 per cent for the middling qualities (Charts V and VI); there was a somewhat smaller fall for pork and bacon prices, but store stock prices seem to have fallen by almost a third over this period, with a further fall in the dry years of 1892 and 1893. Wholesale prices for butter and cheese also fell by about a quarter in these years.[1] Moreover, the costs and output of livestock farmers were simultaneously affected by the general droughts of 1883 and 1893, and by the more localised droughts of 1892 and 1895. During this decade, therefore, the agricultural depression deepened in the arable regions and extended into many of the dairying and grazing districts. And once again, a Royal Commission, that appointed in 1894, investigated its causes and effects and failed to find any remedy.

The immediate cause of this fall in prices for British farm produce was undoubtedly the rising tide of imports, carried to Britain at ever lower freight rates by the growing number of steamships. Their cargoes came from the expanding output of foodstuffs in Russia, the Danubian countries and India, in northern Europe (especially Denmark), in North and South America, as well as in Australia and New Zealand. The 1894 Royal Commission noted that the home production of wheat had been the most affected by imports, which in 1894 supplied three-quarters of the estimated total consumption of wheat and flour; the area grown in Britain had fallen from just over 3 million acres in 1875 to 1·4 million acres by 1895. The imports of other foods had not displaced home production to such an extent, but they had supplied most of the increase in demand brought about by the increase in population and by the increasing income enjoyed by substantial sections of that population. The fall in cereal prices itself had substantially reduced the cost of bread, the basic food for large numbers of the poorer consumers, and had thus enabled them to buy more of other foods. But the competition between the rising volume of imports and the home grown produce brought down wholesale and retail prices for almost every product sold by British farmers.

[1] R.C. 1894, *Final Report*, 1898, C.8540, pp. 43–53.

Thanks to the large organisations, many of them farmers' co-operatives, which dominated the export trade of the United States and some of the European countries, the bulk of the imports of grain, dairy products, pig-meat, eggs and fruit had acquired a good reputation for quality, careful packing and uniformity within grades. At the hotels in which he stayed on his tour of British agriculture in 1901–2, Rider Haggard found that the food was mainly of foreign origin; even the village shops were stocking French and Danish butter, American bacon and tinned meat, Canadian cheese, and Dutch eggs and margarine.[2] And the development of refrigeration threatened similar competition in the meat trade. From the late 1870s, imports of beef, mutton, pig meat and fatstock into the United Kingdom had been running at some 300,000 tons a year, mainly composed of pigmeat from Europe and north America. Ice had already been used in these years to chill carcases before shipment and to keep them cool in holds and trains, but by 1885 technical developments had produced the continuous refrigeration plant which enabled meat to be first frozen and then held almost indefinitely at a low temperature. By 1895 imports of meat had reached over 500,000 tons, supplying (together with the meat equivalent of the fat stock imported live) about a third of the estimated consumption; and a phase of rapid expansion was beginning in exports from Australia, New Zealand and the Argentine, in addition to the established trade from the Middle West of the United States:

Table 1. *Estimated Meat Supply in the United Kingdom*

Thou-sand tons	Home Produce				Imported Meat		
	Beef and Veal	Mutton and Lamb	Pig-meat	TOTAL	Dead	Live	TOTAL
1876–8	657	404	265	1,326	246	90	336
1886–8	710	364	255	1,329	333	124	457
1893–5	731	382	261	1,374	532	157	689

R.C. 1894, *Final Report*, 1898, C. 8540, p. 64.

[2] Rider Haggard, *Rural England*, London, 1903, vol. 2, p. 266; E. A. Pratt, *The Organisation of Agriculture*, London, 1904.

On the average of 1893–5, the United States sent about 80 per cent of the imports of beef and of live cattle, and about the same proportion of the imported pigmeat; about 60 per cent of the imports of mutton and lamb came from Australia, whose exports to the United Kingdom had risen from just under 17,000 tons in 1885 to more than 80,000 tons in 1895.

This frozen meat was not indeed of a quality to compete effectively with home-killed meat of a good standard; but it did compete with the cow beef, ewe mutton and fat pork, whose prices made up a considerable part of the total value of meat sales from which the distributive trades paid the British farmers for their fatstock. The sharp fall in prices for meat and dairy produce which thus occurred in the early 1890s had a serious result on the profits of both arable and grassland farmers. It apparently affected almost all qualities and grades of produce; it came after a long period of falling prices when financial reserves were low; and it coincided with the low output and high feeding costs occasioned by the dry spring of 1892 and the disastrous drought of 1893. As had occurred earlier with grain prices, low output at home no longer brought a compensating rise in prices, but only a more than compensating rise in the volume of imports.

MARKETING OF FARM PRODUCE

The transport of these increasing quantities of foodstuffs across large distances of land and sea was effected by new techniques, such as canning, refrigeration and faster steamships, and by changes in the structure of distributive trades, such as the growth of produce markets with organised dealings in 'futures' and 'options'; the formation of farmers' co-operative societies in many exporting countries; the erection of freezing plants and grain stores at the points of export, and of cold stores, grain and oilseed mills at ports in Britain. But the home trade in foodstuffs appears to have changed little after the establishment of railways and of the auction markets associated with them, except, indeed, in ways which seem to have operated more to the disadvantage than to the advantage of British farmers. The decay of the inland flour mills, for example, removed from many farmers a local market for their grain and a local source of feeding stuffs. There were continuous complaints that the rates fixed by railways favoured the bulk transport of imported produce from ports to cities, while home produce travelling shorter distances on internal lines often paid a higher charge per mile; the railways countered with statistics on the cost of handling irregular consignments badly packed and travelling in small lots.[3] The 1894 Royal Commission was neither the first nor the last body to urge upon farmers the advantages of co-operative action, whether in bargaining over railway rates, or in the bulking of loads before transit, or in the more formal methods of co-operative trading societies.

The few co-operative societies promoted by farmers in the last third of the nineteenth century were insignificant parts of the contemporary pattern of marketing; their importance lay more in the hopes they raised among social reformers and agricultural politicians. The co-operative cheese and butter factories established in the Midlands in the 1870s had few imitators, but they paved the way for a number of privately owned creameries, manufacturing cheese, butter, condensed milks, baby foods and skimmed-milk calf foods as seemed most profitable to the promoters. The half-yearly milk contract became the normal link between these concerns and the dairy farmers from whom they drew their supplies, with prices following the pattern of those customary in the liquid milk market, a difference of $2d-3d$ per gallon between the summer and winter half-years. The growth of the trade in liquid milk and the general habit of dairying off grass meant that little butter was made in winter either on farms or in factories, and the trade in English butter to the large urban markets was consequently lost to the French merchants and to the Danish and Irish co-operative creameries.[4] Similarly, the competition of American factory-made bacon had stimulated similar

[3] R.C. 1894, *Final Report*, 1894 C. 8540, pp. 131–9, and report by F. A. Channing, pp. 348–54.
[4] R.C. 1894, *Final Report*, 1898, C. 8540, p. 124.

enterprises in Britain, but most of them were offshoots of the distributive trades, buying their supplies through auction markets, rather than farmer-controlled co-operatives processing the output of their members. The curing of bacon and hams, previously carried on by consumers, grocers and butchers, became in this period largely a factory trade designed to supply the urban markets.

A more hopeful development arose from the few co-operative societies established for the bulk purchase of farm requirements. The earliest, the Agricultural and Horticultural Association, was founded by E. O. Greening in 1867 for market gardeners round London. Cumberland farmers organised in 1870 the Aspatria Agricultural Co-operative Society for the joint purchase of feeding-stuffs and fertilisers of tested quality, as a preventive against dirty mixtures and fraudulent adulteration. Similar trading societies were later formed in many districts to undertake the same function and also to secure the economies of bulked orders and regular trading. All such co-operative societies required, for their success, the provision of capital, a habit of cash trading, and the willingness of members both to pay for skilled management and to support their society loyally through initial difficulties. Lack of one or other of these qualities killed some co-operative societies within a few years and prevented others from being brought into existence; about thirty were noted by the Central Chamber of Agriculture in 1891.[5] A few of these operated as sellers of their members' output, chiefly for eggs and market-garden produce, but farmers generally preferred to find markets on their own initiative and disliked that sharing of business details between neighbours which co-operation involved. Many small farmers planned their output to supply a local demand for high quality milk, eggs, poultry or fatstock, and the wide range of prices gave opportunities of profit to the energetic and efficient. Presumably all prices tended to follow the downward trend over this period, but the fall seems to have been greatest for the variable

[5] M. Digby and S. Gorst, *Agricultural Co-operation in the United Kingdom*, Oxford, 1957, p. 24.

quantities of indifferent quality put into wholesale markets by farmers who thought of marketing as a social occasion rather than
as an essential business. The persistence of this attitude was shown
by the neglect of the facilities provided, under the Markets and
Fairs Acts of 1887 and 1891, for livestock to be weighed at all
public markets. To weigh their fat beasts before sale, or store
stock before purchase, seems to have been regarded by farmers as
deprecating their skill in estimating live weights, though 'the
judgment of the butcher who is constantly in the market will always
be better than that of the farmer who is only occasionally in the
market'.[6]

For those who sold by private treaty on their farms, or through
auction markets, frequent visits to their county towns provided,
of course, information on trends in prices as well as occasions for
political discussions and social life. It was natural that men with
large arable or stock farms adequately staffed with foremen should
be willing and able to give evidence on depression to Royal
Commissions and to attend meetings of their local Chambers of
Agriculture. The working dairy farmers had little opportunity for
such visits, with their cows to be milked twice a day every day of the
year, and their voices were therefore seldom heard in evidence or
discussion. The relative prosperity of dairy farming over much of
this period was not unnoticed by official bodies – the 1894 Royal
Commission devoted three pages to dairy farming in its final report – but the subject was treated as unimportant compared with
the attention given to the plight of arable farming in some
districts.[7]

CHANGES IN FARMING PRACTICE

Confronted with a still further fall in the prices for their products,
both crops and livestock, many farmers adopted a policy of
economy in cash outlay, including, if at all possible, outlay on

[6] R.C. 1894, *Final Report*, 1898, C. 8540, p. 147; J. D. M'Jannet, 'The Advantages
of the Weighbridge to the Farmer', *Tr. H.A.S.*, vol. 3.v, 1891, pp. 1–24.

[7] T. W. Fletcher, 'The Great Depression of English Agriculture, 1873–1896',
Ec. Hist. Rev., vol. 13.ii, 1961, p. 426.

rent. Spending less, even if the result was less to sell, might at least reduce the annual losses incurred, and thus enable farmers to hold on until prices recovered. So repairs were not done, ditches were neglected, workers not replaced when they retired or emigrated, outlying fields fell out of cropping into rough pasture, stock were taken into graze, and fewer were bred or bought for winter fattening; the outlay on fertilisers was halved, though, thanks to the fall in prices, the quantities purchased did not fall so drastically.[8] Many no doubt survived by such a policy, either till they retired or until prices began to lift at the turn of the century. No doubt thousands of the smaller farms kept going through the worst of the depression only because of the unpaid work of sons and daughters who received no more than subsistence and a contribution in farm stock when they set up a new family for themselves. But it was this kind of farming, without profit, spirit or satisfaction, which made so many of the younger generation look to other occupations for their own future.

The falling prices for wool and store stock pushed many upland farms into a similar policy of economy. Bracken was no longer cut and began to recapture outlying parts; arable fields on the steeper slopes went back to grass; stone dykes and fences were not repaired; open drains not regularly cleaned. Observers commented on the deterioration in the Scottish hill grazings, which was ascribed to over-stocking with sheep, not enough cattle to keep down the rough grass and the bracken, and to an inadequate replacement of lime and phosphate.[9]

In addition to this general lowering of input and output, it was possible to reduce the costs of arable farming by cutting the area under roots, by leaving some leys unploughed until they became 'permanent grass', by summering more stock and feeding fewer in winter. The cropping statistics (Tables 2 and 3) show that a number of farmers in the English arable districts adopted these practices to some extent, thereby reducing the cost of folding sheep on roots,

[8] E. M. Ojala, *Agriculture and Economic Progress*, Table xix, p. 212.
[9] P. R. Latham, 'Deterioration of Mountain Pastures', *Tr. H.A.S.*, vol. 15.iv, 1883, pp. 111–30.

or of hauling roots to the cattle yards and hauling the farmyard manure back to the fields. Skilfully managed, such a policy could reduce costs with little change in output, though it involved the risk of buying store stock dear in the spring and selling them fat when fatstock were apt to be cheap, in the late autumn. Longer leys were successfully adopted by Lord Leicester for his home farm at Holkham in Norfolk; his tenants continued in the older and now less profitable tradition of a one-year ley, being presumably more cautious than his lordship in their use of the new knowledge of the botanical composition of durable leys and of their manurial requirements.[10]

The greater area of grass, whether permanent or temporary, could also be used to grow hay for sale. Many leases had prohibited this practice, but falling rents and failing tenants changed the views of landlords and their agents, while the cheapness of nitrogenous fertilisers encouraged farmers near towns or railway stations to explore this method of obtaining successive cuts of a saleable crop. In the twenty years after 1870, the area of grassland cut for hay increased in England by some 600,000 acres, or by about a quarter of the earlier level, and in Scotland by 140,000 acres, or by nearly a third. Mowers, horse rakes, swathe turners and horse-powered elevators had much eased the work and reduced the cost of haymaking, and hay pressers were also available for those who sold enough to justify the capital cost of this device for reducing the cost of transport. On the light chalky soils, sainfoin and lucerne became economical crops for the hay-selling farms, for they could be left unploughed for several years and, except in years of drought, they yielded several cuts each season when well dressed with fertilisers.

Within the arable rotation, farmers naturally reduced the area under wheat, whose price had by 1895 fallen over twenty years by a relatively higher proportion than almost any other agricultural product. Wheat at 22*s*–23*s* per quarter, as in 1894 and 1895, encouraged the substitution, wherever possible, of barley or

[10] R.C. 1894, *Evidence*, vol. 4, App. D. p. 596; J. T. Coppock, 'Agricultural Changes in the Chilterns, 1875–1900', *Agric. Hist. Rev.*, vol. ix, 1961, pp. 1–16.

oats for which local markets might still provide the chance of a favourable price.

Table 2. *Crops and Livestock in Grazing and Arable Districts of England, 1885, 1890, 1895*

Thousand Acres	Grazing Districts			Arable Districts		
	1885	1890	1895	1885	1890	1895
Wheat	788	717	370	1,562	1,538	970
Barley	614	577	568	1,280	1,199	1,269
Oats	882	884	1,010	766	764	1,035
Pulse, etc.	159	141	102	518	461	394
TOTAL Corn	2,443	2,319	2,050	4,125	3,962	3,668
Potatoes	202	191	183	157	157	190
Root & Green crops	926	864	823	1,453	1,310	1,271
Rotation Grass	1,474	1,508	1,468	1,276	1,283	1,358
Bare Fallow	194	157	118	325	322	341
TOTAL Arable	5,239	5,039	4,642	7,336	7,034	6,828
Permanent Grass	8,088	8,381	8,230	4,142	4,455	5,015
Flax and Hops	11	11	13	63	46	48
Orchards, market & nursery gardens, small fruit	164	182	200	93	135	179
Thousand Head.						
Horses: for agric.	369	374	379	395	391	404
unbroken and mares	179	188	219	139	146	182
Cattle	3,076	3,015	2,833	1,637	1,602	1,640
Sheep	8,961	9,351	8,506	7,849	7,490	7,052
Pigs	1,004	1,221	1,237	1,033	1,135	1,234

Grazing districts: Chester, Cornwall, Cumberland, Derby, Devon, Dorset, Durham, Gloucester, Hereford, Lancaster, Leicester, Monmouth, Northumberland, Shropshire, Somerset, Stafford, Westmorland, Wiltshire, Worcester, Yorkshire (North and West Ridings).

Arable districts: Bedford, Berkshire, Buckingham, Cambridge, Essex, Hampshire, Hertford, Huntingdon, Kent, Lincoln, Middlesex, Norfolk, Northampton, Nottingham, Oxford, Rutland, Suffolk, Surrey, Sussex, Warwick, Yorkshire (East Riding).

The area sown to wheat in 1895 was the lowest on record, less than 1½ million acres in Britain against more than 3 million acres in 1875; not only were wheat prices low, but the wet autumn of 1894 had prevented many farmers from getting their fields ploughed in time for the wheat sowing.

The fall in grain prices was itself a major economy on many live-stock and dairy farms, an economy which might offset, wholly or in part, the fall in the prices for fatstock, milk and dairy

Table 3. *Crops and Livestock in Scotland and Wales* 1885, 1890, 1895

	Scotland			Wales		
Thousand Acres	1885	1890	1895	1885	1890	1895
Wheat	55	62	34	74	69	44
Barley	237	216	217	126	120	112
Oats	1,046	1,014	1,008	247	241	242
Pulse, etc.	32	26	20	6	4	4
TOTAL Corn	1,371	1,317	1,279	452	434	402
Potatoes	149	142	134	41	40	34
Root & Green Crops	511	508	506	83	85	85
Rotation Grass	1,572	1,686	1,575	332	332	329
Bare Fallow	23	13	8	18	16	9
TOTAL Arable	3,626	3,666	3,502	926	907	859
Permanent Grass	1,220	1,225	1,387	1,893	1,956	1,978
Flax and Hops	—	—	—	—	—	—

Orchards, market
  and nursery gardens,
  small fruit
	8	13	15	4	5	6

Thousand Head						
Horses: for agric.	142	142	150	72	75	77
unbroken and mares	47	48	57	68	69	76
Cattle	1,176	1,186	1,180	709	705	704
Sheep	6,957	7,361	7,234	2,768	3,070	3,001
Pigs	151	160	153	216	258	206

products experienced during most of the ten years after 1883. Those who were habitual buyers of cake and cereal feeding-stuffs could, by 1890–95, obtain the same quantity as in 1870–7 for about a third less in outlay, and they therefore suffered little loss of income until the great drought of 1893 coincided with excep-tionally low prices. This cheapness of feeding-stuffs naturally discouraged the ploughing of the more costly land. In the ten years after 1885, farmers in the grazing half of England reduced their arable by some 600,000 acres mainly by reducing the area under bare fallow, wheat, pulse and barley; it can be deduced therefore that it was the heavy land arable which was most generally put out of tillage and into permanent grass, effecting further economies in costs. Most farmers continued to grow oats and barley to provide fodder and essential straw; on the lower area of tillage, they grew about the same proportion as previously of root and green crops to provide fodder for their animals, but they also bought more imported maize and feeding cake in these years.[11]

In spite, however, of cheaper feeding-stuffs, there was no general increase in cattle numbers during these years, only fluctuations round a level of some 4½ million in England, 1·1 million in Scotland, and 700,000 in Wales. But pigs, which (together with the unrecorded poultry) are primarily cereal consumers, increased in number, and there were more sheep in all the grazing areas, until the droughts of 1892 and 1893 brought a sharp fall in the English numbers. In all areas more horses were bred, partly for sale to urban and foreign buyers, but rather more horses were also recorded as used in agriculture in spite of the lesser area to be ploughed and cultivated; possibly farmers used a higher proportion of the young horses before selling them as full workers, or possibly more transport was required to and from the farms, especially in the milk-selling areas.

In contrast to the lower output and lower input that became general, there were some men who saved themselves by the opposite policy, that of increasing output by more than their costs. In all arable areas successful and vigorous farmers could be found who earned (in most years) an apparently satisfactory income by some intensification of the normal routine. Such were the men whose output of pedigree stock was sold to buyers from the Argentine to Canada, from Russia to Australia and New Zealand (Table 4). The successful breeders acquired not merely income but also fame in their generation and in the stud, herd and flock books. Such was the Essex farmer who sold green peas to the

[11] E. M. Ojala, *op. cit.*, Table XIX, p. 212.

London market, feeding the haulms and pods to his pedigree Suffolk sheep. Such were the Tory family at Turnworth in Dorset who, by 1900, were farming some 6,000 acres and breeding Dorset Down sheep; 'overhill, to the south, they raise corn and sheep; underhill, to the north, they are graziers and dairyfolk'.[12] Amos Cruikshank farmed at one time about a thousand acres of Aberdeenshire land to support his Shorthorns; his herd was sold as a unit in 1889 for export to the Argentine, but the shipment was delayed by a financial crisis in that country, and much of the herd was eventually bought by William Duthie of Collynie and Deane Willis of Bapton, two Shorthorn breeders who dominated the decades before and after the turn of the century.[13] Herefords

Table 4. *U.K. Exports of Live Animals: Five Yearly Averages*

	1875–9	1880–4	1885–9	1890–4	1895–9
Cattle: No.	456	2,779	2,295	3,288	4,387
Value £000	37	113	97	69	117
Sheep: No.	2,618	5,245	6,688	7,327	9,171
Value £000	23	41	46	51	102

were bought in large numbers for the American market from the 1870s, and in the next decade a new trade was provided by the stocking of the Argentine ranches. The famous Aberdeen-Angus cow Erica bred for Sir George Macpherson Grant a tribe of animals eagerly sought in succeeding generations both by foreign and British breeders. This trade extended beyond the pedigree herds to include the high-class commercial stock obtainable from many farms, such as those on each side of the Border which specialised in half-bred or Border-Leicester rams for the Cheviot flocks. Though markets were subject to the vagaries of pedigree fashions, exchange troubles and animal epidemics, the demand for breeding stock and for working horses supported the incomes of many farmers through the fall in livestock prices which elimi-

---

[12] Rider Haggard, *op. cit.*, vol. I, pp. 449, 261.
[13] I. M. Bruce, *History of the Aberdeenshire Shorthorn*, Aberdeen, 1923, p. 143.

nated, at times, the profits of those who bought store cattle when they were dear and sold them fat when meat was cheap.

Profits were also secured within the range of customary rotations by changing the type of sheep, the age of marketing and the kind of feeding. Falling wool prices had diminished the value of the older wethers, and this trend was intensified by the fall in meat prices which especially affected the prices of the large joints of fat mutton derived from the Lincoln and Leicester wethers. The statistics show that fewer sheep were kept to be recorded in two successive Junes and more were therefore sold at lighter weights and at younger ages, having consumed less food; more use was made of the rams of the new Down breeds – whether Suffolks, Dorsets, Hampshire or Oxfords – in preference to the slow-maturing Leicesters or the overfat Southdowns, while Cotswold and Shropshire ewes, either pure or crossbred, were becoming a popular method of providing mutton cheaply from grass.[14]

A second form of intensification lay in the introduction of special crops into the normal crop rotation. Swedes, turnips and mangolds were the traditional winter food for fattening stock on thousands of farms; but potatoes, carrots, cabbages, peas, beans and brussels sprouts might be sold for cash, and yet leave residues to support some winter fattening and the production of some farmyard manure. The main difficulties in the production of such crops were, first, the cost of transporting them to a railway station or the nearest town; second, the dislike of land agents for any green crop not consumed on the land; third, the supply of casual workers to plant, pick and pack; and fourthly, the uncertainty of the local markets. These were all crops where a good year implied a glut, low prices and a large proportion unsold, while high prices were only likely to be obtained if yields were generally low. Yet taken over an average of years, such crops might provide a profitable alternative to the traditional roots. The supply of

[14] Reports on Prize Farms, *J.R.A.S.E.*, vol. 25.ii, 1889, pp. 41, 53; W. J. Malden, 'Cross-bred Sheep', *J.R.A.S.E.*, vol. 76.iii, 1895, p. 226; Wilson Fox, *Report on Cambs.*, R. C. 1894, p. 12; T. W. Fletcher, 'Lancashire Livestock Farming during the Great Depression', *Agric. Hist. Rev.*, vol. ix, 1961, p. 28.

potatoes, for instance, was developed in these years by a colony of Scottish farmers round Hatfield; they took farms near railway stations, sold straw and potatoes by the truck load to the terminal markets at King's Cross, taking back to their farms the manure from the urban stables kept by the railway and omnibus companies.[15] Other farmers specialised on seed crops for the seed firms; the work of botanists and chemists employed by the agricultural societies was stimulating the demand for pure strains of seeds reasonably free from impurities and with a guaranteed degree of germination.

Yet another type of intensified production was developing in the East Anglian fens, on farms near large towns, and in north Cambridgeshire, in Bedfordshire and Kent, and round Evesham and Pershore. Here falling profits and rents from the traditional corn-growing enabled enterprising men to acquire land for fruit, bulbs, vegetables and flowers, again using as the basis of fertility the town manure which could be obtained virtually for the cost of carriage; the railways that took away the produce brought back the equivalent manurial value. The light and sandy soils, such as those round Ampthill and Biggleswade, were thus made to support an intensive output of small fruit and vegetables; heavier soils round Evesham and Wisbech were already proved to be suitable for plums and other tree fruit. The family of Chivers began a jam factory outside Cambridge about 1873 which provided a market for occupiers of small farms in the adjacent parishes of Histon, Cottenham, Willingham and Rampton; a similar industry developed in Mechi's parish of Tiptree in Essex, and in Perthshire round Blairgowrie. The statistics of these crops are difficult to interpret, owing to the changes in classification and to the general practice of under-cropping tree fruit and inter-cropping small fruit, but Table 5 shows, for the dozen most important counties, the recorded expansion in this type of cultivation.

In these twenty years, the total recorded area of market gardens more than doubled, and the area under small fruit doubled in the

[15] G. Brown, *Farming Yesterday and Today*, W. E. A., Hatfield, 1962, pp. 35–8 (No. 9 in 'Hatfield and Its People').

seven years for which figures were available; expansion was particularly rapid in Bedfordshire, Kent and Worcester, which includes the area round Evesham and Pershore. As fruit production increased in Kent, Surrey and Sussex, so the area under hops tended to fall in these old centres of hop production, but it was extending in the western counties of Hereford and Worcester. Hop

Table 5. *Area under Orchards, Market Gardens, Hops and Small Fruit. 1875, 1895*

| | 1875 | | | | 1888* | | 1895 | | | |
Acres	Orchards	Market Gardens	Hops	Small Fruit	Orchards	Market Gardens	Hops	Small Fruit
Great Britain	154,584	38,957	69,177	36,724	218,428	92,837	58,940	74,547
England	150,600	35,364	69,171	32,776	212,963	85,398	58,940	68,122
Wales	2,535	712	6	532	3,564	1,395	—	1,175
Scotland	1,449	2,881	—	3,416	1,901	6,044	—	5,250
Bedford	359	819	—	89	820	7,274	—	256
Cambridge	1,106	588	—	1,441	2,718	2,036	—	2,621
Essex	1,038	4,110	—	519	2,072	4,740	—	1,729
Hants	1,177	1,090	3,059	746	1,830	3,137	2,875	2,115
Hereford	24,095	53	5,984	175	26,538	220	7,553	774
Kent	12,032	4,028	43,614	12,344	23,260	12,516	35,018	22,272
Lancashire	1,848	1,052	—	1,360	2,915	2,010	—	2,517
Surrey	1,674	1,656	2,313	674	2,438	3,688	1,783	1,468
Sussex	1,618	809	11,360	483	3,005	2,465	7,489	1,501
Worcester	13,672	1,451	2,468	1,360	19,665	5,586	4,024	3,114
Lanark	482	204	—	1,343	715	1,684	—	2,065
Perth	302	308	—	542	434	636	—	747

* Small fruit was not separately recorded before 1888: some duplication is probable in the areas returned under small fruit and orchards.

growers had recently developed the use of wire instead of strings which had to be renewed yearly; creosote greatly lengthened the life of their poles, and crop sprays were beginning to control the pests of aphis and red spider. But the capital required to equip a hop-field with its poles and wires restricted hop-growing to the larger farms; the smaller men took up the easier investment in fruit and such vegetables as offered the chances of profitable markets in London and Birmingham. The recorded orchards include the large area of cider orchards existing in the western counties since time immemorial; but in these twenty years after

1875 Kent nearly doubled its orchards and there were substantial increases also in Cambridge, Hereford, Sussex and Worcester.[16]

NEW METHODS AND NEW MEN

Where drastic changes had become inevitable in farming systems, they were usually introduced by new men, bringing with them both different skills and different social customs. Let us suppose that an Essex or Suffolk farmer of the old tradition had decided that salvation lay in dairying mainly off grass, keeping only such arable as was required to provide straw for litter and the minimum of roots and fodder crops. It was unlikely that his landowner would have been willing to provide the required new buildings, fences and water supplies, until tenants working the old system had come and gone two or three deep. There would be the loss in valuation on the arable land, representing so much loss of capital to be repaid at the end of the occupation; there would be the expense of getting land into serviceable grass, and of buying the foundation stock.[17] Neither farm families nor the skilled ploughmen and shepherds would be willing to demean themselves by milking cows, churning butter or feeding calves – work done, if done at all on the large arable farms, only by the women servants. Neither the farmer nor his men had the knowledge or the experience to make the best use of grass; permanent grass was notoriously apt to be neglected on the arable farms, and usually received little in the way of manures or cultivation. Therefore, as rents fell to vanishing point in the depressed arable areas, despairing land agents sought tenants from those districts in the north and west where rents had fallen little, if at all, and where farming depended on livestock, grass and the farm families. From Devon and Cornwall the sons of farmers moved into the southern counties; from Wales and the Welsh border they fol-

[16] C. Whitehead, 'Progress of Fruit Farming', *J.R.A.S.E.*, vol. 19.ii, 1883, pp. 368–87; 'Fifty Years of Fruit Farming', *J.R.A.S.E.*, vol. 25.ii, 1889, pp. 156–73

[17] R. Hunter Pringle, 'The Future of Clay Land', *Agricultural Gazette*, May–Nov. 1887.

lowed their store stock on to the vacant holdings in the English Midlands; from Ayrshire and the Scottish uplands young men came east and south to occupy cheap farms from the Lothians down to Suffolk and Essex. Often they followed a previous connection in the potato trade or in livestock marketing or in milk distribution; but once an immigrant was successfully established in a new region, others easily followed from the same family or parish, taking up adjacent farms and thus mitigating for all the loneliness of exile in a strange land.[18]

Enticed by low rents and vacant holdings, these immigrants could afford to choose carefully, and to insist that leases contained no clauses prohibiting free cropping or free sale; they asked for, and often got, repairs, renovations and even new buildings to their own requirements. Hunter Pringle thought that more had been spent on farm buildings in Essex since 1880 than in the previous thirteen years, at least on estates with other income available; small estates were often too heavily encumbered and the buildings too ramshackle to be renovated to the standard required by new tenants.[19] On many farms valuations had lapsed on the bankruptcy of a previous tenant, when the outlying arable had tumbled down to grass; equipment and livestock were cheaper than before, so that less capital was required to stock a new holding; and these men from the north and west were not concerned with keeping up appearances, for they came from farms with lower incomes than the arable farmers regarded as normal. They therefore started with many advantages denied to their predecessors in the farms to which they went, but they also found disadvantages. The old type of corn growing and livestock fattening had proved

---

[18] R. C. 1894: R. Hunter Pringle, *Report on . . . Districts of Essex*, p. 43, and *Report on Beds., Hunts., Northants.*, p. 43; A. Spencer, *Report on Oxfords., Glos., Berks., Wilts.*, pp. 13–14; Primrose McConnell, 'Experiences of a Scotsman on the Essex Clays', *J.R.A.S.E.*, vol. 2.iii, 1891, pp. 311–25; J. Speir, 'Dairying in Scotland', *Tr. H.A.S.*, vol. 18.iv, 1886, p. 302; G. Brown, *Farming Yesterday and Today*, W. E. A., Hatfield, 1962, pp. 35–8; (No. 9, in Hatfield and its People); Rider Haggard, *loc. cit.*, vol. 1, pp. 510, 550; E. Lorrain Smith, *Go East for a Farm: A Study of Rural Migration*, Agric. Econ. Res. Inst., Oxford, 1932.

[19] R. Hunter Pringle, *Report on . . . Districts of Essex*, R. C. 1894, p. 59.

unprofitable, but the drier climate and chalky soils of the south and east were not so favourable to grassland as were other regions. Crushed bones, the standard manure for grass land in Cheshire, and even the new basic slag which was becoming popular in the north, had little effect on East Anglian pastures which gave a comparatively low output over a shorter season. The Ayrshire rotation of potatoes, leys and ryegrass cut for seed also broke down in the run of dry years in the southern half of England that began in 1892 and ended with the drought of 1901, in some parts a worse year even than 1893. Lack of water was also a serious handicap for the type of farming that depended on grazing animals over distant fields, and especially serious if those animals were milking cows. By no means all the immigrants solved these problems profitably, but enough survived to change in many areas the patterns of farming and of social life.

What evolved was a flexible system of cropping which turned farm produce into cash more quickly than the old method of growing roots to fatten, over twelve or eighteen months, animals whose manure, applied to roots, later provided fertility to yield grain for sale. Wherever a local market could be found, and buildings and water supplies were adequate, the new farmers developed milk as their main line, since it brought a regular inflow of cash. They grew oats rather than wheat and beans; they favoured grass rather than roots, for grass was cheaper to grow, it might yield a cash crop as hay, and it could be supplemented by cattle-cake or brewers' grains. They might rear their own calves, or winter young cattle on straw and hay and fatten them off the spring flush of grass to sell in June or July at 2–2½ years old, instead of carrying them on for another winter in yards to sell at heavier weights and a year older. On the clays in Essex and the midland counties, the high cost of cultivation and the profits derived from milk production led the new farmers to convert more and more arable into grass, as fast as landowners could be persuaded to pull down huge barns and rickety sheds and install proper cow stalls and dairies. In such parishes, twenty years of depression often swept away all the old farming families and many of the smaller gentry owning a few farms, together with the immemorial traditions of arable farming.

But local initiative was responsible for an almost equally drastic but quite different change in a number of parishes in Berkshire and Hampshire. George Baylis, the son of a Berkshire farmer, occupied 240 acres at Bradfield in Berkshire from 1866 and lost money steadily on the orthodox rotations. He then decided to apply the basic lesson of the Rothamsted experiments, that corn could be continuously grown without dung or sheepfold by applying ammonia and phosphates in artificial manures. He could not, of course, impose this revolution on a landowner, but in 1875 he bought 400 acres at Wyfield Manor, Boxford, near Newbury, on a series of mortgages, and adopted a rotation of corn, fallow and clover, from which he sold grain, straw and hay. On this light land in a dry climate, he specialised in autumn-sown barley, partly to give employment then to his men and horses and partly to ease the spring rush of sowing; threshing, hay-baling and ploughing occupied his staff during the winter. On this system, which closely resembled that being worked by the Prout family at Sawbridgeworth, he profitably grew grain and hay without livestock, and at a low cost in fertilisers and farm cartage; the only manure to be hauled was that from his stables, and there were no roots. From 1885 onwards, Baylis was offered by despairing owners and mortgagors in possession a series of other holdings, until he was farming 3,440 acres at the end of the century and some 10,000 acres in 1914; he had by then spent £90,000 or so out of his profits in buying the freehold of many of the farms he occupied. This demonstration of how to make profits from corn growing without livestock was largely ignored by his cautious neighbours in more than a dozen parishes, just as the Hertfordshire farmers had ignored the similar demonstration given by Prout for thirty years. But here and there, at the turn of the century, a farmer might be found who grew crops without manure, relying on fertilisers and fallows to maintain the fertility of the soil.[20]

[20] C. S. Orwin, *Progress in English Farming Systems. No. III. A Specialist in Arable Farming*, Oxford, 1930; J. Orr, *Agriculture in Oxfordshire*, Oxford, 1916, p. 22.

PRACTICE WITH SCIENCE

There were not many men who had the courage of Baylis and Prout, who both based their farming on scientific knowledge in defiance of established customs. Yet fifty years of steady and pains-taking work at Rothamsted had illuminated some of the complex problems involved in the nutrition of plants and animals. Sir John Lawes, Bart., and Sir John Gilbert (honoured in 1882 and 1893 respectively) had by 1895 established Rothamsted as the foremost school for agricultural research, and Lawes had endowed a trust which would ensure the continuation of the work after their lifetimes. Their research had elucidated the role of nitrogen in plant growth; their analysis of drainage waters, for instance, had demonstrated that a bare fallow in a dry climate stimulated the active production of nitrates in the soil, while a bare fallow under rain was leached of these soluble elements. Hence arose the disastrous results on the heavy soils after the run of wet seasons from 1875 to 1881.[21] The value of leguminous crops in the rotation had been traced to the existence of a microbe in the soil capable of fixing nitrogen from the air within root nodules which, when decayed, released an additional supply for the use of subsequent crops. This important discovery opened a new chapter in soil science; the concept of soils as an amalgam of chemical compounds became inadequate with the recognition of bacterial activity as a vital influence on the structure of soils and the nutrition of plants.[22] Such basic knowledge had been supplemented over the years by experiments on fertilisers and crop rotations organised by many persons and bodies – by the Royal Agricultural Society on the Duke of Bedford's farm at Woburn, under the charge of Dr Voelcker; by the Highland and Agricultural Society at their experimental station at Pumpherston under Dr Aitkin; and by groups of farmers in Agricultural or Chemical Associations opera-ting under the supervision of these trained chemists.

[21] J. B. Lawes and J. H. Gilbert, 'On the Drainage Waters collected at Rothamsted, Part II', *J.R.A.S.E.*, vol. 17.ii, 1881, pp. 311–50.

[22] J. M. H. Munro, 'Nitrifying Ferments of the Soil', *J.R.A.S.E.*, vol. 2.iii, 1891, pp. 702–17.

That 'amiable and accomplished lady' Miss Eleanor Ormerod [23] was employed by the Royal Agricultural Society at first informally and then formally from 1882 to 1892 as their consulting entomologist, advising on and elucidating the life cycles of insect pests. Much more had become known about the importance in health and disease of such insects, microbes, moulds and animal parasites, arousing hopes of their better control. Worthington Smith, working at Rothamsted, had identified the resting spores of potato blight within decaying crop residues and had thus traced an essential link between successive epidemics. Pasteur's investigation into the yeasts which operated in brewing had been extended to include the bacteria which controlled cheese-making and silage-making. Pasteur and other scientists had also traced the bacteria which caused certain diseases of animals, for example anthrax or 'splenic apoplexy'; they had shown that the anthrax organisms could lie dormant as spores in the soil almost indefinitely until they found a suitable environment for multiplication. [24] Furthermore, it had been discovered how to control anthrax by inoculation, and by the slaughter of infected animals and the burning of their carcases. The general acceptance of 'the germ theory' encouraged better hygiene on farms, and also made farmers more tolerant of the measures periodically imposed to restrict the major epidemics among animals. The exponents of the new knowledge were also pushing local authorities into stricter control over slaughter houses and food markets.

But in dealing with such matters, the veterinary profession and the medical officers of health became aware of the widespread existence of other diseases in animals which not only reduced farming profits but which endangered the health of humans. Such were contagious abortion and tuberculosis, which were found to be rampant in many dairy herds regularly supplying fresh milk. When sent for slaughter, badly infected animals might be

[23] Professor Scott, 'Recent Advances in the Science and Practice of Agriculture', *J. Farmers' Club*, May 1882, p. 81.
[24] Professor Scott, *op. cit.*; G. Fleming, 'Pasteur and his Work', *J.R.A.S.E.*, vol. 22.ii, 1886, p. 104.

condemned and destroyed by the sanitary authorities, but there was no such control over milk supplies; 'that there is grave danger arising from the use of tuberculosis milk must be accepted as proved without any shadow of doubt' was the verdict of one expert in 1891. It also became known that liquid milk might spread such human diseases as typhoid through its contamination from a human carrier while in transit from the cows to the consumers.[25] This new knowledge logically implied an extension of administrative measures, beyond those which discouraged adulteration and which controlled cattle movements in epidemics of pleuro-pneumonia, into the wide field of public health.

These developments in the agricultural sciences were regularly reported in the journals of the national societies and in the weekly farming press, which had flourished under an able group of editors. J. Chalmers Morton edited *The Agricultural Gazette* from its start in 1844 until his death in 1888. Five Macdonalds, four of them brothers, left the same Banffshire farm to become agricultural journalists. William became farming correspondent of *The Scotsman*; James became successively Secretary to the Royal Dublin Agricultural Society and then to the Highland and Agricultural Society; Alexander edited *Bell's Weekly Messenger* until he became the first editor of *The Farmer and Stockbreeder*, in which post he was succeeded by his nephew James; Charles followed William Fream as agricultural correspondent of *The Times*.[26] H. M. Jenkins was secretary and editor to the Royal Agricultural Society from 1869 until his death in 1886, having educated himself, while assistant to the Geological Survey, in geology, botany, languages and in the art of editing papers for publication. In these seventeen years, he regularly wrote reports on the farms entered for the local prizes; he made a special survey for

[25] G. Sims Woodhead, 'Relation of the Diseases of Animals to those of Man', *J.R.A.S.E.*, vol. 2.iii, 1891, p. 639; (with Professor McFadyean & A. P. Aitkin), 'Abortion in Cows', *Tr. H.A.S.*, vol. 19.iv, 1887, pp. 310–22; E. M. Crookshank, 'The Tubercle Bacillus', *J.R.A.S.E.*, vol. 2.iii, 1891, pp. 83–94.

[26] J. Scott Watson and M. E. Hobbs, *Great Farmers*, 2nd edn., London, 1951, pp. 281–6.

the Society on dairying in Cheshire, America, Denmark, France and Holland; he reported on silage and on agricultural education and was an Assistant Commissioner to the Royal Commission of 1881.

The work of such men did much to popularise the ideas of contemporary science among those engaged in the practice of farming. The early development of silage, for instance, was supported and encouraged by the careful enquiries conducted by H. M. Jenkins, Dr Voelcker and Dr Aitkin, and silage was made by a small number of farmers from 1870 onwards. It did not then become popular, partly because the quality of the product was still so variable, and partly because of the cost and difficulty of handling the green crops.[27] Similar informed reports made known the value of cottonseed cake as a cheaper substitute for the better known linseed; of the new potassic fertilisers, useful for the brassica crops; and of basic slag (a by-product of the Thomas process of steel-making, available in the 1880s) which was shown to give a remarkable stimulus to clovers in many pastures in the north and west.[28]

For those who wished to pursue this knowledge further, or encouraged their sons to do so, there were further opportunities available for education in the sciences and practice of agriculture. A few small grants had been provided from 1878 to schools entering candidates for examinations in the elementary principles of agriculture conducted by the South Kensington School of Science, and both the national agricultural societies had by 1895 well-established examinations leading to recognised diplomas. Short courses by travelling instructors in butter and cheese-making and in dairy hygiene had been organised with fair success by some County Councils and by some agricultural associations, such as that in Ayrshire; full-time courses of varying length were

[27] H. M. Jenkins, 'Report of the Practice of Ensilage at Home, and Abroad', and A. Voelcker, 'On the Chemistry of Silage', *J.R.A.S.E.*, vol. 20.ii, 1884; A. P. Aitkin, 'Silage made in Pits and Stacks', *Tr. H.A.S.*, vol. 19.iv, 1887, pp. 333–54.

[28] C. M. Aikman, 'Manurial Experiments with Turnips', *Tr. H.A.S.*, vol. 3.v, 1891, pp. 123–38; H. C. Pawson, *Cockle Park Farm*, Oxford, 1960, pp. 39, 50, 52.

also offered in these and other branches of agriculture at the new schools established by private enterprise at Downton in Wiltshire and Aspatria in Cumberland. At the university level, agricultural degrees were being offered at Leeds, Newcastle and Bangor to supplement those already in existence at Edinburgh, Aberdeen and at the Royal Agricultural College at Cirencester, which, shortly before its fiftieth anniversary, had added a professor of dairy farming to its staff. Yet these facilities attracted but a minute fraction of the agricultural population at which they were aimed. Most farmers and most farm men still learnt their trades by the ancient custom of 'working with father' until they were old enough to move elsewhere, either as hired man or as farmer. The stockman's eye, the ploughman's skill, the grazier's judgment of beast and grass, the ability to make a profit from the complex mixture of soil, climate, crops, animals and men, still could not be taught in schools and colleges; few farmers therefore had sufficient faith in 'book learning' to embark their sons on such courses as were available by 1895.[29] They seem to have been patronised more by those looking for a professional career associated with agriculture, as land agents, surveyors, landowners and journalists. But it was through the work of such men that the new scientific knowledge was gradually spread among farmers and began slowly to influence their farming practices.

One sign of this extension was the greater freedom of cropping adopted by many farmers, and tolerated, though seldom encouraged, by landowners of the more enlightened sort. Yet many estates continued to reproduce for new agreements leases full of ancient restrictions which might or might not be enforced, but whose existence inhibited alike profitable farming, sensible adaptation of rotations, and the more unscrupulous 'land-mining'. The agitation for free cropping and free sale of crops such as hay and straw was based in part on the knowledge that fertility could often be maintained more cheaply by fertilisers, green crops or town

[29] R. C. 1894, Memorandum by T. H. Elliott, vol. 3 of *Evidence*, pp. 481–4; W. Fream, 'Technical Education in Agriculture', *J.R.A.S.E.*, vol. 11.iii, 1891, pp. 95–112; J. Long, 'Education in Dairy Farming', *Tr. H.A.S.*, vol. 20.iv, 1888, pp. 1–105.

manure than by a rigid four or five-course rotation, with all fodder crops fed on the farm. But statistics show that in the main arable areas there was not much deviation from the ancient principle of a regular alternation of grain and fodder crops; there was only greater flexibility in the details of cropping, combined with the inevitable growth of permanent grass over much of the least fertile, most costly or most distant fields.

CHANGE AND CONTINUITY

The collapse of the rural structure in some parishes in eastern and southern England, the spread of bricks and paving stones over suburban farms, the conversion of remote valleys into slag heaps and pit shafts, had indeed changed such areas out of recognition. But over the greater part of Britain, what is surprising is the continuity of the farming traditions which had been established in the early years of Queen Victoria's reign and which were still dominant at the time of her Diamond Jubilee in 1897. The uplands on the boundary of Oxfordshire and Warwickshire have produced two vivid records which illumine the stable traditions of arable cultivation operating within the framework of distant landowners, large arable farms and the subdued, tolerant yet quietly hostile families which provided the manual workers and the craftsmen.[30] There were still the small upland holdings of Wales, depending on sheep and cattle, their families closely knit together by kinship and by the traditions of mutual help at hay-making and sheep-shearing, still separated by language, religion and ill-feeling from those who owned their land. Son succeeded to father on many Scottish farms throughout these sixty years, renewing leases and farming on the same pattern, changed perhaps only by a lower rent, a few more fields lying in grass, fewer men in the cottages and bothies, fewer women at work among the crops. The routine of calving cows, the twice-daily milking, the twice-daily drive to the railway station, or on the milk round was still practised on thousands of farms.

[30] M. K. Ashby, *op. cit.*; F. Thompson, *Lark Rise to Candleford*, Oxford, 1945.

On the other hand, twenty years of falling prices, profits and rents from arable farming had changed many attitudes towards agricultural problems. The process of bringing down rents had created bitterness which found frequent expression in public debates and pamphlets; the ill-feeling between tenants and land-owners was sharpened by the growing conflict between men who wished to farm and those who had newly acquired an agricultural estate as the background to shooting, deer-stalking, politics and social climbing. The collapse of many large arable farms into bankruptcy and dereliction had also stimulated argument over the merits of large and small farms. Social reformers deploring the insecurity of the manual workers and their drift into towns, politi-cal theorists convinced that peasant proprietors were natural conservatives, all argued that small farms produced a greater output per acre, suffered less from falling prices, and kept more families contentedly on the land, than did the large farms. Those who studied small farms and large farms in operation were not so enthusiastic. Small arable farms which were managed on the rotations and systems of the large farms had proved equally liable to bankruptcy, perhaps even more so if occupiers were also heavily mortgaged owners. Small farms flourished where they adopted the intensified systems to which circumstances were also pushing many of the larger men. Poultry, pigs, fruit, vegetables, early potatoes, these could give an income for small farms in the East Anglian fens, round Evesham and Pershore, in the coastal plains of Lancashire and Ayrshire, along both sides of the Hum-ber and Yorkshire Ouse, and, indeed, near any large town. Costs were low, because, it was said, such families applied two men's work for each man's wage they drew; yet some large farms on similar soils were developing an equally intensive output, with more economic buying and selling, better equipment and a larger labour force to cope swiftly with seasonal tasks.

In many parishes there was clearly an unsatisfied demand for small pieces of land to be run with some other interest – shop-keeping, cartage, quarrying, thatching, milling, inn-keeping; large farms unlet in the worst of the depression had sometimes

The Great Depression, 1885–1895

found occupiers if broken up into units that suited these purchasers who normally possessed little capital. A number of sympathetic landowners who had created new smallholdings on their
estates found the larger units taken up by such tradesmen, while
the farm men wanted mainly allotments or a small grazing field
for a cow. About 1870, W. H. Hall established a colony of small
farms on his estate near Cambridge occupied mainly by such
persons, and some 150 allotments were fully taken up by farm
men. Similar experiments were made by Sir Robert Edgcumbe
at Rew Farm, Martinstown, outside Dorchester, by Major Poore
at Winterslow in Wiltshire, and by Lord Carrington at Spalding.[31]
The heavy cost of creating these small units and providing fences
and roads seems to have been largely recouped in these cases, and
the promoters improved the welfare and security of many rural
families some of whom might otherwise have gone elsewhere. If
more were not provided by private enterprise in these years, the
causes must be found partly in the cost; partly in the natural
reluctance to break up established farms which were rent-paying
as they stood; partly in the dislike of many farmers to the idea of
employing men made 'independent' by such possessions; partly
because there seemed to be a large number already existing in
many areas. The special enquiry published in the Agricultural
Returns for 1875 showed that 70 per cent of the holdings in Britain
were under fifty acres in size; they included about 15 per cent of
the area under crops and grass in England and Scotland and 23
per cent in Wales. Yet in some arable counties these proportions
were much lower, from Wiltshire in the south with 7 per cent of
its area in holdings of fifty acres or less, through Northumberland
with 6 per cent, to Edinburgh (Midlothian) with less than 5 per
cent. And so in the 1890s politicians and social reformers were
urging the creation of small farms on many unwilling landowners
and county councils, as is described elsewhere (p. 331).

The historian can also detect in these years the acceptance by
many who were connected with farming of the idea that progress

[31] Rider Haggard, *op. cit.*, vol. 1, pp. 10–14, 273–9; vol. 2, pp. 6, 288; R.C., 1894,
Final Report, 1898, C. 8540, p. 33–7.

had passed them by, that higher incomes and better living were only for urban dwellers. Over much of England south of the Trent, along the eastern belt of Scotland and north of the Grampians, the falling prices of the twenty years from 1875-95 had lowered farm profits and rents, and had kept down farm wages at a time when falling food prices had improved the standards of consumption of many industrial workers. 'The terms of trade' had turned against these areas which were distant from the growing industrial regions; their incomes became stagnant and progressively fell behind those elsewhere. Farm wages in Suffolk, Dorset and Wales were at times barely half of those in the north of England and rents were also considerably lower. Neither the number of farm families nor the number of farm workers fell fast enough to offset, by a higher income per head, the fall in aggregate receipts from arable farming, the value of which in the 1890s has been estimated at barely half that obtained thirty years earlier.[32]

Between the Trent and the Scottish mountains, however, pasture farms and areas of intensive arable land supported higher incomes per acre, higher rents and higher wages than in those other regions to the north, south and west. Probably the very competition for land and labour forced the farmers in this industrialised region into better management and brisker oversight of their enterprises. Certainly, there was here little fall in profits or in rents in the ten or fifteen years before 1890, except in certain areas of arable farms distant from markets as on the Yorkshire wolds. Mr Fletcher has concluded that the value of gross output from Lancashire livestock farms increased by a third during the depression, during which labour costs fell by 15 per cent, rents hardly changed and feeding-stuff prices fell by more than a third.[33] The drought of 1893 and the low prices of milk and livestock at that time did bring a general check to profits and many abatements in rent on a temporary basis. But there was nothing here which resembled the drastic fall which had occurred over so much

[32] E. M. Ojala, *op. cit.*, Table xvi, p. 208.
[33] T. W. Fletcher, 'Lancashire Livestock Farming during the Great Depression', *Agric. Hist. Rev.*, vol. ix., 1961, p. 37.

of eastern and southern England, and which stands revealed in the annual value of lands assessed to Schedule A of the Income Tax, given in Table 6.[34]

Table 6. *Gross Annual value of land*
assessed to Sch. A of the Income Tax (including tithes).

£ooo	1879–80	1893–4	Per cent decrease
England	48,533	37,000	24¼
Wales	3,266	3,066	6
Scotland	7,769	6,252	19½
Great Britain	59,568	46,318	22

It was recognised that these figures underestimated the fall in rents retained. Assessments were only changed if a lower rent was formally agreed; they took no account of arrears and of temporary abatements, nor did they allow for the rise in the costs of maintenance, or for the expenditure often required to find and retain new tenants. A summary of the accounts for 1892 of forty-six estates submitted to the 1894 Royal Commission showed that rents received were 10 per cent lower than agreed rents, maintenance accounted for another 40 per cent, and additional expenditure took a further 11 per cent, leaving about 40 per cent of gross rents as the landowners' net income.[35] Since rents changed little in the grazing half of Britain, it can be deduced that landowners in the arable areas must, as a group, have been receiving little income from their agricultural land at the end of the nineteenth century, in spite of past and current investment.

The immediate effects of a long period of falling prices are almost uniformly disastrous for those whose profits take the first impact, in this case the arable farmers of Britain. Whatever benefits eventually emerged from the great agricultural depression, there remained the personal tragedies of thousands of

[34] R.C. 1894, *Final Report*, 1898, C. 8540, p. 22.

[35] R.C. 1894, *Final Report*, 1898, C. 8540, p. 27.

respected and competent families, who saw their incomes diminish, their capital evaporate and themselves plunged from secure social positions into bankruptcy and destitution. From them, the trail of poverty afflicted their land, which was often left exhausted and weed-infested; their landowners, whose finances were often undermined by falling rents and rising costs of maintenance; and their workers, some of whom were forced, briefly or for longer periods, into the workhouse, as they were thrown out of employment. In these depressed arable districts, farmers, landowners and workers alike suffered, in the years after 1875, from economic forces which they could but imperfectly understand, but which deprived them of those benefits of economic progress enjoyed by other sections of the nation.

11

The Decline of the Landed Interest

Irish Land Reform – The Reform of Local Government – Landlord and Tenant in the Crofting Areas – Commercial Contracts – Private Property in Land – Free Trade in Land – Landlords and the Depression – Death Duties and Land Values

THE peculiar status of landowners in our period – their political preponderance in both Houses of Parliament, their unquestioned supremacy in the social life and local government of the country-side, their wealth from agricultural rents and industrial develop-ment in a period of prosperity – could not be maintained as the century advanced. Other classes rose in economic status and political influence; after 1880 falling rents and capital values in the arable districts in Britain contrasted with urban growth and the expansion of the British Empire overseas; and by the beginning of the twentieth century the status of landowning had changed almost out of recognition.

With the rapid growth of industry and commerce, the repeal of the Corn Laws, and the changes in the general structure of society, agriculture could no longer be the cherished darling of Parliament, and Disraeli's dictum of 1850 '. . . that we should in all our legislation which refers to or regulates the distribution of power, consult the preponderance of the landed interest',[1] could not have been said in the 1880s. Though landowners continued to dominate the House of Lords all through the period, and to be numerically important in the House of Commons, they ceased to dominate both the great political parties. The gradual con-centration of the country gentlemen into the Tory fold, as the Whig influence declined and the parties crystallised into Conserva-tive and Liberal, is one of the characteristics of nineteenth-century

[1] *Hansard*, 19 Feb. 1850.

politics. Parliamentary time during the last thirty years of the century was much taken up by the Irish question, particularly by the problem of Irish land, and the heat generated by this had a profound influence upon the relations of landlord and tenant on this side of the Channel, as well as upon public opinion generally over the status of the landed interest.

IRISH LAND REFORM

It is not proposed to describe in detail the Irish land system and the various attempts made by English politicians to deal with it. The whole set-up of absentee landlords lacking capital or interest in land improvement; tenants on tiny holdings scratching a bare living; over-population and little alternative occupation; rack-renting, ruthless eviction and no tenant right; cattle-maiming, arson and violence when conditions became intolerable; all these called for reform, and after the Devon Commission's Report in 1845, Bill after Bill was introduced into Parliament, but never got very far. It was not till Gladstone became Prime Minister in 1868, saying 'my mission is to pacify Ireland', that things began to move.[2]

His Irish Land Act of 1870 was designed only to give compensation to tenants evicted from their holdings, and it was fiercely resisted, though eventually passed. But it accomplished little. Violence and terrorism went on under the Land League, and eviction continued. Another Land Act was thrown out by the .House of Lords, but Gladstone's Act of 1881 brought in new principles. Its aim was to secure for the Irish peasant the three F's, – Fair Rent, Fixity of Tenure and Free Sale. It set up Land Courts to fix rents by valuation, laid down that no tenant could be evicted so long as he paid his rent, and gave legal recognition to the custom that a tenant could nominate his own successor in the holding and sell his interest to him.

Here was dual ownership with a vengeance! Landlords

---

[2] *See* R. D. Collison Black, *Economic Thought and the Irish Question, 1817–1870*, Cambridge, 1960; J. L. Hammond, *Gladstone and the Irish Nation*, London, 1938.

relegated to being mere receivers of such rent as the courts allowed them to charge, and unable to get possession of their own land if they wanted it! There was bitter opposition to the Bill from Tories and Irish members alike, and it took up fifty-eight sittings in the House of Commons. Nevertheless it was carried at last, but in the state the country had then reached it did little to pacify the extremists or to help the peasants. Their poverty was such that in a time of falling prices many could not even pay the rents fixed by the Land Courts, and evictions continued.

By this time the whole question was exacerbated by the demand for Home Rule for Ireland, and though Lord Salisbury's Government tried for a time to restore order by ruthless coercion, it was becoming clear that a buying out of landlords was the only solution. The final stage of the Irish land question was Balfour's Land Purchase Act of 1903. Most Irish landlords, weary of the unequal struggle to collect their rents, and knowing that the question of Home Rule would soon come to the fore again, were only too willing to part with their land. A substantial loan was made by the British Government to allow tenants to purchase their holdings on easy terms, creating over the years a country of peasant proprietors.

Thus in little over thirty years the whole rural economy of a country had been turned upside down, and the drama and tragedy in the story were such that few in England could be unaware of it. The misery of the evictions, the terrible lawlessness and crime, the attempts at coercion, the murder of Lord Frederick Cavendish just after he was appointed Irish Secretary with a mission of conciliation, the obstructive tactics of the Irish Members in the House of Commons, the divorce case and fall of Parnell – all these were headline news, and to the British public it seemed that the Irish landlords were the root cause of the trouble. They had governed Ireland and had abused their power, and now their power was gone. As Lord Salisbury described it,

... for many generations Ireland has been governed through the influence and the action of the landed gentry. I do not wish to defend that system. There is a good deal to be said for it, and a good deal to be said against it. ...

By the Land Act of 1870, by the Ballot Act of 1872, by the Land Act of 1881, and last of all by the Reform Act of 1884, the power of the landed gentry in Ireland is absolutely shattered.[3]

But the Ballot Act of 1872 and the Reform Act of 1884 applied also to England. Was the power of the landed gentry being shattered here too?

THE REFORM OF LOCAL GOVERNMENT

By the Reform Act of 1867, the Parliamentary vote had been extended to householders in the towns, thus enfranchising a considerable number of working-class men. The extension of this right to householders in the country was a logical and inevitable step on the road to democracy in Britain. But it meant increasing the electorate by some three million voters and the leaders of the two great parties did not think such an extension urgent. The subject was kept alive in Parliament by the radical wing of the Liberals, notably by G. O. Trevelyan, and in the country by the supporters of Arch's Union, who realised that the status of the farm workers would never improve until they had the vote. This step was achieved by the Reform Act of 1884, which was followed by a measure abolishing the old two-member constituencies, and incorporating many of the small boroughs into the county seats. The immediate effect of this legislation was not significant; the counties of England (though not those of Wales and Scotland) continued after 1886 as before that date generally to return a majority of Conservative members. It was, indeed, a long time before farm workers could be induced to believe that the ballot was really secret; and Joseph Arch and George Edwards could tell more stories of victimisation and eviction of labourers for political reasons. The Rev. W. Tuckwell, Vicar of Stockton near Rugby, found that at the first election on the new register labourers in his parish were being asked to sign promises that they would vote for the Conservative candidate. He advised them to sign as

[3] Lord Salisbury. Speech at a dinner in London, 17 Feb. 1886.

asked, and then to vote for whom they pleased, because the ballot was secret, and he also wrote to *The Times* to expose this blatant piece of electioneering.[4]

If Irish landlords could be censured for neglecting their social and administrative duties through absenteeism, English landlords, on the other hand, could be accused of monopolising all the social and administrative power in the countryside. They normally controlled the rural Bench, the County Police, the Boards of Guardians, the Highway Boards, the granting of licences and all the other functions of local government. Their administration of the Game Laws and other offences against property, often making them judges in their own causes, was being fiercely criticised; their autocratic ways towards their own dependants, however benevolent their intentions, were often deeply resented, and the resentment was becoming articulate.

Rural local government had been a haphazard sort of business, *ad hoc* boards and committees springing up as the need arose, and as fresh functions were taken out of private hands by the community; but some attempt to control and direct it was made by the setting up of the Local Government Board in 1871. This body took over the Poor Law Board and matters relating to public health, and at first was concerned chiefly in checking any tendency of local bodies to exuberant spending. In the towns the Board dealt with elected Borough Councillors, but no one could call rural local government in any way representative. As Parliamentary democracy broadened, so public opinion began to demand representation in rural local government, and in 1888 the Local Government Act set up elected County Councils. Here was another whittling away of landlord power. Though landlords at first predominated on the new County Councils, they were joined by farmers, tradesmen, professional men and others, and no longer carried the full responsibility of County affairs which they had exercised for so long. But it took a brave man to contest a seat on the Council against his own landlord, and at that time it was impossible for a working man even to consider such a proceeding.

[4] W. Tuckwell, *Reminiscences of a Radical Parson*, London, 1895.

The difficulty of getting to meetings and the loss of earnings it would involve made it unthinkable.

The 1894 Act for the creation of Rural District and Parish Councils was at first welcomed by the farm labourers, who were encouraged by their Unions to stand for election. But they soon found that the Parish Councils' functions, being limited to the expenditure of a penny rate, were too small to effect any real alleviation in their condition, and as voting at parish meetings was by show of hands instead of by ballot, it was not easy to oppose the powers that be. In a few villages, such as Tysoe, without a resident landlord and with a leader such as Joseph Ashby, Parish Councils got down to the job which their limited powers allowed them, and successfully tackled problems of allotments and footpaths.[5] But in most places the parish meeting was used as an occasion for the squire and his lady and the vicar to explain their wishes to the village, and interest in democratic local government soon died away. Even today, on a wider franchise, a 30 per cent poll is considered quite high in a rural local election. Yet these local government reforms raised the status of the farmers who were able to serve on District and County Councils, giving them a wider experience of power and responsibility, which formerly they had only exercised in parish vestries.

LANDLORD AND TENANT IN THE CROFTING AREAS

In Wales and in the Highlands of Scotland, where the conditions of small family farmers were not so unlike those of Ireland, the parliamentary struggle over the Irish Land Acts was watched with interest by the tenants. Many of their landlords were absentees; they themselves were very poor, their holdings were too small to sustain them and they had little or no security of tenure. In Scotland, memories of the Clearances still smouldered, and the only remedy for poverty which authority had suggested was emigration. A Scottish Land and Labour League on the lines

[5] M. K. Ashby, *op. cit.*, p. 186.

of the Irish Land League was formed, but did not resort to the latter's violent methods.

The failure of the potato crop in 1882 brought great hardship, which was followed in some of the Scottish Islands by rioting and assaults on rent-collecting agents and on tenants of large sheep farms. The Skye crofters issued an appeal which gives some indication of their state of mind:

> Brothers and sisters of the South, we beg you to pull us out of the mire and Slough of Despond, and help us to show the lawyers, the sheriffs, and the Lord Advocate, who is the king of lawyer-eaten Scotland, that the God we worship in common with you intended the soil to provide for the necessities of the many and of the poor, and not to serve as . . . a pleasure ground for the few and the rich . . . .
>
> May God save the people in future from Lords, Lawyers and Liars, and all such Evildoers and unlawful persons who prevent just laws being made for the poor.[6]

The immediate result was the great Crofters' Commission set up in 1883 under Lord Napier to enquire into the conditions in these congested and impoverished areas. Poverty and hardship there was, caused mainly by the smallness of holdings, the primitive nature of their farming, their remoteness from markets, and the over-stocking of the common grazings which provided the main cash crop, store cattle. The crofters had no formal security of tenure and could be evicted at will, though many crofts had passed undisturbed from father to son for generations; the level of rents reflected more the competition for the inadequate area of arable land than the money incomes from the holdings, and yet barely paid the expenses of collection and management. The Commission recommended a double attack on these problems. Each crofting township was advised to elect an executive officer who would control the common grazings, enforce regulations about over-stocking, co-operate with the landowners in improvements, fencing and buildings, and organise the enlargement of the better crofts as others fell vacant. For it was recognised that there were still too many people trying to get a living in glens which could not

---

[6] Quoted by E. P. Thompson, *William Morris*, London, 1955, p. 406.

support them; the Commission recommended that occupiers of holdings rated at less than £6 a year should not be allowed any common rights, which might 'tend to fix them in a condition from which they ought to be resolutely though gently withdrawn'.[7]

The subsequent legislation went considerably further than these recommendations, and further even than the contemporary reforms in Ireland. The Crofters' Holdings (Scotland) Act, 1886, did not try to turn the crofters into occupying owners on the Irish model, for that implied that they would be liable to pay that half of the local rates still paid by their landowners; it gave them instead a unique status as hereditary tenants with fixed tenure and rents. A Crofters' Commission was established consisting of three members, of whom one had to be Gaelic-speaking and one an advocate of the Scottish bar. It acted as a Land Court on the Irish model in fixing rents in the scheduled crofting areas; such rents were to run for a minimum of seven years, and were to be based on the agricultural value of the holding to a crofter of normal ability, not on market value. On appeal by the crofters, the Land Court did generally reduce rents by a third to a quarter of the existing level, and also wrote off much of the accumulated arrears. Crofters were also given a perpetual tenure of their holdings, with right of bequest to members of their family, subject only to certain safeguards about payment of rent, residence and injury to or sub-letting of the holding. Landowners quickly found, however, that the Land Court was not willing to allow eviction even if these safeguards had been disregarded; and the Small Landholders (Scotland) Act, 1911, omitted to re-enact the clause requiring a crofter to be normally resident on his land.

The Crofters' Commission and the Board set up under the Congested Districts (Scotland) Act, 1897, also had powers to compel owners in the scheduled crofting areas to surrender land (even if more profitably let in sheep farms or deer forests) for the creation of new crofts and the enlargement of existing ones, at rents fixed by the Land Court on the basis of the agricultural value to the

[7] R.C. Crofters, 1884, C. 3980, p. 39.

The Decline of the Landed Interest

crofters. About 3,000 crofts were thus enlarged and about 640 new holdings carved out of adjacent farms between 1886 and 1912;[8] this process was also encouraged by the Royal Commission on Deer Forests (1892), which decided that about 11 per cent of the existing area given over to deer stalking for the privileged few was suitable for conversion into crofters' holdings.

A special form of land tenure had thus been devised for these communities in the Highlands and Islands of north-west Britain, which were separated by geography, language and culture from the main stream of economic and social change. Legislation and public opinion shielded them, from 1886 onwards, from any responsibility towards the land. As one commentator put it, 'the landlord was compelled to act in the interest of the crofters; the crofter was not compelled to act in his own interest'.[9] He was not even compelled to co-operate with his neighbours in the township over the improvement of common grazings and the prevention of over-stocking, as the Napier Commission had recommended. The security of tenure granted by the 1886 Act did at first encourage some crofters to erect buildings and to farm more vigorously, but this impetus was short-lived, for a higher proportion of each successive generation moved out of the crofting areas in search of wider opportunities and higher incomes.

Despite all that was done under these Acts, the general trend in population and agricultural production was downwards. Between 1891 and 1911 the total population of the crofting counties fell from 360,367 to 341,535. The agricultural trend in crofting areas may be illustrated by reference to the agricultural returns for the sixty-two parishes mentioned above. In these parishes the tillage acreage fell from some 70,000 acres in 1886 to some 66,000 acres in 1910. In the same period the total number of cattle fell from 95,000 to 84,000 and the total number of sheep from 947,000 to 889,000.[10]

[8] *Report of the Commission of Enquiry into Crofting Conditions, 1954,* Cmd. 9091, p. 14.
[9] J. P. Day, *Public Administration in the Highlands and Islands of Scotland,* London, 1918, p. 195.
[10] *Report of the Commission of Enquiry into Crofting Conditions,* 1954, Cmd. 9091, p. 14, para. 28. The 62 parishes are those in the Highlands and Islands in each of which less than 5 per cent of the holdings are over fifty acres in size (excluding rough grazings). See also R.C. on the Highlands and Islands, 1892; F. Fraser Darling, *West Highland Survey,* Oxford, 1955, Ch. 1.

COMMERCIAL CONTRACTS

The crofting areas provided a special case for which special legislation was thought justified in order to restrain the immediate
effect on rents and tenure of competition for the limited area of
arable land. A Land Court to fix 'fair' rents on the crofting model
was also recommended for Wales in 1896 by the great Royal
Commission on Land in Wales and Monmouth, which collected
evidence from farmers on the strength of their competition for
any vacant farms. But for the remainder of the nineteenth century,
it seemed reasonable to many politicians and most landowners
that the agricultural interests in Wales, as in England and in lowland Scotland, should make their own bargains over farm leases;
they were subject only to the Agricultural Holdings Act, 1883,
which was in the main a re-enactment of that of 1875, save that
it made compensation for tenants' improvements compulsory – contracting out became illegal.

The statutory recognition of the farmers' right to compensation
for improvements dates, therefore, from 1 January 1884. Improvements which changed the character of a holding could not rank
for compensation unless the consent of the owner had been obtained before they were made. For drainage, previous notice had
to be given but consent was not required; in a third class were
improvements for which neither notice nor consent was required,
such as the application of fertilisers and of cake-fed manure.

But agricultural practice is a good deal more complicated than
·even the clauses of an Act of Parliament. Farmers had a right to
claim compensation for the unexhausted value of their improvements at the end of their tenure, but there was no generally
accepted method of calculating this value. Some valuers favoured
cost incurred, with allowances for the time elapsed since the
manures were said to have been applied; the manurial residues
calculated first by Lawes and Gilbert and then by A. D. Hall,
from the Rothamsted experiments, were commonly used, even
upon other soils and under different farming systems. Other
valuers, after spending an evening buying drinks all round at the

local inn, had grave doubts over the documents with which the outgoing tenant supported his claim for costs incurred; they preferred to work on the estimated value to their incoming client, who might have other ideas on how to farm. Such divergences were particularly serious for landowners who could not immediately find a tenant for a vacant farm, as so frequently happened in the 1880s in the areas worst hit by the depression; they might be forced to pay considerable sums by way of compensation to an outgoing tenant for alleged improvements, sums which the incoming tenant, when found, refused to reimburse.[11]

One method of defence against such costs was for the landowner to put in counter-claims for dilapidations and for breaches of covenant – for not carrying out the often antiquated clauses still contained in many leases, which prohibited, for example, the taking of two successive corn crops, or the sale of hay and straw. Such counter-claims might well exceed any value claimed by the outgoing tenant, until a legal decision in 1895 ruled that a landlord could not receive more on his counter-claim than the value awarded to the tenant for his improvements. As a result of this decision, any tenant who wished to run down his landlord's farm could do so with impunity, so long as he refrained from claiming compensation at the end of his tenure.[12]

In spite of these difficulties, the Market Gardeners' Compensation Act, 1895, allowed tenants of agricultural holdings let as market gardens to claim compensation, at the end of their tenancy, for fruit trees and bushes, and for the more permanent vegetable crops, such as asparagus, planted by them. This Act had a wider application than its name might suggest, for landowners in the fruit and vegetable growing districts often allowed stated portions of ordinary farms to be classified as market gardens for the purpose of compensation. Other landowners, however, reasonably took fright at the prospect of being asked to pay, as compensation to an outgoing tenant, sums which might exceed the freehold value

[11] See p. 247.
[12] S. B. Druce, 'Agricultural Holdings (England) Act, 1883', *J.R.A.S.E.*, vol. 6.iii, 1895, pp. 182–5.

of the land, and which they might, again, never obtain from the next tenant. Some forbade the growing of any market garden crops, or specifically wrote into the lease that none of the farm was to be regarded as a market garden; others, especially in the west, themselves provided fruit trees which they bound the tenants to cultivate and prune, thus eliminating the legal right to compensation.[13]

From the point of view of tenant farmers, therefore, their right to compensation for the unexhausted value of improvements (made with or without the consent of the owner) was chiefly hindered after 1884 by the clauses inserted into leases which controlled cropping and the sale of specified products. And it was these residuary powers which were abolished by the next stage in the statutory control of landlord and tenant, the Agricultural Holdings Act, 1906.[14] The Act rendered null and void all covenants which prescribed courses of cropping or prohibited the sale of specified crops; so long as the fertility of the holding was maintained, the tenant could farm as he chose, subject to the right of the landlord to prescribe the rotation in which the farm must be left in the last year of the tenancy. This was the practice introduced by Coke of Norfolk into his improving leases a hundred years earlier.

The provisions for compensation were also extended by allowing the tenant to claim, at the end of his lease, for the cost of repairs which devolved upon the landlord under the contract of tenancy but which the landlord had failed to execute; and to remove from the holding any buildings or other fixtures which he had erected. These clauses reflected the state of poverty to which the long depression had reduced many landowners, who could no longer afford to provide or to maintain the essential equipment of their property.

Finally, tenants of agricultural holdings were given the right to claim compensation for the costs of disturbance if they were given notice to quit or not allowed to renew a lease, for reasons inconsistent with good estate management. The intention, to give

[13] A. D. Hall, *A Pilgrimage of British Farming*, London, p. 179.
[14] Embodied in the consolidating act, the Agricultural Holdings Act, 1908.

greater security of tenure to all tenant farmers, was laudable, but this clause 'opened the door to endless litigation by its bad drafting and by such vague, almost meaningless phrases'.[15] Almost any notice to quit was consistent with good estate management, including that given when a farm was sold to a County Council for breaking up into small holdings under the 1908 Small Holdings Act; the original tenant received no compensation for the costs of being turned out of his tenancy in favour of the tenants of the County Council concerned.

In the years immediately before the first world war, an exceptionally large number of estates came into the market, brought there, it was held, because the successive Agricultural Holdings Acts and the death duties imposed on private estates had destroyed the security of land as a long term investment. Many occupiers were offered the opportunity of buying their farms, but once again it was shown how few farmers wished, even if they were financially able, to assume the responsibilities of ownership, with all that was involved in legal costs on purchase and taxation on capital and income.[16] Jesse Collings several times introduced a Bill into the House of Commons which would authorise State loans to occupiers for the purchase of their farms on the Irish model, but there was not much support for the project. As an alternative solution, the Agricultural Holdings Acts, 1910 and 1914, enforced payment of costs of disturbance whenever a tenancy was terminated on sale of the holding. Another long-standing grievance of many farmers had been mitigated by the Ground Game Act, 1880, which allowed occupiers to destroy rabbits and hares on their farms notwithstanding any clauses to the contrary in their leases; the Agricultural Holdings Act, 1906, also allowed compensation for excessive damage to crops inflicted by other game which tenants might not be allowed to kill, though few tenants were bold enough to operate such powers.

[15] A. H. H. Matthews, *History of the Central Chamber of Agriculture*, London, 1915, p. 199.
[16] *Report of the Dept. Committee of the Board of Agriculture on Tenant Farmers and the Sales of Estates*, 1912, Cd. 6030, p. 12. See also p. 316.

By the outbreak of war, therefore, the State had so far altered the balance of economic advantage between landowners and tenants that occupiers could farm in any way they pleased; and they could claim compensation at the end of their tenancy for the unexhausted value of any improvement made, and for the costs of disturbance. Landowners still had the right to choose their tenants, to agree with them the rent properly payable and (outside the crofting areas) to terminate any tenancy on a year's notice or at the end of a dated lease, subject only to the payment of such costs.

PRIVATE PROPERTY IN LAND

The conviction that private property in land gave too much power to individuals goes far back in British history. In the nineteenth century the desire for a better social order, which grew as the working classes became more politically conscious and better educated, did not at first concern itself specifically with land. Other problems seemed more pressing, such as the right to organise labour and the attainment of the Parliamentary franchise. It was not until the last quarter of the century that British Socialism really became an articulate movement, induced by despair that neither of the two existing political parties would ever do more than tinker with the pressing social problems. The movement drew its philosophy from many sources, both home-grown and imported, and one of its basic tenets was the common ownership of the means of production, of which land was one of the most important. A Land Nationalisation Society was started to advocate the gradual taking over of land by the State, with compensation to dispossessed land-owners, and much play was made over inflated ground rents in growing towns, and the injustice of such unearned increment. Twice during the 1880s the Trades Union Congress passed a resolution in favour of land nationalisation, and it has remained a fundamental principle of Socialism ever since, without yet becoming a practical political issue.

The ruling classes did not take the early Socialist movement very seriously; to them it seemed mere theory, slightly blasphemous and revolutionary, but unlikely to have genuine political repercussions. Then a book was published at the end of the 1870s which stated the case against private property in land in no uncertain terms. This was Henry George's *Progress and Poverty*. George was an American, and his attack on private property was ethical as well as economic, as something contrary to natural law and justice, and the main cause of poverty and distress. His remedy was simple: to abolish all taxes except a single tax on land values, so that the State would eventually become the owner of all land without exercising any of the functions of a landlord, and land would be occupied only by those who worked on it. It is hard to understand today why the book was such a success. It seems curiously unreal and indigestible, but it went into many editions and was widely discussed. Its emotional appeal was strong, and for those in a hurry to improve social conditions it seemed direct and simple. The practical Socialists who found expression in the Fabian Society would have none of it, seeing the economic fallacies upon which it was based. Nevertheless it had a considerable influence on public opinion, and the Land Restoration League was founded to propagate its principles. Subscriptions were raised during the 1890s to send speakers in red caravans into the countryside, where they distributed leaflets and held open-air meetings. The Red Vans were a new phenomenon in the villages, and naturally they had a mixed reception. But the very fact that they could go into the heart of the enemy's country and preach such sedition as this was an indication of how far public opinion had moved in twenty years. In the 1870s it had been hard enough for agricultural workers to form unions to negotiate wages; now they could openly listen to men telling them that their landlords were robbers who had stolen the land from the people. The captions on the Red Vans read 'Fair Rents, Fair Wages, The Land for All' on one side, and on the other 'Justice to Labour, Abolition of Landlordism'. They would pitch on the village green, if there was one, and the speakers would then call round the shops and houses announcing a meeting in the evening. The meeting would open with songs, followed by speeches describing conditions of village life and explaining the aims of the League, and often ending with recruiting for the unions.[17] The labourers heard them with interest. Times were bad, Arch's National Union was dead, and cash wages had dropped from the levels they had reached in the 1870s. But attempts were being made to keep the union spirit alive, and the speakers of the Red Vans worked with the union organisers where they found them.

Landlords could hardly be expected to welcome the vans, and in some places League speakers were turned off and not allowed to hold meetings, but for the most part they were unmolested, and covered large districts in the eastern and southern counties, until their funds ran out. Meanwhile the Land Nationalisation Society was sending out Yellow Vans to some parts of the country to propagate its doctrines in the same way.

FREE TRADE IN LAND

But side by side with these theoretical attacks on private property in land, a more specific attack was developing in other sectors of society. In the 1860s, Britain was prosperous, towns were growing, railways were still being opened in the remoter parts of the country, new factories and housing for workers were needed. The middle classes, with their growing political power and rising standards of living, were moving out from the centres of towns to pleasant surroundings in the suburbs. New schools were being opened, and there was much building activity of all kinds. But the acquisition of land for all these purposes was not easy. As we have seen, family settlement prevented many owners from selling, and the tendency was still for the big landowners to add to their estates rather than to reduce them. The various Settled Land Acts had been passed for the benefit of the landowners, to enable them to grant leases, to borrow to improve their estates, etc. Now the question was beginning to be asked – is it for the common

[17] M. K. Ashby, *op. cit.*, pp. 151–7.

good of the country that land should be in the hands of a comparatively few people, or should it be more widely distributed?

John Stuart Mill drew attention to the idea of community-created value, or unearned increment – the fact that land was limited in quantity, and needed for all sorts of community purposes by a growing population, gave to particular sites an inflated value which those who owned them had done nothing to earn. The operation of the law of supply and demand meant that owners of potential building land, such as that on the outskirts of towns, could, when they were able and willing to sell, get prices far higher than its normal agricultural value. The Land Tenure Reform Association was founded in 1870, with Mill as its Chairman, and he was clearly coming to the belief that the State must intervene to stop the exploitation of the community, but his death prevented his making any real impact upon the problem – a problem which has baffled legislators up to the present day.

The demand for 'free trade in land' thus had a twofold attack. It criticised the stranglehold which a numerically small class had upon one of the nation's most valuable assets, a monopoly of that upon which urban development depended; and it criticised the effect which the monopoly had upon agriculture and the promotion of good farming. The arguments that settled estates prevented expenditure on estate improvement were familiar enough. Pusey and Caird had stated them forcibly, and they were voiced again every time the subject came up in Parliament. The *Report of the Committee of the House of Lords on the Improvement of Land*, published in 1873, had added fresh evidence showing that a vast amount of draining and building was still needed if the land were to be efficiently farmed. In spite of every encouragement in the shape of Government loans, the spread of knowledge of better techniques, and the increased return to be expected from farm improvement, over large parts of the country, owners of settled estates were not doing their job, and the country was suffering accordingly. 'The case for Parliamentary consideration lies in this, that the improvement of land, in its effect upon the price of food and upon the dwellings of the poor, is a matter of public interest.'[18]

There was also the argument that land should be more readily available to men who wished to farm as they pleased, without the restrictions of a lease or covenant. It was almost impossible for a tenant to buy a farm; any freehold which came on the market was generally snapped up by the nearest large landlord, for the idea of 'rounding off the estate' was still prevalent.

The publication of the Census figures for 1871 gave an impetus to the movement. Only some 30,000 people returned themselves as 'landowners', a figure which was clearly absurd, but which gave useful ammunition to those who were attacking the monopoly of an apparently small class, and which they were not slow to use. To combat some of the wild statements which were being made about the concentration of land in a few hands, the Duke of Richmond called upon the Government to compile a more accurate list of owners of land; so another census was undertaken by the Local Government Board, by means of the valuation lists for local rates.

The *Return of Owners of Land*, published in four volumes in 1873, gave the number of owners as nearly a million, an equally impossible figure. When the *Return* was analysed it appeared that some 700,000 people were owners of property of less than one acre, which meant a house and garden, not agricultural land. 120,000 names appeared in the group of owners of one to ten acres, and many of these were also clearly owners of residential property, small parks and orchards, rather than yeoman freeholders. But what really distorted the picture was that great landowners who held land in several counties appeared in each as separate owners, so that the total acreage of their property could not be ascertained. The Duke of Buccleugh appeared fourteen times, and 525 members of the Peerage appeared as 1,800 separate owners. When to all this was added the mis-spelling of names, the confusion of double surnames, the fact that many leaseholders who paid their own rates were put down as owners and that much Church and Charity land appeared under names of individuals,

[18] S.C. 1873 (H.L.) (Lands) p. iii.

it is clear that the *Return* did not begin to give an accurate picture, and did nothing to dispel the accusation that the land of Britain was owned by a very small fraction of the population.

Various people made detailed analyses of the *Return* – the New Domesday Book as it came to be called. They produced startling calculations, such as that four-fifths of the soil of the United Kingdom was owned by under 7,000 people, that the peerage alone owned one-fifth, that nearly a quarter of the whole of Scotland was in the hands of twelve owners, and half of it in the hands of seventy.[19] John Bateman made a very intensive study of the returns, writing personally to all owners of 3,000 acres and over to check their entries, and then tabulating them county by county under the following classes:

Peers, Great Landowners, (commoners owning estates of 3,000 acres and over) Squires, (estates between 1,000 and 3,000 acres), Greater Yeomen, (between 300 and 1,000 acres) Lesser Yeomen, (100 to 300 acres) Small Proprietors, (1 to 100 acres) Cottagers, (all holdings under 1 acre) Public Bodies.

Summary Table of Landowners in England and Wales[20]

No. of Owners	Class	Extent in Acres
400	Peers and Peeresses	5,728,979
1,288	Great Landowners	8,497,699
2,529	Squires	4,319,271
9,585	Greater Yeomen	4,782,627
24,412	Lesser Yeomen	4,144,272
217,049	Small Proprietors	3,931,806
703,289	Cottagers	151,148
	Public Bodies. The Crown, Barracks, Convict Prisons, Lighthouses, etc.	165,427
14,459	Religious, Educational, Philanthropic, etc.	947,655
	Commercial and Miscellaneous	330,466
	Waste	1,524,624
973,011	TOTAL	34,523,974

[19] Joseph Kay, *Free Trade in Land*, London, 1879, pp. 14, 15; G. C. Brodrick, *op. cit.*, p. 164.

[20] J. Bateman, *Great Landowners of England and Wales*, London, 1883, 4th ed., p. 515

His summary given above is probably the most accurate that it is possible to get of the distribution of landownership at the time.

Meanwhile the campaign for the reform of the Land Laws continued. The attackers were careful to emphasise that they were not criticising the institution of private property in land as such. They had no sympathy with the views of Henry George, and no personal vendetta against landlords. Private property in land was highly desirable, they wished to see it more widely diffused, and the reforms they advocated were legal ones, not revolutionary.

Certainly reform was needed. The drawing up of a deed of transfer of real property was then an awesome business. The title to ownership had to be investigated, often back through generations, all the charges and claims on the land, and every possible contingency which might arise, had to be set out in detail. As the legal cost of the transfer was calculated upon the length of the deed as finally drawn up, it was an opportunity for the lawyers of which they took full advantage. And if it came to a serious dispute over title or succession the case went to the Court of Chancery, where it might drag on for years with the costs steadily mounting – as in that of Jarndyce *v.* Jarndyce in *Bleak House*, where the whole estate was finally swallowed up in costs, and most of the interested parties were ruined.

Several great lawyers, successive Lord Chancellors, tried their hands at the reform of 'that tortuous and ungodly jumble, the English law with regard to real property'. Lord Westbury, Lord St Leonards and Lord Cairns each attempted, between 1860 and 1880, to simplify land transfer by such means as setting up a Registry of Titles and so on, but as they were only permissive, they had little success. It was not until 1881 that the Conveyance and Law of Property Act introduced considerable simplification of the whole process, and the Solicitors' Remuneration Act of the same year made the rates payable for conveyancing dependent upon the value of the property, not upon the length of the deed.

Finally, through Lord Cairns's Settled Land Act of 1882, the limited owner was allowed to sell, improve or lease his estate as though he were an owner in fee simple, almost the only fetter being that he could not sell the family mansion without the consent of his successor. Thus the long debate about settled estates was concluded at last, though there were still many complications about the Law of Property which were not unravelled until Lord Birkenhead's Act of 1925.

LANDLORDS AND THE DEPRESSION

The economic effects of the great depression upon farming are considered elsewhere in this book. In the first years, the wet seasons, bad harvests and outbreaks of livestock disease appeared as no more than temporary setbacks – natural phenomena such as were to be expected from time to time, which would pass, leaving things much as they were before. The reaction of farmers after a bad season was to represent that they could not pay their rents in full. So early as 1876 a tenant of Lincoln College, Oxford, was writing to the Bursar: 'The times are very bad with the farmers at this time and I hope you and the other Gentlemen will take our condition into your merciful consideration and take something off the rent.' And in 1880 it was noted in the College Minutes that 'the tenants came to dine but not to pay'.[21] For the most part landowners were prepared to give remissions of rent, hoping to recover them when things improved. But as time went on, there was no rapid recovery of farm prices; the remitted rent seemed likely never to be paid, tenants were going bankrupt, and it was difficult to replace them; then landlords found that economies were necessary if income and expenditure were to be balanced. These economies first took the form of a slowing-down of estate improvement and maintenance; building operations on farms and cottages were drastically cut, and only the most necessary repairs carried out.

The landowners who were hardest hit by the depression were those in the arable areas, who were entirely dependent upon farm rents for their income, and for some of these the situation was becoming serious. Cutting down personal expenditure whilst

[21] V. H. H. Green, *Oxford Common Room*, London, 1957, pp. 288–97.

continuing to live in the family mansion was very difficult, in the expansive way of life in the country which was then traditional. Some of the carriage horses might be put down, the second foot-man given up, the greenhouses closed, part of the park let for grazing, the visits to London curtailed; but these made little difference, for the traditional hospitality, county subscriptions, charity to dependents, and family obligations, had to go on.

John Bateman, in the preface to his *Great Landowners*, gave an analysis of the expenditure of a small estate at that time, which may well have been typical:

... For the benefit of guileless fundholders who have not as yet dabbled in land, I will give them what I consider a fair specimen of what a 'landed income' of 5,000*l* a-year means when analysed. My typical 5,000*l*. a-year squire shall be called –

STEADYMAN, JOHN of Wearywork Hall, Cidershire.

	acres	g. an. val.
b. 1825, s. 1860, m. 1851	3,500	5,000
	£	£
Deduct for value in the rate-books put upon mansion, grounds, fishponds, etc.	220	
Deduct also the value put upon cottages lived in rent free by old workmen and pensioners of the late Mr Steadyman	30	250
Leaving a clear rent roll of ...		£4,750
Now deduct as under:		
His late father's two maiden sisters, Jane and Esther Steadyman, who each have a rent charge of £180 per annum. (N.B. Both these old ladies seem immortal)		360
His mother, Lady Louisa Steadyman, a rent charge of		700
His sisters, Louisa, Marian and Eva (all plain), each £150		450
His brother, Wildbore Steadyman, who was paid off and emigrated but almost annually comes down on the good-natured head of the family for say		50
Mortgage on Sloppyside Farm and Hungry Hill (started when his father contested the county), interest		650
do. on Wearywork End (started when his one pretty sister married Sir Shortt Shortt, Bart., and was paid off), interest		150
His estate agent, Mr Harrable, salary		150
Carried forward		£2,510

Brought forward	£2,510
Keep of a horse for do., £35; house for do. £45	80
Average of lawyer's bill (settlements, conveyances, etc.)	60
Average cost of farm repairs, etc.	350
Draining tiles furnished gratis to tenants	40
Repairs to family mansion	70
Voluntary church rate, school at Wearywork, do. at Wearywork End, pensions and purely local charities	175
(N.B. – If Mr S. is a Roman Catholic, which I do not think he is, a private chaplain, school, etc., would increase this to at least £225.)	
Subscription to county (Liberal or Tory) registration fund	10
Subscription to Cidershire Foxhounds (£25) and Boggymore Harriers (£5)	30
Do. to the Diocesan–? (everything now-a-days is Diocesan, we shall soon be taking pills from Diocesan dispensaries)	25
Other county subscriptions – hospitals, flower shows, races, etc.	35
Returned 15 per cent of rents in 'hard times', averaging perhaps one year in five (would that we could say so now, 1882)	150
Loss on occasional bankrupt tenants (Mr Harrable dislikes distraint) average	30
Arrears of rent, say annually £300, loss of interest thereon at 5%	15
Income-tax at 4d. in the pound on rents paid and unpaid	83
Insurance on all buildings.	55
	£3,718

Leaving our worthy squire the magnificent annual sum of £1,032 to live upon. The subscriptions, I think I may say, are hardly over painted – being, as folks say, 'the least that can be expected from a person in Mr S.'s position.'[22]

Some landowners tried to solve the problem by letting the family mansion, with the shooting and all other amenities, and taking the whole family to live on the Continent, where the cost of living was cheaper. This meant leaving the property to be run by an agent, and did not always make for good estate management. Others, after the passing of Lord Cairns's Settled Land Act, were able to sell part or even all of the estate; in the 1890s fortunes were being made in South Africa and on the Stock Exchange, and it was still fashionable for a wealthy man to want 'a place in the

[22] John Bateman, *op. cit.*, p. xxiv.

country', and to display 'the mystical reverence for the rights of property which is characteristic in all ages of the *nouveaux riches*'.[23]

Landowners who had other sources of income met the depression with less difficulty. The Dukes of Bedford, with all the resources of London ground rents behind them, were able to make generous remissions of rent to farming tenants, in every year between 1879 and 1896, some of up to 50 per cent.[24] At the same time practical steps were taken to help tenants, by assistance with drainage, laying down land to grass, putting up implement sheds, and encouraging in every way farmers who were trying to keep going. But where a farm was being badly run down and it was apparent that the farmer had thrown his hand in, the Duke would take the farm in hand himself and get it into condition again before finding a new tenant. The Bedford property had been a model of good estate management all through the nine-teenth century, and managed to keep up the tradition through the depression when many landlords just let things go.

Another landowner with ample financial resources behind him was Lord Wantage, who owned an estate of 26,000 acres on the Berkshire Downs. Farmers in this area, farming on a four-course rotation with corn, roots and sheep, were particularly vulnerable in the depression, and there were many failures and bankruptcies. On Lord Wantage's estate, in spite of heavy remissions of rent, many tenants threw up their holdings, and successors could not be found for them. Lord Wantage met this by taking the land in hand and farming it himself. He had at one time some 13,000 acres which he farmed as a single unit. He described his system thus:

> You get a superior sort of agriculturalist to manage the land, a better man in knowledge, both theoretical and practical, in training and in capacity, than the neighbouring farmers, so that he can set an example to the whole country round; farmers see the work better done, and the labourers are not slow to find it out. I employ one head bailiff only for all the land I have in hand. He buys everything and sells everything, and under him are only ordinary working foremen. In farming on a large scale there is great economy; you can use

[23] R. H. Tawney, *Religion and the Rise of Capitalism*, London, 1926, p. 148.
[24] Duke of Bedford, *A Great Agricultural Estate*, London, 1897, Ch. vi.

machinery more advantageously, and you can diminish the number both of labourers and horses.[25]

This was a more useful demonstration of landlord farming than the more usual home farm of pedigree stock which lost money every year. At the same time Lord Wantage encouraged the tenants who remained by improving their buildings and erecting good cottages to enable them to keep their labourers. So the Lockinge estate weathered the depression without depreciating the property, thanks to the capital resources from banking which its owner possessed.

The Duke of Bedford and Lord Wantage are examples of what wealthy landlords could do to keep things going in the depressed areas. But it must be remembered that over large parts of the country there was little distress, and small call for landlords to make sacrifices or adjustments. In the regions of family farmers and livestock production, farming went on and rents were paid. Lancashire livestock farmers flourished in the 1880s and 1890s, and the demands for remissions of rent were negligible in that county.[26] On Sir Frederic Knight's Exmoor estate, rents were paid in full, and the landlord's own farming operations (he was farming 9,000 acres) continued successfully.[27] In another part of the country, Savernake Forest, the fifth Marquess of Ailesbury, at the age of fifty-three, succeeded to a practically bankrupt estate in 1894. His predecessor had contracted immense debts, a long and disastrous lawsuit had gone to the House of Lords and been lost, no repairs or maintenance had been done for years, many tenants had given notice to quit, and rents were not coming in. The Marquess immediately set about rehabilitating the estate. By rigid personal economy, letting the mansion and living himself in a small house, he gradually repaired or rebuilt the farms and buildings, and began the replanting of the Forest. It was a gallant struggle, and before his death in 1911 he had pulled round the

[25] *Lord Wantage, V.C., K.C.B. A Memoir, by his Wife*, London, 1907, pp. 375–403.
[26] T. W. Fletcher, 'Lancashire Livestock Farming during the Great Depression' *Agric. Hist. Rev.*, vol. ix, 1961, p. 37.
[27] C. S. Orwin, *The Reclamation of Exmoor Forest*, Oxford, 1929, Ch. vii.

affairs of this ancient estate, which had been in his family since Norman times, and was able to hand it on unencumbered to his successor.[28]

Another effect of the depression upon British landlords was that they gradually ceased to be the leaders of the industry, and the initiative and enterprise in experiment passed to the farmers and to the agricultural scientists. Farmers were better educated, and the Agricultural Holdings Act of 1908 took away the last vestiges of landlord control of farming operations. In the same year, the Lincolnshire Farmers Union was founded by Colin Campbell, a Scottish farmer who had migrated to that county, and this organisation speedily developed into the National Farmers Union. It is significant that voting membership was confined to tenant farmers and owner-occupiers. Before this, the various agricultural societies and clubs, the County Chambers of Agriculture and so on, had been joint affairs of landlords and farmers, with the landlords very much in the ascendant. Now the farmers had their own society, and its rapid organisation of branches in every county soon gave it a position from which it could speak with a united voice for the whole industry. In the First World War it became the political force with which the government could negotiate, a position from which it has never looked back.

DEATH DUTIES AND LAND VALUES

A blow to landlord privilege, the effects of which were not immediately apparent, came in 1894. In the Budget of that year, death duties were for the first time imposed upon agricultural property. Before that estate duty was only levied on other forms of property, but from henceforth it was to include, as defined by the Finance Act 'agricultural land, pasture and woodland, and also including such cottages, farm buildings, farm houses and mansion houses (together with the lands occupied therewith) as are of a character appropriate to the property'. Where a fortune consisted of stocks and shares, it was easy to sell enough to pay the death duties, but

[28] The Earl of Cardigan, *The Wardens of Savernake Forest*, London, 1949.

with land there was not always a ready market, and the old passionate desire to keep and hand on the family estate died hard. But the climate of opinion was changing, and as Lady Bracknell put it: 'What between the duties expected of one during one's lifetime, and the duties exacted from one after one's death, land has ceased to be either a profit or a pleasure. It gives one position and prevents one from keeping it up. That's all that can be said about land.'[29]

The great territorial magnates who had dominated the country for so long had lost their pride of place, as was apparent when a Liberal Government was returned in 1906 with a big programme of social reform. Lloyd George's Budget of 1909 proposed to raise the additional revenue required for Old Age Pensions and Health Insurance by a heavy increase in death duties, and by a scheme of land taxes on future unearned increment of land values on undeveloped land. This famous Budget was thrown out by the House of Lords, provoking a constitutional crisis which resulted, after two general elections, in drastically curtailing the legislative powers of the Upper House.

The proposed land taxes were never put into operation, though the work of valuation for determining the amount of unearned increment was begun. But it was clear that the Liberal Government had far-reaching plans for land reforms, and Lloyd George's speeches during this period were full of attacks on landlords, with picturesque phrases such as 'Labourers had diminished, game had tripled. The landlord was no more necessary to agriculture than a gold chain to a watch.' A Land Enquiry Committee was set up to examine social and economic conditions of rural life in Great Britain, and produced a comprehensive report with recommendations for improving security of tenure, ameliorating the lot of the labourers, increasing production, preventing damage by game, setting up a Land Court to fix rents, and various other matters which would still further have curtailed the powers and prestige of landowners had they been implemented.[30]

[29] Oscar Wilde, *The Importance of Being Ernest*, London, 1895.
[30] *The Land. Report of the Land Enquiry Committee*, London, 1913, vol. 1. *Rural*.

That landowners were beginning to see the red light was brought out in the evidence given to a Committee set up in 1911 to enquire into the position of tenant farmers when estates were sold. There had been an abnormal increase in land sales, caused, the Committee thought, by the apprehensions for the future created by the recent legislation. Landowners were not selling their mansions, but some were selling outlying agricultural land. As one witness agreed, 'Ownership of a rural estate is no longer the same happy business it used to be . . . it is beginning to cease to be a pleasurable business, and beginning to be a bothering business . . . I am keenly alive daily to the sense of insecurity which is permeating all landowners.'[31]

The stage seemed to be set for a wide programme of land legislation, but the landowners were reprieved, for the year was 1914 and the attention of the nation was diverted first by the Irish troubles and then by the outbreak of the First World War.

[31] *Report of the Departmental Committee of the Board of Agriculture on Tenant Farmers and Sales of Estates.* 1912, Cd. 6030, evidence of Mr C. P. Hall, pp. 22, 23.

12

The Changing Villages
1875-1914

*The Structure of Village Society – Wages and Living Standards – Rural Housing -
Allotments and Smallholdings – Farm Workers' Unions.*

No two villages are alike, and any generalisations about them may
be highly misleading; but between 1870 and 1914 it is safe to say
that a marked characteristic of most of them was the steady
decline in the number of their inhabitants. A discussion and
interpretation of the available statistics, sponsored by the Dar-
tington Hall Trust,[1] shows how complex and difficult to measure
was this 'rural exodus'. It was by no means uniform over the
country. Some villages increased in population from the end of the
century, those near large towns tending to become dormitories for
urban workers, while others acquired new industries, such as
creameries and bacon factories, which gave fresh employment.
But they were the exceptions. Over the countryside as a whole
village populations declined, and in general the more remote the
area the greater the decline. The main reason was the restricted
opportunity for employment, as farmers cut down their labour
force during the depression, while the village crafts associated with
agriculture, and other rural industries, contracted or disappeared
under the influence of mass production and cheap transport. At
the same time an increasing awareness of the world outside, which
education, cheaper newspapers and better communications had
brought to the villagers, produced, in many, dissatisfaction with
their own poverty and lack of opportunity, and a longing to get
away to the 'bright lights of the city'.

[1] John Saville, *Rural Depopulation in England and Wales, 1851-1951*, London, 1957.

THE STRUCTURE OF VILLAGE SOCIETY

By the 1870s the isolation and self-sufficiency of village communities were breaking down, but each village remained a compact society with a clear class structure, based mainly on inherited status. The gentry were represented by the squire and his family, the parson, the land agent, perhaps a dowager at the dower house, a doctor serving a number of villages, a retired professional man – but in general, people did not live in the country unless their occupation was there. Social life for the gentry was limited to the range of horses and carriages, but that was quite considerable. In villages where there was no resident landowner, the parson was often the only gentleman, and he generally consorted with the gentry for his social life. Few Nonconformist ministers lived in villages; they came out from the towns to serve the chapels, whose congregations carried on by themselves in the intervals.

Farmers were only a homogeneous social class in the areas of family farms found in Wales, the north-west, parts of Devon and Cornwall, and elsewhere. Over most of England were to be found farms of all sizes mixed together, some occupied by men with considerable capital, directing on horseback big labour forces; others by men who had not long risen above the status of farm labourer, who might employ only the family, or work alongside one or two hired men; between these extremes were farms of every acreage and condition. Even in areas of large arable farms in the eastern counties, the same thing was to be found – small and medium sized holdings intermingled with the big ones. These differences were reflected in the farmers' social status. The bigger men used their profits for a more expansive way of living. They went about more, went to the Royal and other Shows, attended meetings of Chambers of Agriculture and farming conferences and clubs. They might get on to the Bench, take part in County business, and mix socially with the squirearchy. They hunted, shot, and went racing, and left more of the day to day supervision of their farms to their foremen. At home they kept more indoor servants, their wives no longer attended to the dairy and the poultry, but aspired to a more refined social life. Their sons went to boarding schools, their daughters had French governesses and played the piano. Much wit was expended on these piano-playing daughters when the depression came and their fathers were hard put to it to carry on.[2]

The smaller farmers consorted more with the village tradesmen, many of whom were men of substance and employers of labour. The miller, the blacksmith, the wheelwright, the saddler, the maltster, the stonemason, the builder, were all of them essential to agriculture. Then there were the tradesmen serving the community generally; the tailor, the bootmaker, the watchmaker, the dressmaker, the innkeeper, the carrier, as well as other shopkeepers. All of these might be represented in a large village, while the smaller hamlet might have one or two, and would depend on neighbouring places for other essential services. In some localities, rural craftsment of many kinds helped to make up village society, some of them employers of labour, others working alone or with their families. Then came the small family farmers, and at the bottom of the social scale the farm workers, the most numerous and the poorest class of the community. Finally, a new element after 1870, the trained schoolmaster or schoolmistress, coming from outside and better educated than the farmers or tradesmen, not accepted socially by the gentry, but often playing an important part in the life of the village.

All the time Britain's trade and industry were growing, new materials and processes were arriving, and during the 1880s and 1890s goods produced more cheaply in factories were displacing those which used to be made in the villages. In 1881 the Hungarian continuous-process roller mill was introduced into Britain, and imported grain began to be milled at the port of entry. Gradually the little inland wind and water mills were forced out of business, for people could buy their flour more cheaply from the big port mills, and there was less home grown wheat to grind.

[2] For an account of such farmers see Richard Jefferies, *Hodge and his Masters*, London, 1880.

Some of them lingered on into the twentieth century, doing a little business in grinding pig food, etc., for local farmers; but in effect, one of the oldest industries had disappeared from the countryside. Next the blacksmith's business contracted. Ploughs and agricultural implements began to be manufactured in towns, and the forge's activity dwindled to horse-shoeing and minor repairs. Farm carts and waggons, ladders, milking stools and buckets, hayrakes – everything began to be mass-produced; malting was concentrated near the breweries; and one after another the local industries serving agriculture found they could not compete with factory goods. Then came ready-made boots and clothing, and the village tailors and shoemakers were no longer needed, except for repairs. Some of the other local crafts survived, but there was less and less demand for their products as the twentieth century went on.

All this had a profound effect upon village life. In many places, instead of a vigorous community of varied activities, farming was the only industry left, and farmers were reducing their labour force. More boys, as they grew up, could not find work in the villages of their birth. Farmers might take them on at fourteen, for they were a cheap form of labour, but when they grew up and wanted a man's wage, there was often no place for them. The wave of emigration to Canada, Australia and New Zealand, encouraged by Joseph Arch after the lockout, took many of them, but others sought work in the towns, where they soon earned more than their fathers ever would. Except on the family farms, women's work on the land had contracted to a few seasonal jobs. The girls went into domestic service, first to a local farmer's wife, or if they were lucky, to the big house, and then further afield, for there was always a demand for maids from the country.

Parents who had any ambition for their children wanted them to get away from agriculture, with its low wages, long hours and lack of opportunity to rise. In spite of the handicaps of their rural upbringing, for their chances of any further education after they were fourteen were practically nil, these young people were able to show their quality when they got away from the village. Many did well in the police or on the railways; in towns they could generally get a start in jobs with horses, as did Ernest Bevin, and it was only the weaklings and failures who drifted back to the villages.

All this was good for those who got away, but it still further depleted the social life of the villages, which was probably at its lowest ebb in the early years of the twentieth century. The old Benefit Societies were declining, for with fewer young men to support them and more calls on their funds from an ageing population, they could not carry on. Opportunities for recreation were small, for the old traditional amusements were mostly dead and the new ones were still in the future. Bicycles had arrived, but the young men who had them went out of the village for their fun just as they did for their work. There were occasional events such as a penny reading or a concert got up by the vicar, a bonfire, fireworks and feasting for the Diamond Jubilee and King Edward's Coronation, a flower show, a visit from a travelling menagerie, and well-attended political meetings at the time of elections. The Scots and the Welsh had their Sunday School outings, in which people of all ages participated and enjoyed themselves.

Here and there efforts were made by beneficent landlords to improve conditions and brighten village life. Lord Wantage introduced a profit-sharing scheme for his labourers on the farms which he took in hand during the depression. The villages of Lockinge and Ardington which he owned were beautifully laid out with model cottages and gardens, provided with allotments, a reading room, an inn selling tea, coffee and soup in winter, with a salaried manager, not dependent upon beer sales for his profits. There was a co-operative store at which all necessities could be bought, a good school, in fact everything that could conduce to the comfort and well-being of the villagers.[3] It appeared idyllic, but it was a benevolent despotism completely dominated by the great house. People had to do as they were told, and as one man in a neighbouring village put it, 'they daren't blow their noses over at Ardington without the Bailiff's leave'.[4]

[3] *Lord Wantage, V.C., K.C.B. A Memoir by his Wife*, London, 1907, pp. 391–98.
[4] G. F. Mullin, Special Commissioner of the *Daily News, Life in our Villages*, London, 1891, p. 111.

Over the countryside as a whole, life was monotonous and narrow. Then came the motor car, shattering the peace of the country roads, frightening the horses, blowing up the dust, and accentuating class differences, for in the early years of the century it was a rich man's monopoly. The new monied men who had bought country estates often came to them only for the weekends, and did not understand country ways.

WAGES AND LIVING STANDARDS

Farm workers were still a race apart, getting what satisfaction they could from their gardens, their pigs (when they were allowed to keep them), and from the village inn. Not that their work itself was without satisfaction – many of them were artists at their jobs – it was their status which was wrong. They were craftsmen, but they were regarded as unskilled labourers and of no account, and consciousness of this was growing.[5] Of course there were men who, with a combination of tenacity, thrift and luck, managed to acquire some land and to set themselves on the first rung of the agricultural ladder. They might be found anywhere, but there seem to have been more of them in Norfolk than in other counties. But for the most part farm labourers were underpaid, badly housed, under-nourished, with no holidays or weekly half-day, and with no prospect of doing any better.

As the nineteenth century drew to a close, there came an increasing awareness over the country generally of the problem of poverty. A landmark was Charles Booth's *Life and Labour of the People of London*, published in 1889, which stimulated discussion on what came to be known as the 'condition of England'. Commissions and committees put out reports on housing, wages, the sweated trades, etc.; books were written, sermons preached, societies formed and many remedies suggested. In 1901, Seebohm Rowntree made a statistical study of poverty in York, in which he carefully worked out the exact amount of cash needed to main-

[5] See Christopher Holdenby, *Folk of the Furrow*, London, 1913, for a sympathetic study by a young man who lived and worked as one of them.

tain a family, and showed how many unskilled labourers were living 'below the poverty line'.[6] Some years later he applied the same methods to rural workers, and by collecting and analysing household budgets in different parts of England, came emphatically to the conclusion that the wage paid by farmers to agricultural labourers was, in the vast majority of cases, insufficient to maintain a family of average size in a state of merely physical efficiency.

The budgets, collected from families in Oxfordshire, Berkshire, Essex, Yorkshire and Leicestershire, were carefully analysed, and weekly menus given which show the small amount of protein eaten, and the preponderance of tea, bread and potatoes. The account of interviews with wives is full of human interest – the shifts to which they were put to make ends meet, the value of a good garden or allotment, the odd earnings a wife might contribute to the weekly budget, and the impossibility of having enough left at the end of it to spend on anything in the way of pleasure or luxury. Nearly all of them were dependent upon charity or upon help from relatives for much of their clothing, though their cottage rents were very low; perquisites ranged from nothing to milk and/or potatoes, for this form of payment was by now on the wane.[7]

The upward trend in agricultural wages from the 1860s onwards had been checked by the falling prices and profits of arable farming from the end of the 1870s. By the end of the next decade, however, the emigration of experienced men from rural areas had so diminished the supply of farm labour that a slow rise in wages began over most of the country, strongest perhaps in the northeast of Scotland, whence emigration had been most marked. By 1900, weekly cash wages had generally risen by a shilling or two, and a similar increase was obtained in the next ten or twelve years. This trend, however, barely kept pace with the increase in retail food prices from 1900 onwards, and many farm workers with little in the way of perquisites must have found their real wage

[6] Asa Briggs, *Seebohm Rowntree, 1871–1954*, London, 1961, p. 133.
[7] B. Seebohm Rowntree and M. Kendall, *How the Labourer Lives*, London, 1913, p. 31.

tending to fall rather than to rise. Nor did the upward trend obscure those geographical differentials which had developed in the last half of the nineteenth century and which are shown in the map attached to the 1905 *Report* (Cd. 2376). Including the value of perquisites, farm men were earning a pound a week or more in the lowlands of Scotland and up the east coast, in the northern and midland counties of England and in South Wales. Married men in Aberdeenshire, for example, were getting from £22 to £26 a year in cash, a house and garden, a Scotch pint of milk daily, 140 lb of oatmeal, two tons of coal, or peats, a cartload of potatoes and permission to keep a dozen fowls; in return, they worked sixty hours a week in winter and sixty-six in summer. But in north Scotland, East Anglia, southern England and mid-Wales, the average wage (including perquisites) for farm workers was nearer 15s–16s weekly; a substantial number of men must have earned less, since the shepherds and stockmen, the head carters and 'confined men' on large arable farms were comparatively well off. A canvasser during the 1910 general election said to a Lincolnshire labourer 'You are not too badly off, you get 15s a week now'. 'No, Sir, I don't', was the reply, 'I get half-a-crown a day, and last week I took home 10s.'[8]

RURAL HOUSING

A roof over one's head is a basic human need, but standards of housing are by no means constant. The luxury of one generation becomes the necessity of the next, for developments in science, hygiene and education may change social habits. Rural housing

[8] For information on the earnings of farm workers in the twenty years before the First World War, see R. C. on Labour, 1892, *Reports of Assistant Commissioners;* Board of Trade, *Report on Wages, Earnings and Conditions of Employment of Agricultural Labourers in the U.K.*, 1900, Cd. 346; 1905, Cd. 2376; 1910, Cd. 5460; Board of Agriculture, *Wages and Conditions of Employment in Agriculture*, 1919, Cmd. 24 and 25. See also R. Molland and G. Evans, 'Scottish Farm Wages from 1870 to 1900', *J.R.S.S.*, vol. 113, 1950, pp. 220–7; A. L. Bowley, *Wages and Income in the U.K. since 1860*, Cambridge, 1937; J. Cruikshank, 'Changes in the Agricultural History of Aberdeenshire in the Last Fifty Years', *Tr. Aberdeen Philosophical Society*, 1935.

in Britain was a perennial subject of concern all through the period under review. There was great variety of building over the country, according to the locality and materials available – stone, brick, timber-framing, wattle and daub, chalk, etc., and roofs of thatch, slate or tiles. But the standard of accommodation for farm workers did not vary much, consisting mostly of cottages with two or three small rooms, with low ceilings, earth floors, tiny windows, and without damp course, water supply or sanitation. In Scotland there were many houses with only one room.

Farm workers did not complain of these conditions. This was how they had always lived and expected to live. Even the 'black houses' of the Scottish Isles, which so horrified observers from the south, were regarded by their inhabitants as soundly built, warm and weatherproof in an unkindly climate; while the sharing of one roof by the family and its animals seemed to them natural, convenient and patriarchal. Such houses continued to be occupied until well into the twentieth century, and were only relinquished with reluctance.[9] But there was great dissatisfaction with the dilapidation and disrepair into which many cottages had fallen – roofs leaked, water dripped into the bedrooms and ran down the walls, fungus grew on the floors, and holes had to be stuffed with paper and sacking to keep out the draughts. Also there was a serious shortage of cottages, which kept young people from getting married and compelled some men to walk long distances to and from their work.

Various Government enquiries, from the Reports of the Poor Law Commissioners in the 1830s onwards, had drawn attention to the serious condition of much rural housing and its effect on health and morals. The subject was widely discussed, and some progressive landowners, such as the seventh Duke of Bedford and Philip Pusey, had already done considerable rebuilding of cottages on their estates before the turn of the century. But on other estates in the 'close' villages, bad cottages were pulled down

---

[9] See Nigel Nicholson, *Lord of the Isles*, London, 1960, for an account of Lord Leverhulme's attempts to re-house crofters in the Hebrides. See also G. E. Fussell, *The English Rural Labourer*, London, 1949, Ch. ix.

and not rebuilt, for fear of increasing the number of people who might 'come on the rates' in difficult times. This led to still further overcrowding in the 'open parishes' nearby. The Union Chargeability Act of 1865, which spread the Poor Rates of individual parishes over the whole Union, made this sort of action by landowners unnecessary.

Though there was much public concern about the bad state of rural housing in the 1860s and 1870s, the remedies for it were not obvious. Direct Government action was not to be thought of at that time. Landowners could not be compelled to build new houses nor to repair old ones. Tenant farmers could not be expected to build cottages for their labourers, for they would revert to the landowners at the end of their tenancy. Labourers could not afford to build for themselves, nor could they afford to pay an economic rent for new cottages. The only levers which might bring improvements were economic – if cottage building could be shown to be profitable; or philanthropic – if the social conscience could be aroused to do away with intolerable conditions.

The economic argument was that cottage building was as necessary to farm improvement as was the provision of new barns and cowsheds, or land drainage, and that though a single cottage might not earn an economic rent, the increased rent which might be expected from the improved farm might well bring in a handsome return on the whole outlay, including the cottages. Caird was a great advocate of this argument, which comes out in the evidence given before the Select Committee on the Improvement of Land in 1873.[10] Government loans for land improvement might be applied to cottage building, and Caird as an Inclosure Commissioner was responsible for their administration. 'Where you have the best cottages you have the best farm labourers', he said, and this was confirmed by other witnesses, who agreed that good cottages should be a feature of any well-managed estate. The minimum accommodation the Commissioners would sanction was a living-room and two bedrooms, and there should be a water supply from rainwater tank or well. Some of the Scottish witnesses

[10] S.C. 1873 (H. L.) (Lands), p. 349.

thought that this standard was too high and not what the labourers wanted. They preferred the one-roomed house with built-in household bed, and could not afford to furnish anything larger. But others, like George Hope, were emphatic that much needed to be done to improve housing in Scotland.

There was discussion, too, whether cottages should be sited in the villages or out on the farms, and also whether they should be let to the farmer as part of the farm, or kept in the hands of the landlord. The farmers liked to have control of the cottages, letting the men have them free or taking a shilling or two off their weekly wages by way of rent. Some of the land agents thought that landlord control was better, as tenants were inclined to turn men off at a week or fortnight's notice 'and that conduces to a continual change of tenants and you get an inferior class of labourer'. This is the problem of the tied cottage, that running sore in agriculture which has been the cause of so much bitterness and ill-will between employer and worker because power was so often abused; a problem which is still present.

Only some 2,500 cottages had been built under Government loans by 1873, and there was a marked falling off in the next decade, as the depression compelled landowners to reduce expenditure on their estates. Though many labourers were leaving the land from this time onwards, the overcrowding and pressure on rural housing remained, as the worst houses fell down and the general sanitary state of others grew worse as they got older. But public opinion was beginning to move, as the close connection between housing and health was more and more realised, and a series of Acts of Parliament began, step by step, to make standards of housing matters of public concern and responsibility over the whole country.

The Public Health Act of 1875 set up Sanitary Boards in rural districts with powers to inspect properties and to order them to be closed if they were judged to be unfit for human habitation through defective drainage or sewage disposal, disrepair or overcrowding. But part-time Medical Officers to the Boards, generally doctors in private practice, could not effect much improvement, for closing a dilapidated cottage might only lead to over-crowding elsewhere; it was largely a matter of chance whether in any parish bad houses were even inspected, and there was no mechanism for securing their adequate repair.

Though housing was generally bad in the country, it was worse in the towns. The terrible revelations of the Royal Commission on the Housing of the Working Classes in 1885 pushed the State into more positive action to secure certain minimum standards in the interests of the whole community. The Housing of the Working Classes Act, 1890, required local authorities to inspect houses regularly and to condemn and close those judged unfit. Part III of the Act also allowed a local authority to acquire land and to build houses for the working classes, or to buy up unfit houses and repair them if the existing owners would not do so. This was a marked shift in public policy, a recognition that neither self-interest nor philanthropy was adequate to provide for the social needs of those who could not help themselves.

There was, however, little result in the countryside from this Act, as only eight rural districts operated these provisions. The most notable example was that of Ixworth in Suffolk, where an alliance between a progressive parson, the Ixworth Agricultural Labourers' Association and the Medical Officer of Health got a row of cottages condemned and pulled down, and eight new ones built. This was in 1893, just before the new Rural District Councils took over the powers of the Sanitary Boards. As the new Councils mostly consisted of farmers and tradesmen whose main idea was to keep down the rates, little more was achieved under this Act.

The Housing, Town Planning, etc. Act of 1909 made compulsory the permissive powers of earlier legislation, and placed the Rural Districts under the supervision of the Local Government Board and the County Councils in housing matters. Thorough surveys and inspections were to be made to find out defects in existing housing, and the machinery for dealing with unfit houses was simplified. Here was an opportunity for a real improvement in rural conditions, but putting it into practice was another matter.

The Medical Officer of Health for the County of Somerset [11] described some of the difficulties met with in trying to work this Act. The quality of the Medical Officers of Health and the Sanitary Inspectors varied immensely from district to district. The Councils were unwilling to engage any further staff, so that the inspection of houses continued to be irregular and slow. There was no definition of what constituted unfitness for human habitation, and each cottage might need several visits and much paper work before its defects were recorded and the necessary repairs specified. The owners had then to be traced and notices served on them to execute the required work.

Owners were of three kinds. The larger landowners, who regarded cottages as part of the normal equipment of their estates, were generally ready to remedy defects when they were pointed out, though there might be some delay if heavy expenditure was involved, as in providing a water supply for a whole village. Then there were many small owners of cottage property who sometimes derived the whole of their income from such rents, and who could not afford extensive repairs; they would protest that the low rents they received could not justify any expenditure, that sooner than spend they would let the cottages be condemned and closed. Owner-occupiers often had the worst houses of all, could afford least in the way of repairs, and might be driven into the workhouse if there were no alternative accommodation. And usually there was no alternative accommodation, for the combined result of decay and compulsory closing orders had created a serious shortage of houses in many rural districts just before the first world war. Landowners had built few since the depression; the Old Age Pension had allowed old couples to stay on in their cottages instead of going to the workhouse; in some places people working in towns were coming to live in the villages; and with the advent of the motor car, the weekend cottage was beginning to be fashionable. All this made for further pressure upon housing, but the District Councils were unwilling to use their powers to build houses themselves. Between 1909 and 1913, only 470 houses had

[11] William G. Savage, *Rural Housing*, London, 1915.

been built by them over the whole of England and Wales, far fewer than the number condemned and closed under the same Act.

So the consideration of rural housing during the period under review ends on a profoundly unsatisfactory note. Though conditions were never so bad as those in the towns at their worst, rural slums took a heavy toll on the health and happiness of many farm workers and their families, and were undoubtedly a factor in driving men to leave the land.

ALLOTMENTS AND SMALLHOLDINGS

The smallholdings movement began as an anti-landlord movement, part of Joseph Chamberlain's Radical programme of social reform, and it was also supported by the advocates of 'Free Land'. That it caught on and resulted in action was largely due to the untiring work of Jesse Collings, but the idea was not a new one. Arthur Young had commented on the damage inflicted on the prospects of rural workers by Acts of Inclosure which abolished common grazings; as mentioned earlier (p. 189), the provision of allotments was authorised by the General Inclosure Act of 1845, but this mitigation was only partially successful. Too often the allotments were remote from the village, on poor land, and their use hedged about with restrictions. In other places which had not been inclosed under the Act, there were no allotments at all, unless a benevolent landlord provided them. They were unpopular with many farmers, their rent was high compared with the farming land round them, and unless a man could keep a pig for the manure, they were not very productive; but there is no doubt that they were a blessing to many labourers and their families in supplementing their meagre diet, though at a cost of hard work over and above their already long hours of labour. The demand for allotments was strongest in those places where the cash wages were lowest. The extension of allotments was one of the aims of the National Union in some areas, though Arch himself was against it, and it seems to have been the middle class supporters who advocated it.[12]

Allotments, or field gardens as they were called at first, were definitely spare time holdings, limited in size from a quarter to five acres, though generally small; they were unevenly distributed throughout the country, for there appeared to be much less demand for them in the north of England and in Scotland.

In 1882 the Allotments Extension Act laid down that land held by trustees of charities of any parish should be let as allotments if there were a demand for them, and by later Acts the County and Parish Councils were given powers to acquire land for the same purpose. Thus by the end of the century allotments could have been available for any farm labourers who wanted them, though this did not necessarily mean that they got them from Councils composed mainly of landlords and farmers.

The aims of the smallholdings movement were quite different. Collings and his friends were advocating the establishment of full-time holdings of anything from one to fifty acres, which a man could work himself with his family, so as to slow up the drift away from the land of the most promising young men who saw no future for themselves on it. Fewer large estates and multiple holdings, with more peasant proprietors would, it was hoped, result in the land of Britain being more intensively farmed by a much larger agricultural population.

Under a system of land monopoly . . . labourers must always be at starvation wages. But could the peasant – with the passionate attachment to the land which leads him now to seek plots for which he is willing to pay enormous rents – have land of his own to cultivate, he would have an object in life, and while securing a modest competence, would have higher aims and increased self-respect.[13]

Jesse Collings, grandson of a farm labourer in Devon and son of a small builder with some land of his own, was himself in a wholesale ironmongery business in Birmingham, where he became

[12] A. W. Ashby, *Allotments and Small Holdings in Oxfordshire*, Oxford, 1917, p. 18.
[13] *Life of the Rt. Hon. Jesse Collings.* London, 1920. Part I by Jesse Collings. Part II by J. L. Green, p. 129.

a Town Councillor, later Mayor, and a friend of Joseph Chamberlain. But he never forgot his country origins, and supported Joseph Arch in the founding of the National Union. When he got into Parliament in 1880, he proceeded, like Caird in his fight for agricultural statistics, to bring in a motion practically every year pressing for action on small holdings, while outside he formed and led the Allotments Extension Association and then the Rural Labourers League, with the same object. In 1910 the latter became the Rural League, to include all classes interested in land reform, and Collings wrote a copious book on the subject.

Other people, without going so far as Collings in his vision of a peasant England, supported the movement for different reasons. Politicians like Lord Salisbury saw it as likely to build up a stable body of rural electors as a counterpoise to the revolutionary elements in the towns.

> I am very anxious to multiply small holdings and small properties in the country ... But understand what the advantage will be. I do not think it will operate – at least to any great extent – in relieving the peculiar sufferings of the poorer classes. On the contrary, it presupposes the possession of a certain amount of money for a man to undertake a small holding .... I believe that a small proprietory constitutes the strongest bulwark against revolutionary change, and affords the soundest support for the Conservative feeling and institutions of the country ....[14]

Labour leaders thought that the movement might stem the flow of unskilled labour into the towns, which undercut wages in times of depression. Some economists and agriculturists were impressed with the tenacity and survival of smallholders during the depression and thought that more of them would make for the stability of agriculture generally. Sentimentalists saw it as a return to the days of Merrie England and of happy peasants dancing round maypoles. With all this there was genuine compassion for the lot of the farm worker and a desire that he should have a chance to 'get his foot on the agricultural ladder'. The smallholdings movement of this period had no connection with the

[14] Lord Salisbury. Speech at Exeter, 3 Feb. 1892, Quoted by G. Shaw-Lefevre, *Agrarian Tenures*, London, 1893, p. 85.

idea prevalent in the 1930s of settling unemployed miners and others on the land in times of industrial depression. It was not a 'back to the land' movement, but a movement to keep on the land the workers already there.

There were, of course, critics of the movement, who pointed to the very low standard of living of peasants in most European countries, and thought that the creation of small holdings would only increase the prevailing agricultural depression. They held that there was nothing which a small farmer did that a large farmer with his greater resources could not do better, that the latter was more able to take advantage of the discoveries of science and invention and that the way of salvation was in the increasing use of machinery and the reduction of labour costs. But they made little impact on the enthusiasm and emotion which the small holdings movement generated, and propaganda for it, both spoken and written, went on all through the 1880s.

A Select Committee was appointed to consider the question, but Irish affairs occupied the attention of Parliament and it was not till 1892 that the Small Holdings Act empowered County Councils to create small holdings if a sufficient demand existed. The Public Works Loan Commission provided the money to buy the land, but those applying had to put down one-fifth of the purchase money and pay off the rest over a long period. The Act was a failure; only a handful of counties attempted to operate it and less than 800 acres of land were acquired by them in the next fourteen years.

But interest in the movement was still very much alive, and in 1906 a Departmental Committee, appointed to enquire into the working of the Act, found that the demand for holdings was strong. The failure to satisfy that demand was due partly to the apathy of the County Councils and the lack of compulsory powers to acquire land, but chiefly to the insistence on smallholders buying their holdings. The class the Act was designed to help, the labourers, were rarely in a position to put down any money, and what little capital they might have would be needed to stock the holding. But with the example of Ireland before them, the Committee was obsessed with the idea of occupying ownership, though this was really a contradiction of the idea of the 'agricultural ladder'. Once a man had paid his deposit on his holding, it became more difficult for him to move to a larger one, for his capital was locked up.

However, the new Small Holdings and Allotments Act of 1908, which consolidated the earlier Acts, gave powers to provide holdings either for sale or for letting, for, as Asquith remarked, 'the magic of property, such as it is, is derived not from ownership but from security'. The Act was not merely permissive, but required County Councils to prepare draft schemes for the consideration of the Board of Agriculture, of the number, nature and size of holdings to be provided and the land to be acquired. Half of any losses incurred in carrying out a scheme might be recovered from the Board, and Councils were given compulsory powers to acquire land.

Small Holdings Commissioners were appointed to help the Councils, and meetings were held all over the country to explain the Act. There was an immediate rush of applicants for holdings, nearly 12,000 in the first year, but when they came to be examined, the majority of them were found to be quite unsuitable. Enthusiastic townsmen who hankered after a life on the land, but had no experience of its harsh realities, could not be considered as eligible. Some of the farm labourers who applied had misunderstood the conditions of the Act, had thought they would be handed over a fully stocked holding in their own village, and did not want to move away. Many of them, though they had the necessary skill, had not the capital to make a start. Other applications came from small farmers who wanted to extend their holdings or to start off their sons, and from village tradesmen, carriers, innkeepers, butchers etc. who wanted a little land. Only about 2 per cent of the applicants wanted to buy their holdings.[15]

The schemes gradually got going, the County Councils varying very much in the degree of enthusiasm with which they tried to satisfy the demand. Norfolk led the way, and had acquired 10,000 acres by 1912. But some Councils were apathetic and even hostile,

[15] C. S. Orwin and W. F. Darke. *Back to the Land*, London, 1935, Ch. ii.

and most of them were reluctant to use compulsory powers to acquire suitable land. The Land Enquiry Committee found much evidence of landowners and farmers who disliked the Act and who discouraged labourers from applying for holdings.[16]

From 1908 to 1914, some 200,000 acres were acquired by County Councils, and over 14,000 holdings provided. Many of these were holdings of bare land, let to people who already had houses and buildings. Other holdings already had houses on them, and only 886 new houses were built during the period.[17] There were very few failures or arrears of rent, and there was still a large unsatisfied demand. It would appear, therefore that the Act did meet a real need, though farm labourers continued to migrate, and the total number of small farms of under fifty acres did not perceptibly increase.

FARM WORKERS' UNIONS

While these efforts to provide farm workers with land were going on, the workers' efforts to help themselves by collective bargaining were reviving.

The lockout in 1874 was a defeat for Joseph Arch's National Union, but the organisation did not immediately break up. There was a steady falling off of membership, for recrimination and disunity in the Committee undermined confidence; but the spirit was by no means dead and the leaders turned to new activities. A Sick Benefit Scheme was started, which took over some of the moribund village clubs, but it was not a success and had to be wound up after a few years. The agitation for the vote in rural areas was kept alive by meetings and petitions, and Arch himself got into Parliament in 1885, but made no mark there. By 1889 the membership of the National Union had dropped to 4,000 from its one-time peak of over 80,000. Other unions in Kent and the Eastern Counties kept going for a time, but by the end of the decade morale was at a low ebb.

---

[16] *The Land, op. cit.*, pp. 217 seq.

[17] Agricultural Tribunal of Investigation, *Interim Report*, 1923 (Cmd. 1842), p. 329.

Then a new factor appeared. The unskilled urban workers were beginning to organise, but their strikes were generally defeated by blackleg labour, much of it from the country. In the summer of 1889 the London dockers came out for a wage of sixpence an hour, and aroused a great deal of public interest and sympathy. The victory of the 'Dockers' Tanner' was won in August, when farm labourers were not available as strike-breakers, and it was followed by an attempt to arouse them to fresh union activity. This had some success for a short time, helped by the Red Vans of the Land Restoration League. Lord Samuel tells how as an undergraduate at Oxford he and a group of friends used to go out and hold meetings in the Oxfordshire villages in 1890, where wages were then 10s a week, and 9s in winter, to campaign for the Dock, Riverside and General Labourers Union.

> At our meetings we found the labourers silent, and apparently submissive, being very frightened of their employers; but the discontent was deep, and under the surface a current was beginning to move. The revolt of the London dockers had stirred new hopes. ... At Cuddesdon, for example, thirty men joined the Union in a body after one of our meetings. A concerted demand was soon made for higher wages, and an increase of a shilling a week all over the district was secured without difficulty.[18]

But it was hard to keep the enthusiasm going. In 1899 the newly-formed Workers Union did some recruiting in Shropshire, Cheshire and Staffordshire, new fields for unionism, but could not hold its members for long. There was no strong leadership and by the end of the century the trade union movement in agriculture was again moribund.

The eastern counties, always to the fore in agricultural matters, were the scene of the next revival. A new Union was started in Norfolk in 1906, and from that moment the movement never looked back. George Edwards, the Secretary of the new Eastern Counties Agricultural Labourers' and Smallholders' Union, has told the story at length in his autobiography.[19] He was a very different leader from Arch, though with much the same back-

---

[18] *Memoirs by the Rt. Hon. Viscount Samuel*, London, 1945, p. 15.
[19] George Edwards, *From Crow-Scaring to Westminster*, London, 1922.

ground of farm work and Methodism. He had none of the fire and drive of Arch, nor his arrogance, but he had a courage and faith in the cause which led him to work for it from its beginning in the 1870s. Several times the Unions he worked for had to close down, but others were started and he went doggedly on. He was fifty-six when he was called to organise the new union in 1906, a post he accepted at financial loss to himself, and this time the current was flowing with him after the years of frustration. 'A wonderful sower of good seed was this man George Edwards',[20] said one who worked alongside him in those days.

At first the Union was supported and partly financed by Liberal M.P.s, one of whom was its President and another its Treasurer, and by 1910 it had 4,000 members. But this political connection was not happy, and after a dispute over an unsuccessful strike both the politicians resigned in 1911 and Edwards was free to work unhampered. Meanwhile requests were coming in from other counties for help in forming new branches, and the union changed its name to the National Agricultural Labourers' and Rural Workers' Union and became affiliated to the Trades Union Congress.

There were several strikes in different parts of the country in 1913 and 1914, some of which attracted a good deal of publicity. One was in South Lancashire, and it was concerned less with wages than with hours of work. The demand was for a Saturday half-holiday and overtime pay of sixpence an hour, and for the recognition of the union as a negotiating body, for some farmers were still refusing to employ Union men. In that industrial area there was plenty of help forthcoming from trade unionists in Liverpool and elsewhere, in such matters as diverting the boat-loads of Irish immigrants who might have been used for blackleg labour. A threat by the National Union of Railwaymen at Ormskirk not to handle farm produce in the strike district brought this completely successful fortnight's stoppage to an end. This concession of the half-holiday and overtime pay was a real advance for farm workers.

Edwards's Union now had branches in many counties, and in

[20] R. Groves, *op. cit.*, p. 96.

general was able to settle sporadic disputes by negotiation, without resorting to strikes. But there was still great diversity of wages and conditions over the country, and they were still a matter of individual bargaining between farmer and man. The union might arrange a rise of a shilling a week in one parish or group of parishes, while in nearby places they remained at the old level. Many parts were untouched, and it was not easy to get local secretaries, as an active unionist was in danger of losing his job. This question of recognition came to a head in the summer of 1914, when Lord Lilford, a landowner in Northampton, agreed to give a rise in wages to his men on condition that they gave up their union membership. Seven men on the home farm refused, and were dismissed and evicted from their cottages. This raised a storm of protest in the country and in the Press, which only died down with the outbreak of the war.

But George Edwards's N. A. L. U. was not playing a lone hand in these troubled years before the war. In 1910 the Workers' Union began again to draw farm workers into its rapidly growing organisation. Their headquarters were in London, they had much greater resources both of money and of trained organisers, and they set about their campaign in a more systematic way. George Dallas was put in charge of the farm workers' section, and his method was to go round with a van to start branches in a county, and then to call a conference of delegates in the county town to work out a schedule of the wages, hours, conditions etc. suitable to that county, to be used as a basis for negotiating with the farmers. By this time the more intelligent of the farmers, the leaders of the National Farmers Union, were prepared to recognise the unions and to discuss conditions in an orderly way, though the rank and file of the members were still bitterly opposed to the idea. In 1914 E. W. Langford, later President of the N.F.U., said, 'I am of opinion that a big mistake is being made by farmers in refusing to treat through their own Union with the men as represented by their Union.'[21]

[21] Quoted by F. E. Green, *A History of the English Agricultural Labourer, 1870–1920*, London, 1920, p. 226.

Thus things seemed to be moving towards an improvement in the condition of English farm workers, when the outbreak of the war necessarily slowed down Union activity. But the method of discussion on a county or regional basis initiated by the Workers' Union was a valuable precedent, and it was used by the Agricultural Wages Board when it was set up a few years later.

Meanwhile in Scotland, where there had been no trade union activity for many years, things were stirring, and once more the right leader was forthcoming. In 1912 delegates from eight local groups of farm servants in Aberdeenshire met and decided to form a Union. Their Secretary was Joseph Duncan, the son of a farm worker, who had already had some experience of union work as secretary of the Aberdeen enginemen and firemen's union, and who had many contacts all over Scotland. The problem of organisation was very different from that in England and much more difficult. With farm servants mostly living on the farms and changing their job every year, it was hard to get local branches started. Duncan's method was to concentrate the bargaining effort at the hiring fairs. By persuading the workers not to hire themselves at a figure below the agreed rate, the business of hiring was held up until the farmers would accept it. It was uphill work, but after some successes in getting higher wages by this method, the Scottish Farm Servants Union was able to recruit new members and in two years had 200 branches all over Scotland. It ran an attractive journal, *The Scottish Farm Servant*, and by negotiation and regional agreements was able to effect substantial improvements in wages, hours and living conditions.[22]

In the forty years since Joseph Arch organised the National Union, farm workers had come some way towards a better standard of life. The falling volume of employment and the gradual rise in wages were helping to increase their status, and their Unions were now recognised as part of the active labour movement. The Royal Commission on Labour in 1892, and the later Reports into wages and employment by the Board of Trade, kept the

---

[22] Tony Corfield, *Scottish Farm Servants' Jubilee*, Transport and General Workers' Union Record, July 1962.

public informed about farm workers, and the smallholdings movement was designed to help them. Though their housing was deplorable and there was a general lack of amenity and opportunity in their lives, the old age pensions had removed some of the terrors of advancing years.

But whatever the gradual social changes, the face of the countryside as a whole had altered little in the thirty years before 1914. There had not been much new building, except in places where townspeople were beginning to spread out into the villages. Life went on as usual, rain and sunshine, seedtime and harvest; the newspapers, during that summer of 1914, were full of the activities of suffragettes and the danger of civil war in Ireland—all very remote from country life in Britain. No one expected the outbreak of war and the manifold changes which were to follow.

13

Farming in the New Century
1895–1914

Employment and Productivity – Crops and Grass – Meat and Milk – The Liquid Milk Trade – Milk-borne Diseases – Markets and Price Levels – The New Knowledge – British Agriculture in 1914.

T H E declining importance of agriculture in the economic life of Britain had been clearly demonstrated in the thirty years before 1900. From contributing about one-sixth of the national output in 1867–9, agriculture supplied less than one-tenth by 1890 and less than one-fifteenth by 1911–13,[1] pushed down by the scale of the expansion in the industrial sector and in the distributive trades. The fall in output, in rents and in the value of agricultural land over much of eastern and southern Britain discouraged investment in rural estates, where the return on capital seldom compared with that which might be obtained among the opportunities overseas, or among export industries which served the markets of the world. Some farmers fortunately held tenancies on estates maintained out of non-agricultural income for reasons of prestige or social responsibility, but many others were handicapped by dilapidated buildings, unmade roads and undrained fields. Imports of food continued to expand, so that early in the new century British farmers supplied only a quarter of the wheat consumed, less than half the butter, cheese and pigmeat, and about three-fifths of the beef, mutton and lamb.[2] Cheap food from overseas played so large a part in the British diet that most

[1] E. M. Ojala, *op. cit.*, p. 66.
[2] R. H. Rew, 'Observations on the Second and Third Reports of the Committee of the Roy. Stat. Soc.', *J.R.S.S.*, vol. 67, 1907, p. 414; R.C. Food, 1905, pp. 4–6. These proportions relate to the U.K., which then included all Ireland.

farmers accepted, even in the worst of the depression, the hope-lessness of any attempt to impose tariffs which, by checking the decline in food prices, would also check the rising consumption of the food buyers. And each fall in the number of people working on farms emphasised the growing preponderance of food buyers over the food growers within the British nation.

EMPLOYMENT AND PRODUCTIVITY

The population census of 1901 recorded rather more than one million men and boys working in agriculture and allied occupa-tions in England and Wales, with another 165,000 in Scotland; fifty years earlier, the corresponding figures had been 1½ million

Table 1. *Males* Occupied in Agriculture in Great Britain*[3]

Thousands	1861	1871	1881	1891	1901	1911
Farmers†	312	305	279	278	278	280
Others working on farms	1,362	1,157	1,048	961	834	879
Others occupied on the land	105	124	86	112	144	161
TOTAL	1,779	1,586	1,413	1,351	1,256	1,320

* Over 10 years of age.

† Including women returned in this category.

and 232,000. From employing about a quarter of the occupied males in 1851, British agriculture employed about 17 per cent in 1881 and barely 12 per cent in 1901. Changes in classification and the school leaving age, the difficulty of distinguishing women working in agriculture from the domestic servants in farm houses, the problem of part-time employment, the effect of the South

[3] These figures are taken from the careful analysis made by F. D. W. Taylor, *Farm Economist*, vol. viii, no. 4, 1955, p. 39. See also *Agricultural Output of G.B.*, 1912, Cd. 6277, pp. 17–20.

African war on the figures for 1901, all make unsafe a superficial comparison of changes in the agricultural labour force, but they do not obscure the declining employment in farming in the last half of the nineteenth century. There was little change in the recorded number of farmers, but what did change was the number of relatives and hired men they employed.

As noted earlier, the fall in the numbers employed in farming since 1861 was neither caused by the depression nor confined to arable districts. The fall was as marked in the north and west as in the south and east where the depression had been most acute; it occurred as much in Scotland, where the area of arable land continued to rise slowly, as in counties where much arable land went down to grass; and the largest fall occurred between 1861 and 1881 before the depression had done its worst. Between 1891 and 1911, indeed, there was little change in the total numbers working on the land, for the slow decline in the numbers employed on farms was almost balanced by the expanding employment on market gardens.[4]

This 'drift from the land' was the result both of the falling demand from farmers and of the pull of competing trades especially attractive to the younger men. In the earlier decades, the mechanisation of the grain harvest undoubtedly reduced the demand for casual workers, and thus diminished the opportunity for many rural families to earn extra cash. But from the 1890s onwards, many farmers began to experience a shortage of labour which was reflected, partially and locally, in a slowly rising level of farm wages. That new invention the bicycle helped to intensify the scarcity of young men in some districts, for it gave them freedom to take factory employment without leaving home. The brickworks round Peterborough, it was claimed, were thus denuding villages of their active youths who travelled daily to work in them by bicycle and train.[5] The pull of competing trades,

[4] *Report on the Decline in the Agricultural Population, 1881–1906*, 1906 (C. 3273); J. W. Paterson, 'Rural Depopulation in Scotland', *Tr. H.A.S.*, vol. 9.v, 1897, pp. 236–278.
[5] Rider Haggard, *op. cit.*, vol. 2, p. 94.

offering higher wages and a higher social status, a half-day on Saturday and a free Sunday, was thus more strongly felt than before. The difficulty of getting young men and women to work with cows, and especially to milk on Sundays, was frequently quoted to Rider Haggard as the main hindrance to the more general adoption of dairying; it was the smaller farms staffed mainly by family labour that undertook this monotonous task, which demanded one pair of skilful hands twice every day for every ten or twelve cows in milk. Rider Haggard concluded that the scarcity of labour was 'most pressing in the south of England, or near to seaport and manufacturing towns, and least so in some of the eastern and more northerly counties' where the agricultural demand had fallen most and where there were few local industries. It was in Herefordshire, though, that he visited one farm of 180 acres, where the farmer, found ploughing with his pair of horses, said he had one small boy for his staff; and boys from reformatory schools were employed by many family farms in Wales, whose own young men had gone down the valley or overseas.[6]

It was often argued that farmers could easily remedy a shortage of labour by offering higher wages, especially to those men who worked long hours and took responsibility for livestock. To such statements, most farmers would no doubt have replied firstly, that they were paying higher wages in the early years of the twentieth century than they had in the 1860s, when prices of farm produce were far higher; and secondly, that they could not afford to raise wages further, after twenty years of falling prices for the things they sold. The census of production taken in 1908 showed a gross output from agricultural holdings in Britain of a little more than £150 million, of which one-third was derived from the sale of crops and horticultural produce, one-fifth from dairy produce and the remainder from livestock[7]:

[6] Rider Haggard, *op. cit.*, vol. 2, p. 539; vol. 1, p. 297; A. D. Hall, *A Pilgrimage of British Farming*, London, 1913, p. 314.

[7] *Agricultural Output of G.B., 1908* (1912 Cd. 6277), p. 25. The estimate for livestock output (which included skin wool) was revised upwards to £65 million in *Agricultural Output, 1929*, p. 5.

	£ million
Farm Crops	46·6
Fruit and Flowers	4·6
Timber	0·6
Livestock	61·4
Wool	2·6
Dairy Produce	30·0
Poultry	5·0
	150·8

This gross output of £150–£155 million came from 32 million acres of crops and grass, plus the contribution of the rough grazings; if this last item is ignored, there was an average gross output of some £4½ per acre of cultivated land, rather lower than the output of some £5–£5½ per acre assumed to be common in the 1850s from the well-managed mixed farm.[8] Taken over the country as a whole, the increase in physical output per acre had apparently been offset by the fall in prices which had occurred in the thirty years before 1908.

This level of gross receipts was obtained in 1908 with the help of purchased feeding-stuffs and fertilisers costing, it was thought, nearly £30 million, and another £7 million were spent annually on imported store stock from Ireland. Net output per person employed, including occupiers, could not therefore have exceeded £100 a year; if the rent paid in Britain totalled some £40 million (averaging 25*s* per acre), there was barely £80 million available to pay miscellaneous expenses, the profits for the farmers and wages for nearly a million men and boys employed on the land, of whom a third were counted as relatives rather than as hired servants. Most of the 340,000 holdings recorded as being less than 50 acres in size could have brought their occupiers little more than a house, some food and barely the £30–£50 a year in cash earned by farm workers. Even above this limit, there must have been many farmers employing one or two men whose cash income did not exceed the average wage they paid, though their social status was higher. It was the minority of holdings of, say, 150 acres

---

[8] See p. 35.

and upwards which supported the substantial tenant farmers with incomes that were, on average, considerably above the earnings of their men; but these were the farmers with capital, managerial skill and a modicum of education.

Nor was it easy to raise the productivity of the labour force. In field work, the output per man was largely determined by the speed of the horses, the layout of the farm and the type of soil; farm buildings were often antiquated, awkward in arrangement and not designed to economise in labour. Dairying and stockwork involved much lifting and shifting of heavy weights – milk, hay, straw, roots, feeding-stuffs, manure and, not infrequently, water. A few of the large farms might have steam power to pump water, slice turnips, chaff hay and mix home-grown feeds, but on the majority of farms, the output still depended on the muscles of men and horses, from the turning of the first furrow to the lifting of the last sack of grain on to the wagon for sale, from the first cut into the hay field to shifting the milk churns into the railway van. This lack of mechanical power inhibited in agriculture that rising output per worker which was a marked feature of contemporary industry; the divergence between rural and urban wages which developed from the 1870s onwards partly reflected this fundamental disparity in productivity. A. D. Hall noted the contrast between a new condensing plant in Derbyshire embodying the latest knowledge in metallurgy, bacteriology and labour-saving devices, and the primitive methods of producing the milk on which the plant depended – methods which had been little modified by science or engineering in the last century.[9]

[9] A. D. Hall, *op. cit.*, p. 413; E. M. Ojala, *op. cit.*, pp. 152–5, calculated the following indices of changes in productivity in U.K. agriculture and industry after 1867–9, at constant 1911–13 prices:

	Value added per Worker	
	Agriculture	Mining & Manufacture
1867–69	100	100
1870–76	106	109
1877–85	108	119
1886–93	115	123
1894–1903	119	125
1904–10	126	133
1911–13	124	132

In the last third of the nineteenth century, the main labour-saving devices were the mowers, reapers and self-binding reapers which greatly reduced the demand for casual workers for the hay and corn harvests. But when grain prices fell, and arable farmers increased the output of potatoes, fruit and vegetables, they turned away from crops grown and harvested by horse-powered implements to crops which still required large amounts of hand labour for planting, weeding and picking. Such crops might yield a high output per acre but only excellent organisation made them yield a high output per man.

One technical innovation of the 1880s promised some alleviation of the stockmen's work. The stationary oil engine provided cheap power in small units for all kinds of barn work, including that of pumping water for house and stock; by 1908 there were some 13,000 used on agricultural holdings, together with a few of the newer petrol engines.[10] These useful devices encouraged the search for an efficient milking machine, whose basic principles of rubber-lined teat-cups and an intermittent vacuum had been evolved before the end of the nineteenth century. At the Royal Show at Darlington in 1895, the Thistle Milking Machine powered by steam milked ten cows in $12\frac{1}{2}$ minutes with only one man in attendance; at the Trials conducted by the Highland and Agricultural Society in 1897, one milking machine was powered by water, one by horse-gear, two by steam and two by oil engines.[11] But another twenty-five years were to pass before milking machines became sufficiently reliable to be adopted generally; until after the First World War, milking by hand remained the most burdensome of the regular jobs involved in the production of milk.

There was also a continuing improvement in the design and construction of farm implements, much of which was inspired by American experience. The chilled steel plough with a concave mouldboard was directly derived from the American digger-type

---

[10] *Agricultural Output of G.B.*, 1912, Cd. 6277, p. 21.
[11] 'Trial of Milking Machines', *J.R.A.S.E.*, vol. 6.iii, 1895, p. 463; J. Drysdale, 'Trial of Milking Machines', *Tr. H.A.S.*, vol. 10.v, 1898, pp. 166–81.

plough. Used for ploughing grassland on dry soils, it laid a broad furrow almost flat, instead of setting it upon edge; the draught was less and less harrowing was required subsequently. Spring-framed cultivators to which a variety of hoes and ridging ploughs could be attached 'at once made headway all over the country' at the end of the century; in Scotland, many farmers also adopted the rick-lifters, worked by windlass or horse, which lifted the large hay-cocks bodily on to a sledge for quick transport to the barn.[12] The growing use of wire and of barbed wire (in spite of opposition from all the hunts) enabled farmers to erect cheap fences. Yet in spite of these and other improvements, the very durability of agricultural implements ensured that many farms were still using in 1914 the same tools, as well as the same buildings, that had served earlier generations. An Ayrshire farm in 1906 still employed a grain reaper with a manual delivery which must have been bought thirty years previously. The Kentish wooden turnwrest plough, described and criticised in the eighteenth century, could still be found in 1899 in mid-Kent and on the Wealden soils. Although 'corn drills have greatly improved in recent years', grain was in 1906 broadcast by hand on many Scottish farms, falling between the upturned furrows before the harrows covered it.[13] Economy in time, energy and manpower was still on many farms less important than economy in cash outlay, and the maintenance of a routine well understood and known to yield a safe result. The conservatism of skilled workers, the durability of farm buildings and of farm implements, the lack of mechanical power, these were the factors which continuously delayed the rise in productivity of the men and women engaged in British farming.

[12] J. Speir, 'Changes in Farm Implements since 1890', *Tr. H.A.S.*, vol. 18.v, 1906, pp. 46–62; Primrose McConnell, 'Methods of Tillage', *Tr. H.A.S.*, vol. 17.v, 1905, pp. 121–44.

[13] A. Macneilage, 'Farming Methods in Ayrshire', *Tr. H.A.S.*, vol. 18.v, 1906, p. 8; C. Whitehead, 'Agriculture of Kent', *J.R.A.S.E.*, vol. 10.iii, 1899, p. 454; J. Speir, 'Changes in Farm Implements since 1890', *Tr. H.A.S.*, vol. 18.v, 1906, pp. 46–62.

In all parts of Britain there could be found family farms whose inputs consisted mainly of unpaid labour, whose rent was the only large item of expense, and whose household expenditure was kept down to the low level of output. To such farms, the rising prices obtained from their customary output in the first decade of the new century represented so much increase in cash which might be spent on a new plough, but which was seldom invested in any improvement or intensified output that might catch the attention of the landowner's agent. A. D. Hall found that the resorts along the west coast of Wales were apt to run short of milk, butter, cream, eggs, fruit and vegetables in the holiday season, but farms within ten miles, with a climate as mild as that of Ayrshire, were still selling wool and store stock, still growing oats and hay, still seeking nothing better than the subsistence they had gained with difficulty in the years of depression.[14] In contrast, the large arable farms, paying lower rents but higher wages than in the 1860s and 1870s, found their costs rising as fast as their prices; they had to strike a new balance between a high output per acre, the customary standard of good farming, and high output per man, which could be derived either from intensive or from extensive farming. The first could be found in the potato lands round Dunbar, in the highly rented Lothians and eastern fenlands where 'the men who could not alter their system to meet the low prices prevailing only a few years ago have been shaken out of the industry'.[15] Good farmers have always tended to congregate on the better lands where their abilities earn the greatest differential and pay the highest rent, but the depression had given unusual opportunities for able men to rent good farms cheaply and to experiment with new methods. And at the other extreme, many grassland and arable farms found a balance between output per acre and output per man at a low level, partly because of lack of capital for more intensive types of output, and partly because of a generally low standard of management.

[14] A. D. Hall, *op. cit.*, p. 335.
[15] *ibid.*, p. 150.

CROPS AND GRASS

There was a remarkable stability in cropping aggregates within the eastern arable districts of England and Scotland from the early years of the twentieth century up to the First World War (Tables 2 and 3). Cereal prices were somewhat higher than the

Table 2.

Crops and Livestock in Grazing and Arable Districts of England, 1900, 1905, 1910, 1914

	Grazing Districts				Arable Districts			
Thousand Acres	1900	1905	1910	1914	1900	1905	1910	1914
Wheat	535	548	487	512	1,209	1,156	1,230	1,259
Barley	526	456	453	433	1,119	956	997	988
Oats	901	1,001	954	881	909	880	903	849
Pulse, etc.	102	94	83	93	347	375	385	420
TOTAL Corn	2,114	2,099	1,976	1,919	3,585	3,367	3,515	3,516
Potatoes	197	211	178	191	200	224	199	245
Root and Green crops	798	738	747	712	1,248	1,179	1,154	1,154
Rotation Grass	1,473	1,413	1,276	1,143	1,295	1,161	1,084	979
Bare Fallow	82	81	74	79	211	256	269	256
TOTAL Arable	4,664	4,542	4,251	4,044	6,539	6,187	6,221	6,150
Permanent Grass	8,269	8,835	8,948	9,050	4,763	4,925	4,976	5,012
Thousand Head								
Horses: for agric.	426	448	456	362	408	423	429	351
unbroken	173	187	166	146	145	146	134	115
Cattle: Cows and Heifers	1,315	1,379	1,419	1,517	584	612	635	668
Others	1,858	1,902	1,885	1,854	1,091	1,128	1,187	1,080
TOTAL	3,173	3,281	3,304	3,371	1,675	1,740	1,822	1,748
Sheep: Ewes	3,495	3,390	3,692	3,338	2,518	2,192	2,448	1,982
Others	5,574	5,302	5,801	5,024	4,257	3,814	4,333	3,308
TOTAL	9,069	8,693	9,493	8,362	6,775	6,005	6,780	5,290
Pigs	998	1,072	1,029	1,168	975	1,012	991	1,092

Grazing districts: Chester, Cornwall, Cumberland, Derby, Devon, Dorset, Durham, Gloucester, Hereford, Lancashire, Leicester, Monmouth, Northumberland, Shropshire, Somerset, Stafford, Westmorland, Wiltshire, Worcester, Yorkshire (North and West Ridings).

Arable districts: Bedford, Berkshire, Buckingham, Cambridge, Essex, Hampshire, Hertford, Huntingdon, Kent, Lincoln, Middlesex, Norfolk, Northampton, Nottingham, Oxford, Rutland, Suffolk, Surrey, Sussex, Warwick, Yorkshire (East Riding).

Table 3. *Crops and Livestock in Scotland and Wales, 1900, 1905, 1910, 1914*

	Scotland				Wales			
	1900	1905	1910	1914	1900	1905	1910	1914
Thousand Acres								
Wheat	49	49	53	61	52	44	39	37
Barley	240	212	192	194	105	91	88	84
Oats	949	963	958	920	216	208	205	199
Pulse, etc.	21	17	16	12	4	3	3	4
TOTAL Corn	1,259	1,241	1,219	1,187	377	346	335	324
Potatoes	131	144	137	152	33	29	26	25
Root and Green Crops	494	474	465	460	79	78	76	75
Rotation Grass	1,594	1,558	1,511	1,482	397	345	285	260
Bare Fallow	7	7	6	7	8	6	5	5
TOTAL Arable	3,485	3,424	3,341	3,288	894	804	727	689
Permanent Grass	1,408	1,451	1,505	1,491	1,929	1,989	2,049	2,055
Thousand Head								
Horses: for agric.*	153	156	156	136	91	95	97	79
unbroken	41	50	47	47	62	67	61	56
Cattle: Cows and Heifers	434	437	431	454	287	280	282	300
Others	764	790	740	761	471	450	458	458
TOTAL	1,198	1,227	1,171	1,215	758	739	740	758
Sheep: Ewes	2,978	2,919	2,988	2,975	1,360	1,435	1,538	1,518
Others	4,337	4,105	4,157	4,051	2,073	2,100	2,147	2,089
TOTAL	7,315	7,024	7,145	7,026	3,433	3,535	3,685	3,607
Pigs	132	130	133	153	228	211	196	222

* Including mares.

lowest points reached in the 1890s. Wheat at a price of about 30s per quarter could be a paying crop on good land; a yield of 4–5 quarters of grain (32–40 bushels per acre), with 1½ tons of straw fetching another £3 per acre, brought in a satisfactory return of £9 per acre, or more on many farms. A good sample of malting barley, perhaps five quarters to the acre, and selling at much the same price, also provided straw to be sold or used for litter.[16]

[16] A. Hutcheson, 'Past and Future of Scottish Agriculture', *Tr. H.A.S.*, vol. 11.v, 1899, p. 124.

Wheat preceded by two green crops, and followed by barley, roots, barley, clover and wheat again became a common rotation on the light soils of southern England. This 'Wiltshire rotation' was thought to give a more even sample of malting barley than that grown after the hasty ploughing which followed roots; the catch crops required for sheep-feed fitted more easily into the two years of green crops taken together in alternate courses and the land was less likely to develop finger-and-toe disease.[17] But barley that only made the price of a feeding grain could hardly pay for growing, in the face of cheaper maize, and the area tended to fall in all parts of the country. This was especially the case in Wales and the western counties of England, where the total area of tillage shrank slowly throughout these twenty years from 1895, while year by year there was always more land in grass in these districts where grain yields were often below the average. But most farms continued to grow some roots and a grain crop for both fodder and straw, and a patch of potatoes for their own use or for local sale.

Along the Ayrshire coast, round Girvan, some farmers ran an almost continuous succession of early potato crops, manured from the Glasgow stables and usually followed each autumn by ryegrass, barley or rape fed off by sheep for the Christmas market; but potatoes every second or third year was more common. The earliest crops in Ayrshire might be sold 'in the field' for £35-40 per acre at the turn of the century, with the second earlies fetching £25 per acre and upwards according to season. Here and elsewhere in the northern half of Britain, the crops were lifted by gangs of hired workers, generally itinerant Irish, paid by the merchants; the farmers provided the horse teams and digger ploughs that lifted the tubers on to the surface for easy picking. The red soils round Dunbar grew potatoes that were becoming favoured for seed by growers in southern England, where farmers found by experience that Scotch seed was less liable to disease

[17] J. M. H. Munro and E. S. Beaven, 'Manurial Conditions affecting the Malting Quality of English Barley', *J.R.A.S.E.*, vol. 8.iii, 1897, p. 70; H. E. H. Rice, 'Rotation of Crops for Light Chalk Soils', *J.R.A.S.E.*, vol. 9.iii, 1898, p. 183.

than seed saved from local crops; the high prices obtained by farmers in East Lothian were reflected in the high inputs of Edinburgh manure and of fertilisers, as well as in high rents that ran up to £4 per acre or more. Here, well-dunged potatoes were usually followed by wheat, ryegrass cut for hay, roots and barley, four cash crops in each five years from these fertile and well-farmed fields.

In Cheshire there were rather fewer potatoes grown in 1910 than in 1895, but there was a larger area in the western side of Lancashire, in the Vale of York, and in the eastern fenlands of Norfolk, the Isle of Ely and the Holland Division of Lincolnshire. It was the large commercial growers in these regions who were the best customers for the Scottish seed potatoes; they supplied London and the midland towns with their potatoes after Christmas, first clamping them in straw-lined pits and dressing them out in the biting winds of January and February. In Bedfordshire, some farmers worked a rotation of potatoes, vegetables and grain, yielding a continuous succession of cash crops as well as the straw needed whenever potatoes were clamped.[18]

The practice of sprouting potatoes indoors in shallow trays was widely adopted at the end of the century, as a method of getting both heavier yields and also earlier crops, a matter of importance in such districts as Cornwall and Ayrshire, where the difference of a week in time of harvesting could alter receipts by £10 per acre. The disadvantage of sprouting was that careful handling was then required, for the sprouts could easily be broken in planting. Another innovation was spraying against blight with 'Bordeaux mixture', a mixture of copper sulphate and lime-water; first used in France for the protection of vines against mildew, the practice was adopted by English hop growers for the same reason and then by large potato growers in the early years of the new century. Engineers quickly provided spray-booms, either horizontal or vertical, which could be mounted at the

[18] A. Macneilage, 'Farming Methods in Ayrshire', *Tr. H.A.S.*, vol. 18.v, 1906, p. 11; A. D. Hall, *op. cit.*, pp. 133–39; Primrose McConnell, 'Rotations', *J.R.A.S.E.*, vol. 69, 1908, p. 31.

back of an ordinary cart and fed by hand pump from a barrel, while a steady horse was led between the hop poles or potato drills.

These rotations with frequent crops of potatoes represented the intensive farming which might combine high output per acre with a profitable level of output per man; round Dunbar and on the alluvial soils, potato yields might run up to 10 tons per acre, compared with the national average of 6–7 tons. Yet some serious problems were developing for the future in the accumulation of disease. In spite of sprays, blight spread easily across large areas of potatoes concentrated in the favoured districts; eelworm and wart disease were becoming worse in Lancashire, Staffordshire and Cheshire, and these pests were spreading, as seed from infected soils was used elsewhere. A number of men wrestled with the problems of breeding potatoes that were resistant to the main diseases, and especially blight, the earliest and most destructive scourge of the potato crops. James Clarke (1825–90) of Christchurch in Hampshire evolved 'Magnum Bonum', sold by Suttons from 1876 onwards; it proved resistant to blight for many years and was the most popular English variety till the end of the century. John Nicol of Forfar bred 'Champion' which was especially favoured by Scottish and Irish growers from the 1870s. Archibald Findlay (1841–1921), working at Markinch in Fife, bred 'Up-to-Date' and 'British Queen' in the 1890s, when James Clarke also produced the famous 'Epicure' – one of the most successful of the early varieties.

In spite of these efforts, few crops escaped the blight in such years as 1894, yet there was always a hope that potato breeders would succeed in their quest for immune varieties. Short crops in 1902 and 1903 pushed up seed potato prices and there suddenly developed in 1903 the 'potato boom' centred on Findlay's two new introductions 'Northern Star' and 'Eldorado'. Unscrupulous merchants claimed them to be immune to all known diseases, and found a number of gullible buyers who were willing to pay tens of pounds sterling for a pound weight of tuber. The good crops of 1904 pricked this speculative bubble, and potato prices fell to the low level common when there was a surplus of output over consumption, but the trade was left in still greater confusion over varieties and their alleged immunity. Over 200 synonyms were thought to exist for the popular 'Up-to-Date'; 'Abundance' and 'British Queen' were each sold under perhaps seventy different names. The economic importance of the potato crop led the Board of Agriculture to set up in 1914 a Wart Testing Station at Ormskirk in Lancashire, an area known to be badly infected with this disease; farmers had to wait until after the war for a thorough investigation into potato varieties.[19]

One new crop was tested by East Anglian farmers in the years just before the war. As far back as 1871, an attempt had been made to import into England the practice of growing sugar beet which was well established on the Continent, thanks to high tariffs and much Government support. The first factory, set up in Lavenham in Suffolk, did not survive more than two to three years, partly because its effluent destroyed the local fishing; a second attempt in 1884 was no more successful. But a more methodical start was made nearly thirty years later, when a limited company organised by local landowners and farmers set up a factory at Cantley in Norfolk and processed the output of some 4,500 acres in 1914; a small grant from the Development Commission by way of encouragement was not sufficient to offset the financial loss incurred in this experiment.[20]

In Scotland, there was a greater use of timothy grass to provide hay, a practice apparently imported from America. On heavy soils, such as those in the Carse of Gowrie and the Carse of Stirling, a field of timothy, once established, gave a high yield of hay for several years which could be sold profitably or used for winter fodder; the area to be ploughed annually was thus reduced, costs lessened and the timothy stubble, when finally ploughed in,

[19] R. N. Salaman, *op. cit.*, pp. 167–73; A. W. Sutton, 'The Potato', *J.R.A.S.E.*, vol. 9.iii, 1898, pp. 581–654; D. Young, 'The Potato Crop', *Tr. H.A.S.*, vol. 18.v, 1906, pp. 143–65.
[20] A. H. H. Matthews, *History of the Central Chamber of Agriculture*, London, 1915, pp. 335–7; Development Commission, *Third Report*, 1913 (273), p. 6.

provided valuable humus for succeeding crops.[21] In spite of this innovation, there was no tendency in this period for the area of temporary grass to increase. In the arable districts of England, the cropping statistics indicate that most farmers took three grain crops in five years, roots once, while temporary grass and potatoes occupied the other fifth of the land; Scottish farmers were still generally taking two years in grain and one in roots or potatoes, with a two-year ley.

Basic slag was perhaps the innovation of greatest value to grassland farmers in these years. The adoption of the Thomas process in steel-making in the 1880s enabled smelters to use iron ores containing phosphorus, which combined with lime to form a product of no use to the industry but eminently useful in agriculture. Its value for poor pastures on clay soils was demonstrated by W. Somerville, T. H. Middleton and D. A. Gilchrist, successive Directors of Cockle Park. (This upland farm near Morpeth was leased by the Northumberland County Council in 1896 for an experimental and demonstration centre, in conjunction with the teaching of agriculture at what was then known as Armstrong College, Newcastle.) Basic slag was cheap; it could be finely ground and evenly spread; it contained lime and phosphates and liberated them slowly over a period of years, encouraging the growth of wild white clover, a hitherto inconspicuous component of many poor swards. A creeping strain, known as 'Kent wild white clover' was found to be exceptionally persistent and fast growing in a horizontal direction; with basic slag it gave a luxuriant growth of nutritious fodder which stimulated in turn the subsequent crops taken when the ley was ploughed under.[22] Unfortunately, basic slag proved of less value in the south and east of England, where the lack of moisture and the alkaline reaction of many soils hindered the liberation of the phosphates.

Another type of grassland improvement was popularised by Robert Elliot, of Clifton Park in Roxburgh, across the border

[21] A. Hutcheson, 'Rotation of Crops', *Tr. H.A.S.*, vol. 21.v, 1909, pp. 51–8; J. Drysdale, 'Timothy Meadows', *Tr. H.A.S.*, vol. 18.v, 1906, pp. 17–23.

[22] H. C. Pawson, *Cockle Park Farm*, Oxford, 1960.

from Cockle Park. By sowing a variety of grasses, clovers and deep-rooting herbs (such as chicory) on his upland fields, and by controlled grazing, he much improved his pastures and the subsequent crops, with little expenditure on fertilisers and tillage. The herbs broke up the sub-soil, tapped sources of nutrients out of reach of the shallow rooted plants and gave a tasty bite to the livestock.[23]

Farmers in touch with new ideas had therefore considerable scope for raising the output of their grassland. They must have used, year by year, rather more fertilisers of all sorts, for the aggregate quantity applied was in 1911–13 nearly double that used in the 1880s; and there was also a substantial rise in the import of animal feeding-stuffs whose manurial residues went back into the soil.[24] But farmers seemed to have limed less frequently, as wages rose and crop prices fell; further, the supply of urban horse-manure began to decrease in the years before the First World War, as motor vans and omnibuses supplanted the town stables.

MEAT AND MILK

For nearly thirty years after the first collection of agricultural statistics in 1866, the number of cattle increased in almost every county in Britain. The dry year of 1893 and the severe drought of 1894 coincided with a sharp fall in meat prices, and cattle numbers fell from a peak of 6,945,000 head in 1892 to a low point of 6,347,000 in 1894. Then a recovery began, and although meat prices in 1902–4 were almost as low as ten years earlier, cattle numbers increased slowly beyond the previous record to reach a new peak of just over 7 million in 1911.

But throughout these years, the age structure, the purpose and

[23] R. Elliot, *The Clifton Park System of Farming*, London, 1908, first published in 1898 under the title *Agricultural Changes*.

[24] E. M. Ojala, *op. cit.*, estimated the annual average import of feeding-stuffs and consumption of fertilisers for the United Kingdom as follows:

	1886–93	1894–1903	1904–10	1911–13
Thousand Tons				
Imported Feeds	4,627	5,863	6,113	6,432
Fertilisers (excl. lime)	647	912	1,050	1,281

the density of the cattle population showed considerable changes which are summarised in Table 4 for the years 1890 and 1910. Compared with the figures for 1870 (given earlier on p. 137), the most striking feature is the fall in the proportion of the cattle aged two years and over, a sign of the more rapid maturity of the

Table 4.

Cattle Enterprises in Britain, 1890 and 1910

Per 100 cows and heifers	1890		1910		
	Cattle 2 yrs & over	Cattle under 2 yrs	Cattle 2 yrs & over	Cattle 1–2 yrs	Cattle under 1 yr
1. Fattening on arable and leys	78	114	80	75	63
2. Fattening, some rearing, 13 Scottish counties	99	163	101	100	66
3. Fattening on grass, 7 English counties	140	142	136	88	72
4. Mixed with dairying	59	97	51	60	52
5. Lowland rearing, some fattening, 7 English counties	63	118	50	68	63
6. Hill rearing: Wales and 4 English counties	43	115	42	65	69
14 Scottish counties	51	120	45	66	64
7. Dairying: English counties	29	64	25	32	31
6 Scottish counties	28	66	26	29	27

1. Bedford, Cambs., Essex, Notts, Sussex, Warwick, Yorkshire (East Riding); in 1910, Essex and Sussex shift to Group 7.

2. Aberdeen, Berwick, Clackm., Fife, Forfar, Haddington, Kinc., Kinross, Kirkcudb., Linlithgow, Perth, Roxb., Stirling.

3. Hunts., Leicester, Lincoln, Norfolk, Northants., Northumberland, Rutland.

4. Berks., Bucks., Herts., Kent, Oxford, Suffolk; in 1910, Berks. shifts to Group 7.

5. Cornwall, Devon, Glos., Hereford, Monmouth, Salop, Worcs.

6. Cumberland, Durham, Westmorland, Yorkshire (North Riding); Argyll, Banff, Bute, Caithness, Dumfries, Elgin, Inverness, Nairn, Orkney, Peebles, Ross and Cromartie, Selkirk, Shetland, Sutherland.

7. Cheshire, Derby, Dorset, Hants., Lancs., London and Middlesex, Somerset, Staffs., Surrey, Wilts., Yorkshire (West Riding); add Berks., Essex and Sussex in 1910. Ayr, Dumbarton, Edinburgh, Lanark, Renfrew, Wigtown.

beef animals, and of their slaughter before they laid on too much fat. By 1910, there were in England and Wales only 47 cattle aged two years and over to every 100 cows and heifers in milk and calf, compared with 56 in 1890 and 62 in 1870. In contrast, more calves were reared, both absolutely and as a proportion of the breeding stock; there were 103 cattle under two years of age in 1910 for every 100 cows and heifers, compared with 98 in 1890, and 83 in 1870.

Within this general change, a few counties showed peculiar features which indicated shifts in the dominant type of enterprise. In 1890, the higher ratio of other cattle to breeding stock in Huntingdon and Norfolk brought these counties from Group 1 into Group 3, from the primarily arable group into the mainly grassland group; it is probable, however, that winter figures, if available, would show that Norfolk farmers continued to fatten cattle in yards on a large scale over the winter months. A fall in the same ratio in Suffolk, combined with an increase in cow numbers, brought this county out of Group 1 in 1870 into Group 4 in 1890, reflecting the greater importance of dairying; and the same trend shifted the West Riding of Yorkshire from Group 6 in 1870 into Group 7 by 1890. By 1910, the age structure in Essex and Sussex (Group 1) and in Berkshire (Group 4) showed that dairying had become their principal cattle enterprise; these counties then came into Group 7, which contained fourteen English counties in 1910 against only ten in 1870.

In Scotland, the changes were less marked, for the extension of dairying was more limited and the conversion of arable to grassland insignificant. But there was the same decline in the proportion of the cattle aged two years and over, and the same increase in the younger cattle, showing the same tendency as in England and Wales to rear more calves from the breeding stock. Outside the main dairying district of the southwest, the lowland farms remained substantial importers of store stock, whether from the Scottish hills or the Irish pastures; they needed cattle and sheep to graze their leys, in summer, and to turn their oats, straw and turnips into meat for sale and into muck for the potatoes.

In 1908, farmers were asked to state the breed or type of their animals.[25] Out of almost 7 million cattle, $4\frac{1}{2}$ million were returned as Shorthorns, to which group most of the 200,000 cattle returned as 'Irish' probably belonged. The Devons and Ayrshires had about 450,000 each, there were nearly 400,000 Herefords, 250,000 were described as Welsh, and Aberdeen Angus accounted for just under 200,000 animals. Two-thirds of the cattle in Britain were thus predominantly Shorthorn, though many classified under this heading were, no doubt, indifferently bred and poorly reared. The spread of intensive dairying seems to have been one factor in the poor quality of the cattle stocks found over much of the English Midlands. Cowkeepers near towns cared little for pedigree or even for good commercial breeding; they bought their down-calvers by eye, and many found it less trouble to fatten dry cows for the butchers than to get them in calf for another lactation. Good milking cows were thus continually being killed young, or put to any cheap bull. A high level of commercial Shorthorn was to be found chiefly in the north of England and in eastern Scotland away from the dairying influence. The greater part of the English milk supply came from animals that were nominally Shorthorns, for the two southern dairy breeds, the South Devons and the Channel Islands, only included some 100,000 animals each in 1908, against the 440,000 Ayrshires that supplied the Scottish milk market; and Friesians (or Holsteins) were not even mentioned in this enquiry.

A dozen breeds thus accounted for the cattle of Britain, but thirty-three headings were required for the 27 million sheep. The ten most popular breeds, accounting however for only 20 million animals, were:

Blackfaced Mountain	5·6 million	Shropshire	1·6 million
Cheviot	2·7	'Scotch'	1·2
Welsh Mountain	2·6	Oxford Down	1·1
Lincoln	1·9	Kent or Romney	1·0
Hampshire Down	1·7	Suffolk	0·9

[25] *Agricultural Output of G.B.*, 1912, Cd. 6277, p. 57.

The big long-woolled Lincolns still took pride of place among the lowland sheep, and took also a considerable part of the export trade. The Hampshire Downs and Oxford Downs were increasing in popularity, either pure-bred or as second crosses on half-bred ewes, producing animals which were sold fat at 80 lb or thereabouts in weight by the time they were a year old. Suffolks and Southdowns were still found mainly in the south and east of England, being folded on the chalky and dry soils there; here the decline in arable brought a corresponding fall in sheep numbers, which persisted through short fluctuations caused by droughts, disease and changing prices. After the recovery from the 1894 drought, there was little change in the total number maintained in the English grazing counties and in Scotland, but Welsh farmers increased their flocks steadily up to the war. The Welsh mountain sheep, a type more than a breed, and the dark or speckle-faced Cluns and Kerrys, were favoured by the English midland graziers, for the draft ewes, though smaller and wilder than the Scottish half-breds, were also cheaper. Crossed with an Oxford or Hampshire Down ram, they produced useful, quick-maturing animals which could be folded on the light cornbrash soils.

The 1908 census also recorded 2·8 million pigs upon agricultural holdings, but did not attempt to count the number kept in sties and back gardens. Of the pigs included, more than a million were described as White or Large White; there were 460,000 Berkshires, and about 400,000 Middle Whites, more specifically a pork pig favoured in the Midlands; the remainder were small white, blacks, Tamworths and crossbred. The Yorkshire or Large White was thus easily the most popular breed. Evolved in the northern mining districts as a supplier of pork or bacon, it was developed through local shows until it attained the dignity of classes at the national shows and a Herd Book. Breeding stock was sought, during the last third of the nineteenth century, by such countries as Denmark and Holland which were building up a trade in mild cured bacon and hams for the British market. Further south, the small black pigs, variously known as Essex,

Suffolk or Wessex, had been bred as porkers for the London market but their excessive fat was making them less popular, as the British townsmen consumed more butter on their bread and less lard with their meat.

The commercial fattening of pigs was concentrated in those areas which possessed suitable foods – Cheshire and Lancashire with their milk and whey; the south-western counties with their milk, orchards and vegetables, and the eastern counties depending on potatoes and beans. The breeding and rearing of pigs for the commercial and household fatteners was in most areas a different business, the prerogative of small holders and family farmers. The two sides of the trade were linked by the 'pig dealer', buying and selling, matching supply and demand with the help of an old pony and trap. The activities of such men, operating often without records or premises, continually defeated the efforts of 'authority' to control outbreaks of swine fever by controlling movement of pigs within a scheduled area. The trade in weaners was also affected by sanitary regulations which prohibited the keeping of pigs near houses or roads; but local inspectors were often unwilling to deprive a cottage housewife of her pork and bacon by condemning her pig-sty.[26]

THE LIQUID MILK TRADE

The census of output taken in 1908 recorded the value of dairy produce sold from farms in Britain at about £30 million, about one-fifth of the total agricultural output. Some 850 million gallons of milk were thought to have been sold liquid, of which an unknown quantity was manufactured by dairies into a variety of products; another 140 million gallons were sold by farms as butter, with possibly 17 million gallons of skim milk also sold, as it was at Lark Rise at a penny per container to anyone who cared to come and buy at the farm's back door.[27] Farm cheese makers used

[26] *Interim Report of the Dept. Committee on Swine Fever*, 1911, Cd. 5671, and *Evidence*, 1911, Cd. 5680; S. Spencer, 'Pigs on the Farm', *Tr. H.A.S.*, vol. 11.v, 1899, pp. 263–287; National Pig Breeders' Association, *Herd Book*, St Ives, 1885.

[27] F. Thompson, *Lark Rise to Candleford*, Oxford, 1945, p. 17.

another 56 million gallons of milk. In one form or another, there-fore, farmers sold in that year rather more than a thousand million gallons of milk, and most of it went either direct to consumers of liquid milk or to wholesale milk distributors.[28]

The extension of dairying in the forty years after 1870 was partly indicated by the analysis of cattle figures given earlier (p. 358). By 1910, liquid milk was being brought into the London market from 130 miles away by the Great Western Railway, though most of the trade was carried from stations in Berkshire, Hampshire and Wiltshire. The Great Northern Railway ran a special milk train daily to London from Eggington Junction outside Burton-on-Trent, carrying milk from farms in Derbyshire and Staffordshire 150 miles to market. The London terminal stations reserved special platforms for the milk traffic; there was a considerable market in what was known as 'accommodation milk', milk consigned either to the railway, or to a wholesaler, for sale at the station to any trade buyer. Glasgow was drawing milk from Kirkcudbright and Wigtown, though most of its supplies came from the nearer counties of Ayr, Lanark and Renfrew; the more distant farms often made cheese in the summer, but obtained a higher price from the milk wholesalers by selling to them for a couple of months at each end of the season.[29]

The farmers who regularly sold milk on wholesale contracts normally paid the transport costs to their buyers' station; they sometimes also paid a further halfpenny per gallon or so for 'insurance', against their milk souring in transit. At the distance from the urban markets where transport costs and insurance together amounted to some 2*d* per gallon, it usually became worth while to sell milk to a local factory, or to manufacture it into cheese or butter, using the whey or skim milk for rearing calves or pigs. The basic prices obtained from London contracts in 1905–6 averaged 9*d* per gallon for the winter half-year and 7*d* for the

[28] *Agricultural Output of G.B.*, 1912, Cd. 6277, p. 14; *Final Report Census of Production*, 1912, Cd. 6320, p. 462.

[29] E. A. Pratt, *The Transition in Agriculture*, London, 1906, pp. 11–17; J. A. Gilchrist, *West of Scotland College of Agriculture*.

summer half-year; they tended to rise slowly in keeping with other prices and with the increasing demand, and by 1913–14 averaged about 10½*d* and 8*d* per gallon respectively. In the northern markets, prices were somewhat lower and the seasonal differential rather larger; in 1914, the Glasgow prices ranged from 6½*d* per gallon in June and July to 10*d* in January.[30]

The flow of milk into these large towns was thus balanced between the net price received on farms for wholesale contracts, and the net price received from other methods of sale, which was in turn largely dominated by the prices for imported butter and cheese. The liquid markets were supplied through wholesalers, buying on contract from farmers and selling to the retailers, or as in the northern towns, direct to the consumers. From about 1890 onwards, wholesalers also tended to become processors of milk, with plant for cooling, 'pasteurising', and perhaps bottling, thus providing consumers with a better quality of a less perishable product; they also installed churning facilities or condensing plant to manufacture milk surplus to the liquid demand. These new processes required expensive premises and complicated machinery, and could only be economic if operated continuously on a large scale. Inevitably, the few firms which were first to install this equipment in each large town tended to expand rapidly at the expense of smaller or less alert businesses; and farmers who were not satisfied with their contracts from one such firm might find it difficult to obtain better terms from any other. It is note-worthy that retail prices in London remained virtually unchanged at 16*d* per gallon from 1892 until 1915, in spite of considerable variations in seasonal prices on the wholesale contracts, and large variations in the prices obtained by 'accommodation milk'.[31]

A number of attempts were made at co-operative selling by dairy farmers over this period, in order to obtain better prices, especially during the summer months when they might be getting 5*d* or 6*d* per gallon for milk retailed in London at 16*d*. Farmers

[30] R. L. Cohen, *History of Milk Prices*, Oxford, 1936, p. 18; R. B. Forrester, *Report on the Fluid Milk Market*, Ministry of Agriculture, Economic Series No. 16, 1927.
[31] *ibid.*, p. 18.

in Staffordshire and Derbyshire combined about 1897 to pay a London agent to sell their milk direct to retailers; a similar agent was at one time operating in the Manchester market on behalf of the Cheshire farmers, and in London for dairy farmers in the eastern counties. Such efforts may have helped to secure that rise in contract prices from 1906 onwards which was obtained from the London market while retail prices were held unchanged. The big retailing firms were still subject to competition from producer-retailers who operated from their own farms on the edges of the suburbs; hundreds of milk floats clattered twice a day down the streets of outer London and of the smaller towns, retailing 'farm milk' as distinct from 'railway milk'.

Outside the range of the liquid milk trade, farms combined stock rearing with the seasonal manufacture of butter or of cheese, as occurred throughout much of Wales and the west of England. Such butter was often of poor quality and fetched only low prices, but the farmers' wives might reckon that it cost nothing but their time in the making and its sale brought in useful cash. Farmhouse cheese-makers were perhaps more professional, if only because the equipment was more costly and the process more laborious. The work of dairy bacteriologists had explained and codified many of the cheese-making mysteries, and had shown that almost any type of cheese could be made anywhere, given the appropriate 'starter' and subsequent treatment of the curd. Farmers in north Somerset had thus largely abandoned the 'truckles' of Cheddar cheese, of which huge quantities were imported; by the early years of the new century, they were generally making the 5 lb Caerphilly cheese which sold so well among the coal-miners on the other side of the Bristol Channel. Some farms, and a small number of co-operative factories in Leicestershire and south Nottingham, were then making the traditional Stilton for the London market; the oldest co-operative factory here was that at Scalford, established in 1903 with the support of the Duke of Rutland. But butter-making and duck-rearing were almost extinct round Aylesbury by 1905, and whole milk went instead to the new condensing factories at Aylesbury, Buckingham and Winslow.

In Derbyshire, the co-operative factories set up in the 1870s had largely turned to the collection and cooling of milk before dispatch to the towns; but a few farmers here also made Stilton cheese, taking in milk from their neighbours in order to build up a worthwhile output. The manufacture of Cheshire cheese was declining in its native county; and by 1905 Ayrshire farmers mainly sold liquid milk rather than the original Dunlop cheese, or the Cheddar introduced into the district forty years earlier.[32]

Another co-operative effort was the British Dairy Farmers' Association, founded in 1876 during the first London Dairy Show, largely through the initiative of Professor John Sheldon, then teaching at the Royal Agricultural College at Cirencester. The financial support and enlightened views of the members of this association created in 1888 the British Dairy Institute at Aylesbury, where courses were given in milk hygiene and processing; here was the origin of the National Institute for Research in Dairying which developed later at Reading from these modest beginnings at Aylesbury. In 1905, the British Dairy Shorthorn Association was formed by a group of breeders and dairy farmers, including R. Hobbs, at Kelmscott, whose herd traced back (through that of his father, C. Hobbs at Meysey Hampton) to the dispersal sale of Bates's cows at Kirklevington in 1850.[33]

MILK-BORNE DISEASES

Farmers who, in 1900 or in 1910, signed contracts for the sale of milk did more than engage in business; they also put their farms under the supervision of a variety of local authorities concerned with public health. Adulteration, sanitation, and tuberculosis summarise the three major problems of the milk trade in the years before the First World War.

[32] E. A. Pratt, *op. cit.*, pp. 220, 358–9; A. D. Hall, *op. cit.*, p. 409; A. Macneilage, 'Farming Methods in Ayrshire', *Tr. H.A.S.*, vol. 18.v, 1906, pp. 1–17.

[33] E. Capstick, 'The Past One Hundred Years', *J. Soc. Dairy Techn.*, vol. 3, 1950, p. 153; G. T. Burrows, *History of Dairy Shorthorn Cattle*, London, 1950; A. D. Hall, *op. cit.*, p. 168.

The Sale of Food and Drugs Act, 1875 (and subsequently), gave local authorities powers to prosecute sellers of food which was judged unfit for human consumption or which was sold under a description that disguised its real nature. The sale of milk-and-water as milk clearly contravened this legislation, and public analysts devised methods of detecting the grosser forms of adulteration, leaving to lawyers the problem of proving where, in the chain from cow to consumer, such dilution might have taken place. But analysts quickly discovered that milk itself varied greatly in composition, apart altogether from any question of adulteration. Where milk was bulked from a number of farms, its variability was of course not large. Producer-retailers with a few cows each were most likely to be prosecuted for selling a genuine, if thin, milk when the Board of Agriculture introduced, under the Sale of Milk Regulations, 1901, minimum presumptive standards of 3 per cent butter fat and $8\frac{1}{2}$ per cent of solids-not-fat.

The association of dirt in the dairy with souring of milk was well known before bacteria were discovered, but that association became of public interest when it was shown that infected milk could convey a number of diseases from one human being to another. Under the Dairies, Cowsheds and Milkshops Orders, 1885 (and subsequently), local authorities began to require certain minimum standards of ventilation for cows kept indoors, of purity for their water, and of cleanliness in the handling of their milk. The Infectious Diseases Prevention Act, 1890, gave powers for Medical Officers of Health to prohibit the sale of milk if they had reason to believe it was conveying infectious disease from one human being to another. Difficulties arose, of course, in enforcing such regulations when the farms concerned might be 100 miles away from the Medical Officer and under the jurisdiction of another sanitary authority; the Central Chamber of Agriculture consistently tried, from the 1890s onwards, to persuade Parliament to enact a single uniform code for milk-selling farms which would avoid these difficulties of over-lapping jurisdictions.

These problems were intensified when medical science

demonstrated that tuberculosis could be conveyed from cows to human beings through the medium of infected milk or infected meat. Local authorities had powers under the Sale of Foods and Drugs Acts to condemn meat offered for sale that was judged unfit for human consumption because of tuberculosis; as it was an offence to offer such meat for sale, no compensation was paid to its owner. In 1908, a few butchers' associations threatened not to purchase fatstock unless farmers provided a warranty that they were free from disease; the Chambers of Agriculture urged farmers to resist, and to press instead for compensation to be paid, not from the local rates, but from national funds, since public health was a national concern.

Meat inspection showed that a considerable proportion of dairy cows were tubercular at death; the development of tuberculin enabled tests to be made on cows while alive, and revealed that a substantial minority, possibly a majority, of dairy cows supplying milk to the liquid market were infected with tuberculosis. Public concern over this disease was shown in the enquiries conducted by no less than three Royal Commissions in fifteen years – that of 1890, re-appointed in 1894 to consider fresh evidence, and that of 1904. Many local authorities took powers, in private bills going through Parliament, to impose varying regulations to prohibit the sale within their respective areas of milk from tubercular cows. Here again, the Chamber of Agriculture opposed these unco-ordinated and variable controls; it managed to persuade most local authorities to adopt uniform 'model clauses' which made it an offence knowingly to sell milk from cows affected with tuberculosis of the udder, and placed the enforcement of this regulation in the hands of the Justices in the area where the suspected dairy was situated.

When national legislation was at last introduced, in 1909, it did provide for compensation to be paid to the owners of cows condemned because of tuberculosis, but this was to be paid out of the rates, which fell most heavily, of course, on owners and occupiers of land. These clauses met with such opposition that the Government withdrew the bill; when again brought up, in

1914, a sum of £60,000 was allowed from taxes for five years for this purpose.[34]

By 1901, about 40 per cent of the British people lived in seven industrial conurbations – Greater London, southern Lancashire, the west Midlands round Birmingham, west Yorkshire, Merseyside, Teeside and Clydeside. The provision of food for these urbanised masses involved the assembly of small lots from farmers; subsequent grading, sorting, packing and processing; storage over time; transport over land or seas; financing the goods in progress from the first seller to the final buyer; bargaining over prices and transport charges at each stage; and, finally, the breaking up of the bulked consignments for delivery to the retail shops and thence to the housewives.

The arrival of the first cargo of frozen meat from New Zealand in 1882, with the carcases of 4,000 sheep and 600 lambs, was followed before the end of the century by rapid developments in distribution. The importing firms built refrigerated stores at the main British ports, which enabled them to hold frozen meat for long or short periods and which were also used for the storage of other imported produce. Dealing in truck loads and ship loads, they secured favourable terms from railways and ship-owners for their custom; by 1896, it was calculated that a lamb could be killed in New Zealand, frozen, shipped to London and delivered there to a retailer for a little under 2*d* per lb. Private companies and a few of the urban councils also built cold stores in other towns in which space could be rented by local traders; those using this facility were chiefly agents handling imported meat for the 'Colonial Meat Stores which are springing up ovei the country'.[35]

---

[34] A. H. H. Matthews, *History of the Central Chamber of Agriculture*, London, 1915, pp. 43–69, 300–302.

[35] D. Pigeon, 'Cold Storage', *J.R.A.S.E.*, vol. 7.iii, 1896, p. 609; *Report of the Dept. Committee on Combinations in the Meat Trade*, 1909, Cd. 4643, and *Evidence*, 1909, Cd. 4661.

The trade in British produce was little affected by such innovations. As towns grew bigger, direct contact between growers and
consumers became less possible, and the weekly markets fell out
of use or became converted to the trade from farmers to merchants;
and the country traders and local higglers extended their activities
in rural districts. Market gardeners and farmers selling potatoes
and vegetables continued to send their consignments to the towns
to be sold at the produce markets by their agents. It is recorded
that one day's despatch of vegetables from Wisbech station in the
season weighed about 53 tons but consisted of more than 17,000
consignments, as each grower sent a variety of produce to a
variety of salesmen, at the rates appropriate to the cost of handling
and invoicing the separate parcels. Politicians, earnest Fabians,
improving land owners and some farmers all emphasised the reduction in costs, or the rise in prices, that might be obtained by
co-operative action in getting produce from the farm gate to the
first point of assembly, in controlling the flow into the main
markets especially in times of glut, and in setting up facilities such
as freezing plants or cold stores.[36]

The new century saw a considerable burst of co-operative
activity in Britain, following a lead given, in this case, by Irish
farmers with their co-operative butter factories. In many parts of
Britain, but especially in Wales, groups of farmers did set up in
business, either in co-operative societies under the Industrial and
Provident Societies Acts, or in joint-stock companies, in order to
supply themselves with seeds, fertilisers and feeding-stuffs of better
quality, or at cheaper prices, than could then be secured from
the local traders. More than 100 such societies were thought to be
in existence in 1908, and about 200 in 1914, with a combined
turnover then of about £1·7 million annually, and with about
24,000 members. Many of these societies were small in members
and in turnover; a few successfully overcame initial difficulties
and evolved into large businesses, but many also quickly faded
out or were finally wound up after a few years, for a variety of
reasons – hostility from existing merchants to whom farmers were

[36] E. A. Pratt, *op. cit.*, pp. 45, 219.

often in debt, unwillingness or inability to provide adequate finance or an adequate volume of trade, the general apathy of many members.

Co-operative selling organisations were also tried in some numbers in these years before 1914. The most durable and successful were those established in areas of smallish farms following much the same pattern of production – the Leicester cheese factories, the milk cooling centres in Ayrshire, Derbyshire and in the Dorset vale; and the horticultural co-operatives round Evesham and Pershore, which either organised auction sales or bulked and packed produce for dispatch to Birmingham and other markets.

These local improvements in the first stage of marketing were accompanied by more conspicuous activity at the national level. Enthusiastic reformers established a confusing variety of associations and societies to advise the co-operatives, or to stimulate their creation, or to federate them into larger and more economic trading units. Those who are interested in these early attempts can refer to the references below; the many creations, conversions and dissolutions give the impression that little was achieved in the face of the apathy of most farmers. For the distributive trades contained, among many thousands of firms, a number of the highest repute and efficiency, already performing for farmers, at reasonable cost, the services that they needed in marketing and in the supply both of inputs and of credit.[37]

Two events occurred at the turn of the century which demonstrated the extent to which prices received by British farmers were dominated, not by their own supply, but by events outside this country. In 1898 a sharp rise in wheat prices was caused by the combined effects of poor crops in Europe, a famine in India which reduced exports from that country, and an American 'corner' in wheat operated on the Chicago market in May when supplies were at their lowest. This particular monopoly was short-lived, but it marked the beginning of a period when the growing

[37] Ministry of Agriculture, *Report on Co-operative Marketing*, Econ. Ser. No. 1, 1925; *Report on Co-operative Purchase of Requisites*, Econ. Ser. No. 5, 1929.

demand for wheat caught up with that vast increase in supply which had occurred in the last quarter of the nineteenth century; wheat prices after 1898 were generally above those of the depression years.[38]

And in the summer of 1908, beef suddenly became dearer. Popular opinion blamed the American firms of 'meat packers', which had recently acquired a control over the exports of meat from the United States, and, it was feared, controlled also the refrigerated cargo space and some of the wholesale firms in the British market. An official enquiry concluded that there was still plenty of competition on this side of the Atlantic, much of it indeed stimulated by the new practices and methods introduced by the American firms themselves; the rise in prices was attributed to an unexpected fall in cattle sales from the American ranches which sharply reduced the volume of meat available for exports.[39] Whatever the cause, the result was no doubt welcomed by British livestock farmers. For ten years from 1893 a run of exceptionally dry summers reduced the output of grass, roots and hay, and forced them on to purchased feeds at a time when cereal prices were rising, and those of meat and wool remained relatively low. They remained low, partly because imports were increasing in these years, and partly because lack of employment in many British industries created a lack of purchasing power. Depression in many export trades only slowly gave way in the new century to fuller order books and more employment, while wage rates tended to lag behind the rise in the prices of cereal foods, thus restricting the demand for meat. But from 1906 onwards, meat prices followed the general upward trend which lasted, with only minor checks, until the outbreak of war in 1914. The farmers who survived the great depression had managed to cut their costs to match the fall in prices; their successors in the new century had the different task of holding down their costs in a time of rising prices and rising wages.

[38] R.C. Food, 1905, p. 9; W. T. Layton, 'Wheat Prices and the World's Production', *J.R.A.S.E.*, vol. 70, 1909, pp. 105–6.

[39] *Report of Dept. Committee on Combinations in the Meat Trade*, 1909, Cd. 4643, p. 11.

THE NEW KNOWLEDGE

The development of the sciences in the last decades of the nineteenth century had provided farmers with some assistance in this
task. Chemical analysis had reduced the adulteration of fertilisers
and feeding-stuffs and had yielded useful information on the
extent to which one type could be substituted for another type if
relative prices changed. Such knowledge was important, for
fertilising was no longer a choice between guano, superphosphate
and nitrate of soda; a variety of phosphatic and potassic rocks
were imported, as well as nitrate of lime. Many farmers still
bought no fertilisers, preferring to rely on the traditional muck;
others judged a fertiliser by their nose, on the theory that the
more the contents of the bag smelt like ripe manure, the more
potent would be the effect on the crop.[40] On the other hand,
farmers were aware of qualities important to them which were
still not explicable by the scientists. Continued use of nitrate of
soda was found to have deleterious effects of the structure of some
soils and on plant growth, effects which could not be correlated
with known facts, until further research into soil microbiology
explained the release of carbonate of soda which gradually de-
flocculated the clay particles. Livestock fatteners knew that cotton-
seed cake was a more economic feed, weight for weight, than linseed cake for sheep, but suited bullocks less well; it was only just
before the First World War that scientists began to analyse the
plant 'albumens' and 'proteins' into different groups and to
recognise that animal nutrition involved complex changes, going
far beyond the absorption of fats, albumens and carbo-hydrates
for use in the same form. It was surely a sign of better mutual
comprehension when a scientist decided that in feeding dairy
cows 'farmers have in most cases come wonderfully near to what
would be regarded as up-to-date scientific requirements'.[41]

[40] This traditional practice was reported by Professor Sir Frank Engledow.
[41] A. D. Hall, 'Some Secondary Actions of Manures upon the Soil', *J.R.A.S.E.*,
vol. 70, 1909, pp. 12–35; J. Hendrick, 'Nitrogenous Constituents of Foods', *Tr. H.A.S.*,
vol. 22.v, 1910, pp. 142–51; T. B. Wood, 'Chemistry of the Proteins', *Tr. H.A.S.*,
vol. 23.v, 1911, pp. 84–92; A. S. Grant, 'Feeding of Dairy Cows', *Tr. H.A.S.*, vol. 25.v,
1913, p. 16.

Marked improvements in the purity and germination of commercial seeds had occurred as the result of the work of such botanists as William Carruthers, who advised members of the Royal Agricultural Society from 1871 to 1909. The more reputable firms of seed merchants and seed growers had, by the end of the century, developed methods of seed testing for their own products, or sent their seeds to the new testing stations in Switzerland, Denmark or Germany, since no such official organisation existed in Britain. Temporary leys were less likely than before to consist of a mixture of unspecified weeds, rye-grasses and clovers; the campaign against rye-grass, led by Faunce de Laune and Robert Elliot of Clifton Park, had encouraged the use of more complex mixtures, with timothy, cocksfoot and meadow fescues, which could give a higher yield over a longer grazing season; the use of basic slag and of selected strains of wild white clover also improved the output and lengthened the useful life of many leys.[42]

Botanists and seed merchants had long recognised that most crops sown in Britain contained a variety of types; by continuous selection and careful breeding from strains most suited to particular environments, a marked improvement could often be effected in the average crop, whether of grain, potatoes, clovers or rye-grass. Hybridisation – the crossing of distinct varieties – had also been used to improve such important farm crops as wheat and potatoes. In the 1890s, a Lancashire firm of seed merchants put on the market some new strains of oats which gave generally higher yields than the old Potato or Sandy; their stiff-strawed Tartar King was of special value to farmers on fertile soils. In 1893, E. S. Beaven (1857–1941) began his lifetime's work at Warminster on the breeding and manuring of barley; in the next decade, he produced pure strains of the 'Plumage' and 'Archer' varieties which were widely adopted. These normally yielded more than Chevallier, the barley previously favoured in the east and south of England, or than Goldthorpe, much grown in the

[42] *Report of the Dept. Committee on Agricultural Seeds*, 1901, Cd. 489, and *Evidence*, 1901, Cd. 493; Wm. Carruthers, 'The Botanist's Work 1871–1909', *J.R.A.S.E.*, vol. 70, 1909, pp. 5–12.

north and west. But it was the rediscovery in 1900 of Mendel's theory of heredity which laid the foundations of the modern science of genetics, and which gave contemporary scientists some clues to the complex problems of the inheritance of such qualities as yield of grain and strength of straw. In 1906, R. H. Biffen (1874–1949) at Cambridge, demonstrated that Mendel's theory also illuminated the inheritance in wheat of susceptibility to yellow rust; by 1910 he had bred 'Little Joss' which combined a resilient straw with a notable resistance to this disease. 'Little Joss' came to be much grown on the black soils of the East Anglian fens; its rust resistance was derived from a Russian wheat which Biffen crossed with the old Squarehead's Master 'for many years the most widely grown wheat in this country'.[43]

By the early years of the twentieth century, the pioneers in the agricultural sciences had revealed exciting possibilities in the further study of soil colloids and soil micro-biology, of animal and plant physiology, of the pathology of their diseases and of the mechanism of heredity. But the developments thus foreshadowed threw up two major problems in the decade before the First World War, one of organisation and one of education. The scope and expense of agricultural research had outrun the facilities which could be provided by the agricultural societies and by private benefactors such as Lawes in Hertfordshire, his neighbour the Duke of Bedford, and E. S. Beaven at Warminster; nor could such facilities offer a worthy career to the new profession of agricultural scientists. Secondly, there was a growing gap between the knowledge and practice of the majority of farmers, educated not in the sciences but in the school of profit-making, and the thought and language of the research workers, mostly trained in the pure sciences. The career of A. D. Hall in the twenty-five years after 1890 is noteworthy for its contribution towards bridging this gap.[44]

Born in 1864 in the textile town of Rochdale, Hall received his training in the natural sciences first at Manchester Grammar

---

[43] F. L. Engledow, 'R. H. Biffen', *Obituary Notices of Fellows of the Royal Society*, vol. 7, 1950, p. 16.
[44] H. E. Dale, *Daniel Hall, Pioneer in Scientific Agriculture*, London, 1956.

School and then at Oxford where he read chemistry. From 1885 he taught science at two schools and seemed to be launched on the normal career of a schoolmaster. But in 1891, he accepted the challenge of a new appointment as a University Extension Lecturer in Surrey – a post under the Oxford Delegacy for Local Examinations, but paid by the County Council from the new grant for technical education. Most of the lecturing was concerned with physics and chemistry, but in the course of much travelling, he also studied the local agriculture and the local audiences. When the County Councils of Kent and Surrey established in 1894 an agricultural college at Wye, on the site of an ancient but decayed College of Priests, Daniel Hall became its first Principal.

In this capacity he was both a teacher of agricultural science and practice, and the servant of two County Councils dominated by critical farmers. It was Hall's peculiar genius that he was able to meet the farmers on their own ground, to discuss their problems in language which they understood and to interpret to them the value of the research work which he and his staff instituted at Wye, where they elucidated some complex problems in hop drying, fruit growing and horticulture. The new Principal rapidly became an expert himself in the breeding and cultivation of sweet peas and tulips. In 1905, he combined with T. H. Middleton, R. H. Biffen and T. B. Wood (all then at Cambridge) to launch the *Journal of Agricultural Science*, designed to serve the workers in the new profession of agricultural research and experiment.

While Wye was growing into an established institution, a number of other colleges were set up by enlightened County Councils or by generous benefactors, with the same double function – the systematic training of young men in the agricultural sciences and the spread of the new knowledge among farmers. The lectures in agricultural chemistry begun at Cambridge in 1892 with the support of local County Councils evolved in 1899 into a degree course in agriculture; the Worshipful Company of Drapers provided endowments for a Chair, occupied successively by William Somerville and T. H. Middleton from Cockle Park, and then by T. B. Wood. The Extension College at Reading (later the University of Reading) established degrees in agriculture and dairying; three County Councils organised an agricultural college at Kingston, near Nottingham; others were provided by private generosity at Newport to serve the county of Stafford, and near Newton Abbot for the county of Devon; advanced schools of agriculture were set up in Cheshire, Sussex and Penrith. Farmers, County Councils and the Highland and Agricultural Society promoted agricultural colleges at Edinburgh, Glasgow and Aberdeen to serve the south-east, south-west and north of Scotland, absorbing the existing Chair of Agriculture at Edinburgh and the Scottish Dairy School at Kilmarnock. Many of these institutions at first prepared their pupils for the diplomas in agriculture or dairying already established by the two national societies which combined from 1900 to hold joint examinations; but the new colleges at the University level soon developed their own diplomas or degrees.

When A. D. Hall gave evidence in 1908 to the Reay Committee on agricultural education, he spoke from much experience in teaching and administration, for he had moved from Wye in 1902 to become Director of Rothamsted after the death of Sir John Gilbert. In both positions, he was aware of the inadequacies of the existing facilities for agricultural education and research. A start had been made, thanks to the generosity of private benefactors, the energy of a few farmers and landowners, and small contributions from the rates in some counties; but the results could not compare with the organisation provided in other countries through such institutions as the Danish Folk Schools, the German State-supported research stations or the American land-grant colleges. The Reay Committee were particularly concerned by the virtual lack of agricultural education at the lower levels; it recommended that County Councils should establish farm schools which would combine winter courses for the 17–20-year-olds with advisory work for farmers. But it also thought that the existing courses at University level could not provide enough qualified teachers, or enough research scientists, without greater assistance from the State; the Board of Agriculture provided grants totalling only £12,300 in 1909–10 for all agricultural education and research.[45]

In 1910 the new Liberal Government established a Development Commission charged with the 'economic development' of the nation through grants in aid of approved non-profit-making schemes; A. D. Hall became a Commissioner and was concerned primarily with the development of agriculture and forestry. For two years he combined this post with his work at Rothamsted, but the burden grew too heavy, and in 1912 he resigned from Rothamsted to become one of the two full-time Commissioners.

In the early reports of the Development Commission, there appeared the skeleton of an organised structure of agricultural education and research. By 1912, twelve teaching colleges in England and Wales, and three in Scotland, were providing full courses at University level, aided by grants from the Board of Agriculture for their ordinary work, and from the Development Commission for their buildings, equipment and research. At a lower level, County Councils were being encouraged (they could not be compelled) to set up farm schools, to be run in conjunction with advisory work among farmers, as envisaged by the Reay Committee. Finally, fundamental research in the agricultural sciences was financially supported on a systematic basis which allocated the main subjects to specific institutions; Hall's experience at Rothamsted had convinced him that specialisation was becoming a necessity for the advance of knowledge. The scheme for England and Wales was described in the third report of the Development Commission, covering that last year of peace, 1913–1914:

Plant Physiology	Imperial College, S. Kensington
Plant Pathology	Kew
Plant Breeding	Cambridge: John Innes Institute for horticulture
Fruit Growing	Wye: Long Ashton Institute linked to Bristol University

[45] *Report of Dept. Committee on Agricultural Education*, 1908, Cd. 4206, pp. 36–8

Plant Nutrition and Soils	Rothamsted
Animal Pathology	Royal Veterinary College; Veterinary Laboratory of the Board of Agriculture
Dairying	Reading University
Agricultural Zoology	Manchester and Birmingham Universities
Animal Nutrition	Cambridge and Leeds Universities
Agricultural Economics	Oxford

It was characteristic of Hall's commonsense that the Development Commission approved the setting up at Oxford in 1913 of an Institute for Research in Agricultural Economics. In his evidence to the Reay Committee in 1908, he had argued that the book-keeping commonly taught to agricultural students was useless as a guide to better farm management. From 1905 to 1912, he had acted as technical adviser to an experimental hop farm run by the brewing firm of Guinness where, in conjunction with their accountant, he had evolved a system of 'costs book-keeping', designed to ascertain the balance of costs and profits for individual enterprises. It was this kind of analysis that he felt was urgently needed, if farmers were to be shown that the new knowledge could improve their profits as well as increase their output.

BRITISH AGRICULTURE IN 1914

It was in the intervals of this busy life as teacher, research scientist, author of successful text books and administrator that Daniel Hall, accompanied by E. S. Beaven and T. B. Wood, surveyed British agriculture in 1910–12 for *The Times*, as James Caird had done 60 years earlier. They did not take to horse, like Daniel Defoe, Arthur Young and William Cobbett, nor use a combination of horse and railway, like Caird himself and Rider Haggard in 1902–3; they travelled by motor car, a temperamental Leon Bollee which frequently boiled in that hot summer of 1911, when the dust from the untarred roads lay thick on the hedges. The

vacation tours showed to these, as to earlier, travellers the be-
wildering variety of crop rotations, feeding systems and social
traditions which existed within the confines of British agriculture.
Fream's popular textbook *The Elements of Agriculture* gave seven
standard rotations commonly found in England, but 'a sound
farmer should be competent to introduce a modified rotation to
meet his special requirements'.[46] All over the country, farmers
adapted the established rotations to the conditions of their soils,
the layout of their farms, the peculiarities of their climate, the
supply and cost of their labour, their need for fodder throughout
the year, the local opportunities for profitable markets. The new
fertilisers and the new implements gave farmers more choice in
their methods than had been available to their fathers and grandfathers, but the basic problems remained the same – to choose a
rotation of crops and a combination of enterprises which gave a
maximum level of profits with a minimum level of weeds and
pests.

Hall's first vacation tour in 1910 took him through the arable
regions in the southern half of England and then up the east coast
into Scotland. Farmers were then being faced with renewed
agitation for higher wages, a Saturday half-day, and by the first
organised 'strikes' in agriculture for thirty years. The threatened
rise in labour costs was serious to the intensively cropped farms,
many of which kept no livestock of their own, and were also being
affected by the falling supplies and rising prices of town manure.
Vegetable growing in Bedfordshire, corn, vegetables and bulbs in
the Fens and along the Yorkshire Ouse, the early potato production in Lincolnshire and Lancashire, these were the exceptions to
the general rule of feeding the soil through the manure of livestock
fed on the farms. Outside these specialist areas, the majority of
arable farmers looked to wheat, malting barley and, in some areas,
to potatoes for their income; they grazed sheep in summer or
fattened bullocks and hoggs in the winter because they could not
take more than three grain crops in five years without a drastic

[46] W. Fream, *Elements of Agriculture*, 8th ed, rev. by J. R. Ainsworth-Davis, London,
1911, p. 313.

fall in yields; the animals turned the inevitable straw, roots and grass into money and, when cake-fed, added fertility for the subsequent crops.

In Britain as a whole, however, the output of livestock and livestock products much exceeded in value the sale of crops; the Census of Output, 1908, showed that crops accounted for about one-third of the total sales from British farms.[47] The majority of farms, especially those in the north and west, devised their cropping to supply fodder for the livestock; crop costs and profits were therefore measured only indirectly, by the balance between receipts and expenditures for each farm as a whole. In the grassland regions, explored by Hall and his friends in 1911 and 1912, they found some land intensively used in dairying, but much that was indifferently farmed at a low level of costs and output. In spite of technical improvements in the twenty years after 1895, in spite of basic slag, wild white clover, improved seeds, more fertilisers and more knowledge of their use, the official statistics recorded little rise over this period in the average yields of hay or of the major crops:

Table 5. *Average Yields per Acre in Great Britain*

	Wheat	Barley	Oats	Potatoes	Hay Clover	Hay Meadow
	bus.	bus.	bus.	tons	cwt.	cwt.
1885–1894	29·3	33·0	38·2	5·8	28·2*	23·9
1905–1914	32·3	33·5	39·5	6·2	29·5	23·5

* Average for 1886–94.

Good farming there certainly was, but it was obscured in the national picture by large areas of underfarmed grassland, unlimed, barely fertilised and inadequately drained. The practice of liming seems largely to have died out after 1880, when the prices of crops fell, but the cost of digging, carting, burning and

[47] See p. 345.

spreading rose with rising wages and shorter hours; marling – the mixing of the underlying clay with light soils – had also been abandoned for the same reason. To Hall's charges of slipshod farming, there was always the easy defence, that the years of depression had eroded profits, credit and capital from landowners and farmers alike; that if the nation wanted better farming, it must pay higher prices for its food. Yet much of the contrast between good and poor farming was due, as always, to differences in the abilities of farmers as managers and employers of labour. Not all farmers who succeed to their fathers' farms are born managers, but Hall noted many on his tours who lacked that degree of education which might have made them more willing to look over their own hedges, less contented with traditional standards, less suspicious of their neighbour's success. And the contrast between good and poor management became more conspicuous when farmers were less bound by conventional rotations, when the new freedom could be used either to improve fertility or to exhaust it more quickly.

For raising the general level of efficiency, agriculture lacked not only education from below but also leadership from above. The political agitation against land owning seems to have inhibited many owners from getting rid of inefficient tenants, while the succession of Agricultural Holdings Acts limited their powers of control.[48] Owners and agents often tolerated poor farming because they themselves were unbusinesslike in the management of family estates, or because they preferred not to disturb long-established tenants who at least demanded little in the way of repairs and nothing in the way of improvements.

Nor was there much contact between the small family farmers, who had perhaps worked up from the ranks of cowmen or shepherds, and the educated and wealthy men who supported the national and breed societies and the Chambers of Agriculture. The continuing multiplication of separate breeds seemed only to intensify the contrast between the standards of the show ring and of the commercial market. One attempt was made to bridge the

[48] See Ch. 7 and 11.

gap from 1895 onwards, when the annual Christmas show at Smithfield was supplemented with carcase competitions; although the prize-winning animals seldom won a prize after death, the fatstock judges took little account of this difference in standards. A more hopeful development in these years was the initiation of milk recording in the south-west of Scotland. Pushed forward by John Speir of Newton (d. 1909), the Highland and Agricultural Society provided £200 a year for five years from 1903 towards the cost of professional recorders, who travelled from farm to farm testing herds in rotation every fourteen or twenty-one days. This innovation was at first opposed by some pedigree breeders who sold their bulls by conformation rather than on the milking records of their female relatives, but by 1914 there were thirty-six Milk Recording Societies in this area, with 6–700 herds regularly recorded. A few English members of the British Dairy Farmers Association and of the Dairy Shorthorn Association also kept and published similar records, but the first English Milk Recording Society, on the Scottish model, only began operations in 1914, at Cadbury in Somerset, encouraged by a grant from the Development Commission.[49]

The Royal Agricultural Society had been handicapped by troubles of its own in the early years of the new century. It had recently bought a new and expensive house in London and had enlarged its office staff to suit. By 1900, the overhead costs of its headquarters exceeded the annual receipts from the subscriptions of its members; and the cost of the annual show rose until that also exceeded the receipts from exhibitors and from admissions. It was then decided to acquire a permanent site near London on which the show could be staged more economically; one was bought in 1902 between Willesden and Ealing, and christened Park Royal. The decision was disastrous, for attendances dropped from 65,000 in 1903 to 24,000 in 1905; the loss on the 1904 show

[49] J. Speir, 'Milk Records', *Tr. H.A.S.*, vol. 21.v, 1909, pp. 175–96; Dept. Committee on the Export Trade in Livestock, *Evidence*, 1912, Cd. 6032, q. 5630–5667; B. Ridler, 'Origin, Development and Influence of Milk Recording . . .', *Dairy Science Abstracts*, vol. 23, 1961.

exhausted the accumulated reserves, and the guarantee fund raised in the next year did not cover the loss of nearly £8,000. A reorganised Council sold both Park Royal and Harewood House, moved the Society into more modest premises in Bedford Square, reduced the numbers and the salaries of the office staff, and reverted to the peripatetic show, beginning with a resounding success at Derby in 1906. But economy in expenditure and accumulation of fresh reserves were the principal cares of the Society for some years after this episode.[50]

Yet members of the two national societies could justly claim that they had greatly benefited farming in the last half of the nineteenth century. They had been pioneers in the analysis of feeding-stuffs and fertilisers, by which adulteration had been greatly reduced; their botanists had encouraged the seed trade in providing purer seeds in better condition; they had propelled the Government into more efficient measures for the control of animal diseases; the experiments supervised by their chemists had elucidated many details of manuring and animal nutrition; their regular tests had facilitated the improvement of farm machinery and implements; their journals, textbooks, annual shows and regular meetings kept their members in touch with products of science and engineering; their examinations and diplomas provided a foundation for the later growth of agricultural education. But having initiated so many desirable reforms in the nineteenth century, the Societies seemed less alert to the needs of the twentieth, to the new problems of management and of marketing, of changes in demand and in distribution.

Nor was the State concerned with the broader issues of agricultural policy. Although farming had been given a Board of Agriculture and a good share of attention from the Development Commission, the net results were only a weakening of landlord control over the farming community; a few grants to encourage research; a few County Council small holdings, and some sanitary regulations about adulteration, animal diseases and plant pests.

[50] J. A. Scott Watson, *History of the Royal Agricultural Society of England, 1839–1939*, London, n.d., Ch. V and VI.

Chamberlain's campaign for Tariff Reform, for import duties on foreign produce to provide a preference in the British market for all farmers within the Empire, was perhaps the most important political question for five years after the South African War, but it again split the Conservative party and finally brought into power in 1906 a Liberal Government pledged to free trade and social reform. From 1846 to 1914, therefore, the official policy for British agriculture was one of leaving landowners, farmers and farm workers substantially free to make the best incomes they could from the play of market forces.

For the greater part of this period, those markets embodied a rising demand for agricultural products from a population that was steadily growing larger and, in many sections, wealthier. In the last quarter of the nineteenth century, cheap grain from overseas seriously reduced the incomes derived from arable land, but cheap grain also increased the real incomes both of the town dwellers and of those livestock farmers for whom it was a raw material. The twenty years of depression after 1874 ruined many farmers and their landowners, destroyed flourishing communities and left some land derelict; on the other hand, it encouraged among the better farmers independence of judgment and a flexibility in practice which embodied such cost-reducing innovations as were available towards the end of the era of the farm-horse. The best farming seen by A. D. Hall between 1910 and 1912 was very good indeed, whether measured in output or in profit, but there was little corporate effort in Britain to improve the average standards whether in farming or in marketing.

There is more in farming, however, than business efficiency and profit per acre. Dungair was not less of a man because he farmed under a series of trust deeds for the creditors of the Aberdeenshire holding which his father and grandfather before him had won from moor and heather.[51] Of the men who turned the hay and carried the harvest in that glorious summer of 1914, some stayed on the farms, to improvise and worry and over-work for the

[51] J. R. Allan, *Farmer's Boy*, London, 1935.

harvests that were to keep a hungry nation from starvation. Others went overseas, to the trenches in Flanders and the beaches of Gallipoli, into the navy and the merchant fleet; and many did not return. In every parish in Britain their names are inscribed between the dates of 1914 and 1918. The hamlet of Lark Rise composed one epitaph for them which described not only their farming but also the men themselves—'they did not flinch'.

Charts

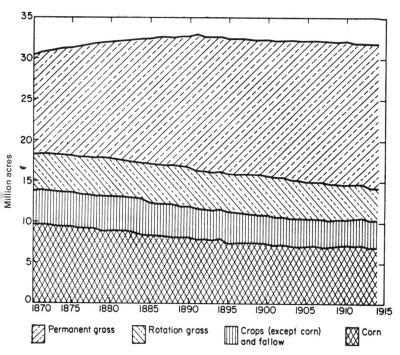

Permanent grass   **Rotation grass**   **Crops (except corn) and fallow**   **Corn**

Chart I. Area under corn, tillage and grass in Great Britain, 1870–1914

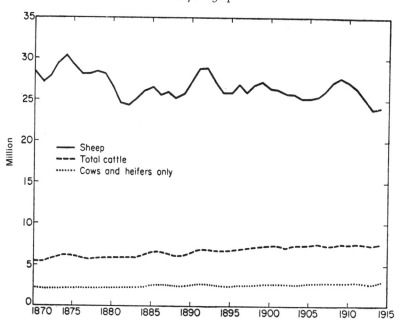

——— Sheep
‒ ‒ ‒ Total cattle
········· Cows and heifers only

Chart II. Numbers of sheep and cattle in Great Britain, 1870–1914

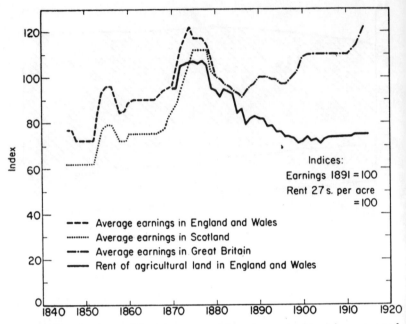

Chart III. Indices of I. Average earnings in agriculture in a normal week: 1846–1914; II. Rent per acre of agricultural land: 1870–1914

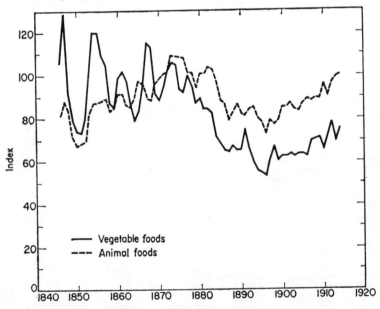

Chart IV. Indices of wholesale prices of food, 1846–1914
(1867–77 = 100)

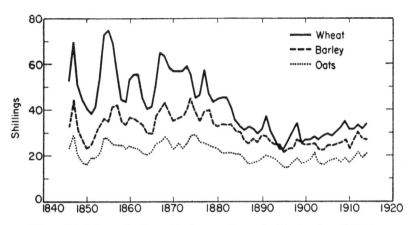

Chart V. Prices of wheat, barley and oats in England and Wales,
1846–1914

Prices in s. per quarter

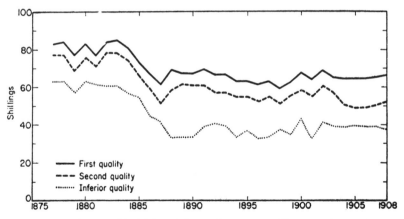

Chart VI. Prices of British cattle at the metropolitan cattle market,
1877–1908

Prices in s. per cwt.

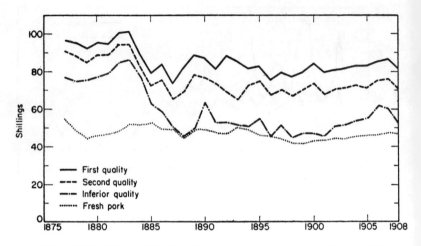

Chart VII. Prices of I. British sheep at the metropolitan cattle
market; II. Fresh pork: 1877–1908

Prices in s. per cwt.

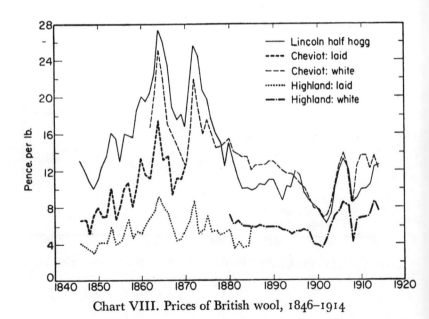

Chart VIII. Prices of British wool, 1846–1914

Index

Index

Guest, Lady Charlotte, 42
Guinness, hop farm of, 379
Guthrie, Rev. J., 74–5

Haggard, H. Rider, 260, 270*n*, 275*n*, 285*n*, 343*n*, 344, 379
Haldane, A. R. B., 27*n*
Hall, A. D., 298, 300*n*, 346, 349, 352*n*, 366*n*, 373*n*, 375, 378, 379–80, 385
Hall, C. P., 316*n*
Hall, W. H., 285
Hamilton, Henry, 167*n*
Hammond, J. L., 290*n*; J. L. and B., 62*n*
Hampshire, 273, 363
Hampstead Heath. 65
Handley, J. E., 77*n*
Harding, Joseph, of Marksbridge, 145
Hardy, Thomas, 85, 204, 233–4
harvest
  in eastern counties, 83–4, 205
  effect of, on commerce, xvii, xviii
  labour for, 9, 16, 76, 113
  mechanisation of, 8, 111–14, 254–5, 343
Hasbach, W., 73*n*, 190, 210*n*
Hatfield, W. E. A., 272*n*, 275*n*
Haxton, J., 36*n*
hay, 18. 19, 37
  acreage of, 266
  sale of, 166, 266, 276, 277, 282
  yields of, 381
hay tedders, mechanical, 7, 110–11
health
  of farm workers, 93, 219, 330
  public, 280, 293
Health Insurance, 315
Healy, M. J. R., 125*n*
Heath, F. G., 206*n*, 222*n*
Hebrides, 21–2, 25, 31
hedgerows, removal of, 105, 126, 164
Hendrick, J., 373*n*
Herbert, Auberon, 230
Herdwick sheep, 141
Hereford cattle, 13, 15, 25, 134, 135, 370
  exports of, 270
Herefordshire
  crops in, 123, 273, 274
  farm workers in, 227, 233, 344
Hertfordshire, 227, 272
Highland and Agricultural Society, 31, 32, 55, 280
  experimental station of, at Pumpherston, 278
  inquiry of, into methods of engaging farm workers, 221
  milk recording by, 383
  prizes offered by, 145
  shows of, 14, 29, 140

Highland and Agricultural Society—*cont.*
  statistics collected by, 118, 181.
  tests of machinery by, 103, 195, 347
  Transactions of, 145
Highland cattle, 14, 132, 135
Highland Clearances, 21, 23, 55, 217, 294
Highway Boards, 293
hill farming, 20, 120, 137
hill grazings, 265
hill sheep farming, 21, 142, 215, 244
hiring fairs (feeing markets), 76, 80, 81, 213, 220–1, 226, 338
Hirst, F. W., 44*n*
Hobbs, C. and R., of Meysey Hampton and Kelmscott, 366
Hobbs, M. E., 177*n*, 280*n*
hobjobbers, 84
Holdenby, Christopher, 322*n*
holdover, custom of, 153–4
Holland
  export of breeding pigs to, 361
  imports of cows from, 133–4
  imports of food from, 24, 145, 260
Hood, Thomas, 71
Hope, George, of Fenton Barns, 15–17, 91, 101, 116, 174*n*, 176, 205, 327
hops, acreage of, 251, 267, 273
horse hoes, 8, 109, 117, 255
horse rakes, 7, 266
horses
  acres cultivated per pair of, 35–6
  breeding of, xviii, 143
  at Fenton Barns, 16
  and machines, 114, 115
  numbers of, 114, 119, 120, 121, 251, 252, 267, 268, 350, 351
  urban, fodder for, 18, 123, 253; manure from, 272, 282–3, 352, 353, 357
Hoskins, W. G., 193*n*
Hoskyns, C. Wren, 5, 7, 82, 110
housing of farm workers, 81, 82, 83, 92–3, 196, 198, 204, 211, 306, 313, 324–30
  in Scotland, 215–16, 219–20
Houston, G., 78*n*, 206*n*, 225*n*, 249*n*
Howard, H. F., 160*n*
Huntingdonshire, 123, 243, 246, 359
Hutcheson, A., 351*n*, 356*n*
hypothec, right of, in Scotland, 173–4

implements and machinery, 7–10, 51, 102–14, 254–6, 320, 347–8, 384
import duties, on farm produce, repeal of, 40, 97
imports
  of dairy produce, 40, 97, 144–5, 260, 341
  of feeding-stuffs, 357

Index

imports—*cont.*
of meat, 260-1
of wheat and flour, 38-9, 240, 259, 341
improvements, xx, 156-8
compensation for tenants', 150, 171, 298, 300
in the depression, 309
loans for, 194-200
on settled estates, 65-7
Inclosure Commissioners, 181, 182, 187-94
and loans for improvements, 101, 195-9, 326
inclosures, *see* enclosures
India, 259, 371
infant mortality, 207
insect pests, 273, 279
Inspectors
for cattle plague, 200, 201
of meat, 368
of the Poor (Scotland), 74
'insurance', against milk souring, 363
interest, rate of, on loans for improvements, 195, 196, 198
International Agricultural Congress, Paris (1878), 182
International Exhibition, Battersea (1862), 112, 134
Inverness-shire, 21, 217
Ireland
butter from, 24, 40, 144, 145, 262, 370
cattle from, 19, 25, 27, 99, 132, 345, 359, 360
famine in, xix, 31, 39
farm workers from, 77, 79, 352
land reform in, 290-2
Irish Land League, 290, 296
Ixworth Agricultural Labourers' Association, 328

jam factories, 272
Jefferies, Richard, 319n
Jenkins, H. M., 146n, 280, 281
Johnes, Thomas, of Hafod, 58
Johnson, C. W., 4, 6-7, 31
Jonas, S., 4
Jones, E. L., 125n
journals, agricultural, 33-4, 280, 376
Justices of the Peace, 44, 53, 200, 293, 318, 368

kale, 3
Kay, Dr, 73
Kay, Joseph, 307n
Kelso, ram market at, 140
Kendall, M., 323n
Kendall, S. G., 245n
Kent, 12, 24, 348, 376

Kent—*cont.*
crops in, 123, 272, 273, 274
farm workers in, 227, 230, 335
Kent (Romney) sheep, 142, 360
Kerrison, Sir Edward, 236
Kerry sheep, 361
Kingsley, Charles, 204
Kinnaird, Lord, 215
Kirk Session, 56, 73-4, 91
Kirkcudbrightshire, 214, 216, 363
Knatchbull-Hugesson, 172
Knight family, of Exmoor, 3, 66, 159, 313
kohlrabi, 124
Kyloe cattle, 13

labour, *see* farm workers
labour, cost of, 35, 36, 248, 256, 286
Labourers, Federal Union of, 231, 237, 239
'Labourers' Revolt' (1830s), 31
lambs, market for meat from, 142-3
Lanarkshire, 118, 214, 273, 363
Lancashire
crops in, 18, 273, 284
farm workers in, 78, 205, 211, 237
livestock in, 18, 286, 313, 362
potatoes in, 123, 353, 354, 380
Lancet, The, 147-8
land
annual value of, 287
death duties on, 314-17
exchanges of, 194
free trade in, 304-9
private property in, 302-4
transfer of, 179, 308
land agents, 163, 282
Land Commission, 182, 202
Land Courts, 290, 296, 298, 315
Land Department of Board of Agriculture, 182
Land Enquiry Committee, of Liberal Party, 315, 335
land laws, campaign for reform of, 308
Land Nationalisation Society, 302
Land Restoration League, 303, 336
landowners, 41-67, 289-316
corporate, 56-7, 160-1
numbers of, xviii, 306, 307
as privileged creditors, 173-4
and tenants, 42-3, 151-77; in crofting areas, 294-7
Langford, E. W., 338
Latham, P. R., 265n
Laune, Faunce de, 374
Lavergne, Léonce de, 10, 167
Lawes, J. B., 244, 375; and Gilbert, 30, 31, 34, 125n, 129n, 278, 298
Layton, W. T., 372n
leaching of soils, 30, 243, 378

402

Index

market gardens—*cont.*
  acreage of, 251, 252, 267, 268, 273
  employment in, 343
markets, 13, 23–8, 32, 261–4
  and cattle plague, 200, 201
  and price levels, 369–71
  and railways, 23, 25, 97–100
  see also hiring fairs
Marlborough, Duke of, 161–2
marling of land, 157, 382
Martelli, G., 47n
Martineau, Harriet, 48
Matthews, A. H. H., 138n, 301n, 355n, 369n
Maud, market at, 98–9
Maxwell, John Hall, 118
meat
  marketing of, 25, 99; *see also* Smith-field market
  prices of, 40, 250, 258–9, 261, 271, 357, 372
  supplies of, 10, 260, 261
  tuberculosis and, 368
mechanisation
  of harvesting, 8, 111–14, 254–5, 343
  and productivity, 346
Mechi, J. J., 125–9, 130
Medical Officers of Health, 207, 367
Mendel, G., 375
Meredith, George, 66
Merionethshire, 169
Methodism, 52, 53, 92, 229, 232, 337
Middlesex, 18
Middleton, T. H., 356, 376
Midlands, 2, 4–5, 275
  dairying in, 276, 360
  farm workers in, 80–1, 206, 234, 324
  livestock in, 12, 13, 15
migration of farm workers, 222–3, 227, 237, 257, 274, 275
  see also emigration
milk
  carriage of disease by, 279–80, 366–9
  condensed, 262, 346, 365
  cooling of, 148, 150, 364
  for farm workers, 205, 216, 323, 324
  prices of, 18, 148–9, 250, 262, 363–4
  for towns, 18, 19, 36, 134, 147–9, 249, 276, 283, 362–6
  yields of, 36–7, 147
  see also dairies, dairying
Milk Recording Societies, 383
milking machines, 347
Mill, John Stuart, 89, 305
mills, flour, 262, 319
Mills, Stephen, of Elston, 12
mole ploughs, 100, 106
Molland, R., 249n, 324n

Morgan, K. O., 169n
Morley, John, 42n, 151n
Morley, Sam, 236
Morton, J. Chalmers, 5, 6, 34, 115n, 144n, 147, 149, 280 .
motor cars, 322, 329, 357, 379
mowers, mechanical, 110–11, 266
Mullin, G. F., 321n
Munro, J. M. H., 278n, 352n
Murray, Rev. D. R., 227
Murray, G., 139, 145n, 150n
mutton
  breeds of sheep for, 12–13
  prices of, 95, 96, 142, 271
  (and lamb) supplies of, 260, 261, 341, 369
Napier Commission, 295, 297
National Agricultural Labourers' Union, 228, 230–2, 234, 237, 238, 239, 248, 292, 304, 330, 332, 335
National Agricultural Labourers' and Rural Workers' Union, 337, 338
National Farmers' Union, 314, 338
National Institute for Research in Dairying, Reading, 366
National Society for the Education of the Poor according to the Principles of the Church of England, 90, 91
nationalisation of land, 302
'*New Domesday Book*' (*Return of Owners of Land*, 1878), 306–7
New Zealand, 269, 320
  imports from, 259, 260, 369
Nicholls, Sir George, 73n
Nicholson, Nigel, 325n
Nicol, John, of Forfar, 354
nitrates, 16, 102, 125, 149, 373
  on fallows, 278
nitrogen, 29, 30, 125, 278
nitrogenous fertilisers, 266
Nonconformist churches, 90, 169, 229, 318
Norfolk
  Brecklands of, 47
  crops in, 36, 123, 243; 4-course rotation of, 3, 124, 158
  farm workers in, 236, 336
  livestock in, 13, 15, 97, 359
  smallholders in, 322, 334
  tenant right in, 158–9, 247
Northamptonshire, 163
Northumberland, 10, 13, 75, 356
Nottinghamshire, 123, 163, 365

oats
  acreage of, 118, 119, 121, 122, 241, 251, 252, 258, 267, 268, 350, 351
  in crop rotations, 4, 16, 252–3, 276